A
Scientific Autobiography
of
Joseph Priestley
(1733-1804)

Selected Scientific Correspondence
Edited With Commentary
by
Robert E. Schofield

The M.I.T. Press
Massachusetts Institute of
Cambridge, Massachusetts, and L

A Scientific Autobiography of
Joseph Priestley (1733–1804)

Joseph Priestley as a Young Man
*Artist Unknown. Courtesy of the Unitarian Church,
Cambridge, England.*

Preface

THE MEMOIRS OF *Dr. Joseph Priestley, to the Year 1795, written by himself* . . . (London, 1806) was written, Priestley tells us on its first page, because, "Having thought it right to leave behind me some account of my *friends* and *benefactors,* it is in a manner necessary that I also give some account of myself." When to this singular reason for writing an autobiographical sketch is added the emphasis on theology (thought by Priestley to be his most important activity), it is not surprising that his *Memoirs* provide very little information on his scientific career. Fewer than thirty of its one hundred and twenty-eight octavo pages have even the smallest relevance to those discoveries which made Priestley for almost a quarter of a century the foremost name in science. There are scattered references to some autobiographical details in other works by Priestley, e.g., his *Familiar Letters, addressed to the Inhabitants of Birmingham* (1790), his *Appeal to the Public, on the subject of the Riots in Birmingham* (1791), and his *Letters to the Inhabitants of Northumberland* (1799), but these also emphasize the theological aspects of his life, not the scientific.

Fortunately, Priestley was committed on principle to the

most rapid public communication of his scientific observations. For example, he wrote in the preface to his first volume of *Experiments and Observations on different Kinds of Air* (1774), praising men "who, from a natural ardour of mind, engage in philosophical pursuits, and with an ingenuous simplicity immediately communicate to others whatever occurs to them in their inquiries" and insisting that "all unnecessary delays in the publication of experiments . . . are peculiarly unjustifiable." As a result, his reports of experiments are charmingly discursive ramblings, having all the appearance of elaborated research notes. The modern custom, apparent in its beginnings even then, of the *post facto* rationalizing of experiments and conclusions into an impressively consistent, but unreal and unhistoric, picture of scientific logic and rigor was not for Priestley. Even in his *History of Electricity* (1767), accounts of his own work describe false starts, misleading experiments, and temporarily faulty conclusions, while it was not until 1790 that he finally "abridged and methodized" the chemical experiments of almost twenty years, breaking the chronological pattern of his report of one line of investigation after another, as is seen in his six volumes of *Experiments and Observations* and in his papers for the Royal Society of London.

For the fortunate few with access to these volumes and to the *Philosophical Transactions of the Royal Society,* a partial account of the development of Priestley's scientific ideas is therefore obtainable. But Priestley's scientific works have now become collectors' items, and even if one can consult them, additional information is still necessary before the picture can be completed. Such information is available in Priestley's vast scientific correspondence. These letters give an insight into Priestley's private speculative thinking that his published writings, however discursive, do not give. They reveal more of his relationships with contemporary scientists, more of his influence on and his debts to the scientific thinking of the day than can be obtained without the most searching analysis of his books and papers. They constitute a continuing, year-to-year, firsthand account of Priestley's scientific career, which for the most part has yet to be drawn upon to any significant degree.

The failure adequately to use these letters is primarily the result of their inaccessibility. Most of the letters which have survived are scattered in private hands and archives throughout the world. The majority of them have never previously been published, or have appeared scattered in the published correspondence of other men, in historical journals, or the pages of Unitarian periodicals. Two collections of Priestley letters have appeared, but are now almost as hard to find as the original letters themselves. The earliest edition of Priestley letters was that edited by John Towill Rutt, to accompany and illustrate his 1831–1832 edition of Priestley's *Memoirs.* Rutt had the good fortune to know personally some of Priestley's correspondents and the immediate descendants of others; his edition of the letters was prepared before the dispersal or disappearance of many private collections. Unfortunately, Rutt was not interested in science, and his standards of scholarship were very different from those of today. A comparison of Rutt's versions with the originals in a large collection of letters to the Reverend Theophilus Lindsey and the Reverend Thomas Belsham, now preserved in the Dr. Williams's Library (London), reveals changes in wording and punctuation, the frequent omission of paragraphs without indication, and, on some occasions, the combination of parts of two or even three letters into what appears in the printed version to be a single letter! In the present selection of letters, Rutt's edition is used as a source only when it has not been possible to locate the originals.

In 1892, the American historian of chemistry, Henry Carrington Bolton, published privately ninety-six Priestley letters in a volume entitled, the *Scientific Correspondence of Joseph*

Priestley. In the many instances in which the originals could be compared to Bolton's published versions, the latter were found to be substantially correct; there are occasional differences in the reading of obscure words or phrases, there are again changes in spelling, paragraphing, and punctuation, but the content of these printed letters can be depended upon. Bolton's selection is, however, primarily limited to letters written by Priestley to Josiah Wedgwood between 1780 and 1794 (now preserved as "Miscellaneous Manuscripts, volumes 5–6, 1–33," in the Archives of the Royal Society of London), with the addition of scattered letters to other persons, from 1780 to 1804. Where the originals were not found, I have confidently adopted the Bolton text for those letters chosen for republication here, but it must be admitted that Bolton's collection is not of the greatest importance; this period was neither the most significantly productive nor the most illustrious one in Priestley's scientific career.

The letters in this volume have been selected from a total of more than four times their number, covering the period from 1762 to Priestley's death in 1804. Most of Priestley's letters are principally concerned with theological subjects, though many of these also mention or discuss scientific problems. The selection includes all unpublished letters found of scientific interest and a majority of those in print. To include all the letters published in Bolton's *Scientific Correspondence of Joseph Priestley* would increase the size of this volume beyond manageable proportions; many are repetitive, not all are on scientific subjects, and their earlier publication by Bolton reduces the value of reprinting them here. The letters chosen for republication are those of greatest scientific and autobiographical interest, which repeat neither themselves nor the content of other letters previously unpublished.

The whole of a letter, when found, has been included, even when substantial parts of the text are theological. Reasons of scholarship aside, this procedure serves to emphasize that

Priestley's science was an activity of his leisure, that he was by profession and conviction a minister who prized his scientific reputation, because, as he wrote in his *Memoirs,* it gave weight to his "attempts to defend christianity." Because correspondence is generally an exchange of ideas and information, some letters to Priestley have been included in this collection. Unfortunately, few of these are letters to which we have answers. The bulk of the correspondence to Priestley was destroyed in the Birmingham Church-and-King riots of 1791; the remainder was burned by Joseph Priestley, Jr., on his father's death in 1804, in what now seems an excessive regard for the privacy of the writers. All our letters to Priestley are derived from manuscript drafts or published versions. In no instance, however, has such a letter when published by Priestley in one of his works been included. An occasional letter between third parties and a few rare, published items are also included in the collection when they appeared to have a peculiar relevance to Priestley's scientific career.

The text of the letters whenever possible has been taken from the originals, and the spelling, punctuation, and paragraphing have been left unchanged; transcriptions from printed sources have been changed only to correct obvious typographical errors. Where obscurity, illegibility, or destruction of text has made a reading questionable or impossible, this has been indicated by square brackets in the transcript. The complimentary close, usually following the eighteenth-century formula, has in all cases been omitted.

The sources of the originals are identified in a bibliographical appendix. I am grateful to the following owners or custodians of these originals for the permission to publish copies in this collection.

Biblioteca Nazionale Centrale, Florence, Italy.
Österreichische Nationalbibliothek, Vienna, Austria.
Universitetsbiblioteket, Uppsala, Sweden.
The British Museum, London, England.

Birmingham Public Libraries, Birmingham, England.

Birmingham Assay Office, Birmingham, England.

The John Rylands Library, Manchester, England.

Bodleian Library, Oxford, England.

Devonshire Collections, Chatsworth, Bakewell, England.

Wellcome Historical Medical Museum and Library, London, England, by courtesy of the Wellcome Trust.

Trustees of Dr. Williams's Library, London, England.

The Royal Society, London, England.

Cambridge University Library, Cambridge, England.

Hollandsche Maatschappij der Wetenschappen, Haarlem, The Netherlands.

Archives du Loiret, Orléans, France.

Manuscript Division, New York Public Library, Astor, Lenox and Tilden Foundations, New York, New York.

Boscovich Archive, General Library, University of California, Berkeley, California.

Pennsylvania Historical and Museum Commission, Harrisburg, Pennsylvania.

Historical Society of Pennsylvania, Philadelphia, Pennsylvania.

Historical Library, Yale University School of Medicine, New Haven, Connecticut.

Charles Roberts Autograph Collection, Haverford College Library, Haverford, Pennsylvania.

Massachusetts Historical Society, Boston, Massachusetts.

University of Pennsylvania, Philadelphia, Pennsylvania.

The Franklin Institute, Philadelphia, Pennsylvania.

The New York Historical Society, New York, New York.

American Academy of Arts and Sciences, Boston, Massachusetts.

Sidney M. Edelstein, Dexter Chemical Corporation, New York, New York.

Burndy Library, Norwalk, Connecticut.

American Philosophical Society, Philadelphia, Pennsylvania.

Dickinson College, Carlisle, Pennsylvania.

Istituto Lombardo, Accademia di Scienze e Lettere, Milan, Italy.

Musée de Mariemont, Mariemont, Belgium.

Earl Fitzwilliam and Earl Fitzwilliam's Wentworth Estates Company; and the Sheffield City Libraries, England.

I wish also to acknowledge my gratitude to the librarians and archivists who aided my search for Priestley letters, to my colleagues and to fellow admirers of Priestley for their advice and assistance, and to the secretaries and editors who helped to bring some order from chaos. I would likewise be grateful to anyone who can inform me of the existence of Priestley letters that I may not have seen. A substantially complete collection of extant letters could not but be invaluable for the biography of Priestley I hope some day to write.

It was originally intended to make this an account, in his own words, of Priestley's scientific career, through the combination of selections from the *Memoirs* and the correspondence, with a minimum of editorial commentary. It is hoped that the spirit of this intention has remained and that the flavor of the work is still predominantly that of Priestley, though the "minimum" of commentary has insensibly grown in an attempt to relate the letters to Priestley's scientific work as a whole. The definitive study of Priestley as a scientist remains to be done and will ultimately require the reading of all his published work, nonscientific as well as scientific, but this collection of correspondence will perhaps add a dimension to the present view of Priestley and make the ultimate larger task an easier one.

Special thanks are due to the many institutions that provided the time and funds to make this work possible. I was first enabled to follow Priestley's trail by a fellowship grant under Public Law 584, 79th Congress—the Fulbright Act. Subsequent trips to England were made possible by the American Philosophical Society, on grant No. 2189 of the Penrose Fund; and a research grant from the National Science Foundation, which also gave me the leisure for investigation and covered the manifold expenses of photographing and transcribing. The University of Kansas regularly assisted me with research grants while I was there, and the Case Institute of Technology has continued that assistance and further eased my labors with its enlightened policy to encourage research. Finally, the John Simon Guggenheim Foundation made it possible first to clear an earlier task from the path to this one and then to begin collating and arranging the materials for this volume. I am deeply grateful to these institutions for their support.

ROBERT E. SCHOFIELD

Cleveland, Ohio
1966

Contents

CONTENTS

[xiv]

A Scientific Autobiography of
Joseph Priestley (1733–1804)

CHAPTER ONE

Introduction

THE EARLIEST DATE for the beginning of Joseph Priestley's interest in science is given by his brother Timothy.

My brother [writes Timothy] began to discover a taste for experiments when about eleven years of age [i.e., 1744]. The first he made was on spiders, and by putting them into bottles, he found how long they could live without fresh air.

The second was the power of the leaver, and I well remember how much these experiments pleased him. He soon told me how many men he could lift from the ground in a moment, &c. &c.

My brother, when he began to learn astronomy, would be in the fields with his pen and papers; this spread his fame, as it was at that time a science very little known. When he found out any thing new, I was soon acquainted with it: I remember when he was making much progress in electricity, in showing me how to melt steel; when the mettle melted, he called, Oh had Sir Isaac Newton seen such an experiment! and his pleasure on those occasions cannot well be described.[1]

Unfortunately, this claim was made in a funeral sermon in which theological animus so vies with family pride that, be-

[1] Timothy Priestley, *A Funeral Sermon occasioned by the Death of the late Rev. Joseph Priestley* . . . (London, Alex. Hogg, and Co., 1805), pp. 42-43.

[1]

tween predictions of Joseph's damnation and fraternal reminiscences, it is impossible to place confidence in any part of it. Without substantiation, Timothy's statement suggests only a pardonable desire to find in Joseph's early life signs of his later scientific greatness — and there is nothing in other sources to suggest in him any predilection toward science at so early an age.

Except for a letter to Priestley, dated 31 December 1750, which does not mention science, the earliest letters found to or from Priestley date from 1762.[2] In these there is some casual indication of his scientific interests, but for reliable information on Priestley's science before 1762 during the first twenty-nine years of his life, we are dependent upon scant references in Priestley's *Memoirs* and the hints these offer. Though all these references suggest a perhaps more than average education in science for that time, they fail to justify much opposition to Priestley's own flat disclaimer of having experimented to any original purpose before 1765.[3]

Priestley himself dates his beginning acquaintance with science as the interval between 1750 and 1752, when he "attended two days in the week upon Mr. Haggerstone . . . who had been educated under Mr. Maclaurin. Of him I learned Geometry, Algebra and various branches of Mathematics, theoretical and practical. And at the same time I read, but with little assistance from him, Gravesend's Elements of Natural Philosophy. . . ."[4]

[2] The 1750 letter may — according to J. T. Rutt, who prints at least parts of it in his *Life and Correspondence of Joseph Priestley* (London, R. Hunter, 1831–1832), vol. 1, pp. 9–10 — indirectly refer to Priestley's early thoughts of becoming a physician. It seems equally likely that the reference is to the possibility of his becoming clerk to a merchant, as Priestley mentioned in his *Memoirs*.

[3] For a detailed analysis of Priestley's preparation in science, see Robert E. Schofield, "The Scientific Background of Joseph Priestley," *Annals of Science*, *13* (1957), 148–163.

[4] *Memoirs of Dr. Joseph Priestley, to the Year 1795, written by himself* (London, J. Johnson, 1806), p. 9.

W. J. S. v. 'sGravesande's *Physices elementa mathematica* (presumably in the English, *Mathematical Elements of Natural Philosophy Confirmed by Experiment, or an Introduction to Sir Isaac Newton's Philosophy,* translated by J. T. Desaguliers) specifically encourages observation and the performing of experiments as confirmation of the principles of astronomy and elementary mechanics. In light of Priestley's repetition of the experiments he intended to describe in his *History of Electricity* (London, 1767), it is probable that he performed the exercises recommended by 'sGravesande and that this is the source of Timothy's misdated memories. There is little electricity and no chemistry in 'sGravesande, however, and *those* experimenting incidents described in the *Funeral Sermon* must have occurred considerably later than Timothy remembered them, if, indeed, they happened at all.

From 1752 to 1755, Priestley attended the dissenting academy at Daventry. The only scientific work in Daventry's curriculum found worthy of specific reference in Priestley's *Memoirs* was the reading of "Dr. Hartley's Observations on Man," to which his attention was drawn by a reference in the course of lectures. We may perhaps relate Priestley's unusually firm belief in mechanistic and strictly causal relationships in science to his reading of this work, a cornerstone in the development of mechanistic, associationist psychology; but Priestley remembered Hartley's work primarily as a justification for a theological "doctrine of necessity." Only the comment, "My attention was always more drawn to mathematical and philosophical studies than his was," in reference to a fellow-student justifies any inference from the *Memoirs* that Priestley's interest in science continued into his school years.[5]

From Daventry, Priestley went to minister to a small dissenting congregation at Needham Market, Suffolk. There, he tells us, "I applied with great assiduity to my studies, which

---

[5] Priestley, *Memoirs,* pp. 18–19, 21.

[3]

were classical, mathematical and theological. These required but few books. As to Experimental Philosophy, I had always cultivated an acquaintance with it, but I had not the means of prosecuting it." His income at Needham Market being inadequate, he hoped to supplement it by teaching "the classics, mathematics, &c." and when this scheme failed:

> . . . I proposed to give lectures to grown persons in such branches of science as I could conveniently procure the means of doing; and I began with reading about twelve lectures on the *use of the Globes*. . . . I had one course of ten hearers, which did something more than pay for my globes; and I should have proceeded in this way, adding to my apparatus as I should have been able to afford it, if I had not left that place.[6]

These remarks force a reappraisal of Priestley's experiences at Daventry, for where else could Priestley previously have afforded cultivating an acquaintance with "experimental philosophy" and where else could he have learned the mathematics or the "branches of science" on which he so confidently planned to give lectures? A re-examination of Daventry's course of studies is rewarding. Dissenting academies regularly offered the most complete formal instruction in contemporary science available in eighteenth-century England. Exact information on the science course at Daventry during Priestley's stay seems unavailable, but its broad outline can be determined by inference. The academy at Daventry had originally been founded by Philip Doddridge, under whose direction the curriculum included:

> . . . lectures on the Principles of *Geometry* and *Algebra* . . . the knowledge of *Trigonometry, Conic—sections* and *celestial Mechanics* (A Collection of important Propositions, taken chiefly from Sir Isaac Newton, and demonstrated, independent on the

---

[6] Priestley, *Memoirs*, pp. 29, 37–38.

[4]

rest. They relate especially, tho' not only, to centripetal and centrifugal Forces). A system of natural and experimental Philosophy, comprehending *Mechanics, Statics, Hydrostatics, Optics, Pneumatics,* and *Astronomy,* was read . . . with reference to the best Authors on these Subjects. This system was illustrated by a neat and pretty large *philosophical Apparatus.* . . . A distinct view of the Anatomy of the human Body was given them. . . .[7]

That Caleb Ashworth and Samuel Clark (successors to Doddridge, and Priestley's tutors) continued this program is not entirely clear, but in 1781 Thomas Belsham, then directing the course of studies at Daventry, included in an outline of the subjects studied: Euclid, algebra, trigonometry, "the doctrine of the Human Mind" (presumably Hartley), conic sections; natural philosophy, including mechanics, hydrostatics, pneumatics, "with the new discoveries upon Air," astronomy, and electricity, and declared, "The philosophical apparatus is very complete in Mechanics, Hydrostatics, Pneumatics, Electricity, and the Airs; its principal defects are in the Optical and Astronomical departments."[8] With the exception of the later emphasis on "the Airs," to be expected as current fashion, the similarity between Doddridge's course before 1751 and Belsham's of 1781 supports the conclusion that Daventry's scientific curriculum was maintained at an equivalent position during Priestley's attendance there.

To this inferred program of Priestley's scientific studies at Daventry can be added the direct evidence from his diary for 1755, his last year there. Priestley regularly kept a record of his work in a series of diaries, the majority of which were destroyed in the Birmingham riots of 1791. The diary for "1754, 1755 and several of the subsequent years" was saved,

---

[7] Quoted in J. W. Ashley Smith, *The Birth of Modern Education* (London, Independent Press Ltd., 1954), p. 131.
[8] Quoted in John Williams, *Memoirs of the Late Reverend Thomas Belsham* (London, for the Author, 1833), pp. 224–226.

however, and though even that seems now to have disappeared, it was in the possession of Joseph Priestley, Jr., at the time he prepared his father's *Memoirs* for publication, and sections of it are quoted in the posthumous continuation of that work. During 1755, we find that Priestley read: "Maclaurin's Algebra to part 2d," "The Anatomical Articles in the Universal Dictionary, several principal Algebraic ones, and all the letter A," "Euclid, Lib. 1, 2, 3, 4, 5, 6, 11 and 12 slightly," "Boerhaave's Theory of Chemistry a good part of Vol. 1st; Rowning's Philosophy half of Vol. 1st, and part 2d and 3d."[9] After such preparation, Priestley might well face the task of lecturing to his untutored neighbors on the sciences.

In 1758, Priestley left Needham Market for Nantwich, in Cheshire. This was a more thriving community, and though he had no friends of similar interests, "besides Mr. Brereton, a clergyman in the neighbourhood, who had a taste for astronomy, philosophy, and literature in general," he was able to start a school there and exploit his scientific training.

> . . . at Nantwich my school soon enabled me to purchase a few books, and some philosophical instruments, as a small air pump, an electrical machine, &c. These I taught my scholars in the highest class to keep in order, and make use of, and by entertaining their parents and friends with experiments, in which the scholars were generally the operators, and sometimes the lecturers too; I considerably extended the reputation of my school; though I had no other object originally than gratifying my own taste. I had no leisure, however, to make any original experiments until many years after this time.[10]

He continued at Nantwich until September 1761, when he was invited to become tutor in languages and belles lettres at Warrington Academy.

9 Priestley, *Memoirs*, collected from long list of reading, pp. 178–184, *passim*.
10 Priestley, *Memoirs*, pp. 41–43.

This I accepted, though my school promised to be more gainful to me. But my employment at Warrington would be more liberal, and less painful. It was also a means of extending my connections. But, as I told the persons who brought me the invitation, viz. Mr. Seddon and Mr. Holland of Bolton, I should have preferred the office of teaching the mathematics and natural philosophy, for which I had at that time a great predilection.[11]

It is hard to see what he thought to gain by mentioning his preference for mathematics and natural philosophy. Warrington already had a tutor in these subjects, John Holt, who had been selected for that post in 1757 because of his reputation as a teacher of mathematics near Liverpool. Even in 1761, Priestley would probably have made a better tutor of natural philosophy than Holt, who had occasionally to be reminded to make his course more experimental and practical; but Priestley was not yet known as a scientist and had no reputation as a science teacher. The letter which had first recommended him to the attention of Warrington's trustees in 1758 spoke of his "unexceptionable character . . . steady attachment to the Principles of Civil & Religious Liberty; and . . . Degree of Critical & Classical Learning not common in one so Young . . ."; while the recommendations of 1761 praised him as "an able master of the learned Languages; and a considerable proficient in many of the modern: To which is added, that he has always attended to the duties of a private school with indefatigable labour; and has discovered a singular genius for the management of youth."[12]

If his science teaching in Nantwich had "considerably extended the reputation" of Priestley's school, the news had not yet reached his friends in London or his new employers at

[11] Priestley, *Memoirs*, pp. 45–46.

[12] MS., Minutes of the Warrington Trustees, p. 55; and *A Report of the State of Warrington Academy, by the Trustees at their Annual Meeting, June 25th MDCCLXI*, p. 2, n.p.; both are preserved in the library of Manchester College, Oxford.

[7]

Warrington. It was there, however, that Priestley blossomed as a scientist, though according to the *Memoirs* this was not in any way connected with his academic duties, which were "to teach elocution, and also Logic and Hebrew. The first of these I retained; but after a year or two I exchanged the last two articles with Dr. Aikin for the civil law, and one year I gave a course of lectures in anatomy."[13]

Here again the *Memoirs* is inadequate. He was to remain at Warrington for six years, and only the electrical studies connected with his *History of Electricity* are described by Priestley, but for this period other information is available to fill out the picture and to amplify a reference made later in the *Memoirs* to "a course of chemical lectures delivered in the academy at Warrington by Dr. Turner of Liverpool."

On 16 March 1762, Dr. Matthew Turner wrote to John Seddon at Warrington. After estimating the length of his proposed course in chemistry — "As near as I can guess it may be finished in twenty Lectures" — Turner mentions that he already is acquainted with Priestley and adds:

I greatly admire Mr. Priestley, and am certain any School must flourish that has such teachers in it, he seems to possess all the Qualifications necessary for encreasing and diffusing Knowledge.[14]

John Seddon was the chief dissenting minister of Warrington and had been instrumental in establishing the academy there. Though not at this time a member of the faculty, he was, so far as it had one, the administrative officer of the school. From a letter of 9 April 1762 from Priestley at Warrington to Seddon, then visiting London, it appears that Priestley, though the newest member of the faculty, was acting

13 Priestley, *Memoirs*, pp. 48–49.
14 Matthew Turner to John Seddon, 16 March 1762; from the library of Manchester College, Oxford.

as Seddon's deputy, and that he and Seddon were responsible for bringing Turner to give the chemical lectures.[15]

Under the circumstances, Turner's expressed admiration for Priestley may partly be judicious flattery, but it was to be stated again in a different and more public context. Turner was a professed atheist who wrote an answer to Priestley's *Letters to a Philosophical Unbeliever* (1780) under the name of Hammon. In this answer he expressed a high opinion of what Priestley might have done in science had he not "from . . . [your] first initiation into science, been dedicated to what is called the immediate service of God."[16] Turner has been described as "A good surgeon, a skilful anatomist, a practised chemist, a draughtsman, a classical scholar, and a ready wit." He is credited with the first commercial preparation of sulphuric ether, he supplied both Josiah Wedgwood and Matthew Boulton with varnishes, lacquers, and metallic powders for their various manufacturies, and may be said to have guided Wedgwood into truly scientific investigations from his previous empirical researches.[17] Turner's praise is surely an indication of Priestley's capabilities in chemistry, some five years before the *Memoirs* note any chemical experimentation and ten years before there was public knowledge of it.

The only specific account of work done in Turner's course is Priestley's reference in his *Philosophical Empiricism:*

---

[15] See Joseph Priestley to John Seddon, 9 April 1762, in the *Christian Reformer*, 10 (1854), 625–626. For a description of Warrington Academy, see the Reverend William Turner, *The Warrington Academy*, edited with an introduction by G. A. Carter (Warrington, Library and Museum Committee, 1957).

[16] See Priestley, *Additional Letters to a Philosophical Unbeliever, in Answer to Mr. William Hammon* (Birmingham, J. Johnson, 1782), p. 303.

[17] *Dictionary of National Biography* (London, Smith, Elder, &. Co., 1909), article "Matthew Turner," vol. 19, p. 1277; Turner, *op. cit.*, p. 42; and R. E. Schofield, "Josiah Wedgwood, Industrial Chemist," *Chymia*, 5 (1959), 187–188. Matthew Turner introduced Wedgwood to Thomas Bentley, a trustee of Warrington, who became his dear friend and partner. Bentley may be the link between Priestley and Turner, as he was between Priestley and Wedgwood.

. . . when I attended a course of chemical lectures, delivered at Warringon, by the ingenious Mr. Turner of Liverpoole, I was one who assisted in making a quantity of Spirit of nitre [nitric acid], in a manner not so expeditious, indeed, as that which I suppose is now generally used, but in which I am pretty confident there was no opportunity for any common air to get into the composition of.[18]

The course was probably based, however, on William Lewis' *Commercium Philosophico-Technicum or the Philosophical Commerce of Arts* (London, 1763–1765), since that work was purchased for the Warrington Library and the Trustees' *Report* of 1762 emphasizes the commercial aspect of the instruction. Turner's lectures were apparently very successful. The Warrington Trustees noted in that *Report:*

This last Spring Mr. Turner of Liverpool, a gentleman deservedly esteemed for his abilities as a chemist, went through a full course of practical and commercial Chemistry in the Academy, very much to the satisfaction of all who attended him. A room is properly fitted up, and an useful Apparatus provided for the cultivation of this most valuable branch of natural knowledge: and Mr. Turner will continue to favour the Academy with his assistance in this way, as often as shall be thought convenient.

While the Trustees' *Report* for 1766 adds:

A very useful Apparatus for Experimental Philosophy consisting of most of the capital instruments, is already purchased; and additions will be made to it from time to time. Some progress hath likewise been made in forming an apparatus for some of the most useful processes in Chemistry: this hath been principally done by the favour of a gentleman, who is himself a considerable artist this way; and whose love of natural knowledge hath induced him to offer to go through a course of chemistry in the academy, as

[18] Priestley, *Philosophical Empiricism* (London, J. Johnson, 1775), p. 45.

often as a sufficient number of students may call for his attendance.[19]

Though there is no specific information that Turner's course was repeated after 1762, the implication is that it was. At least it can be said that both apparatus and instruction in chemistry were available to Priestley after 1762, even while he was interrupting his chemical studies for electrical investigations.

[19] *A Report of the State of Warrington Academy, By the Trustees at their Annual Meeting, June 30th. MDCCLXII,* p. 1, and *June 26th. MDCCLXVI,* p. 2.

CHAPTER TWO

Electrical Experiments
and the History of Electricity
1765–1767

THE MOST SIGNIFICANT scientific work of Priestley's Warrington phase was the electrical experimentation and
writing, done in connection with his *The History and Present
State of Electricity, with Original Experiments,* first published
in 1767. The first serious and extensive references to science
in Priestley's *Memoirs* are in connection with this study of
electricity. Priestley writes:

I was in this situation [at Warrington] when, going to London, and being introduced to Dr. Price, Mr. Canton, Dr. Watson,
(the Physician,) and Dr. Franklin, I was led to attend to the subject
of experimental philosophy more than I had done before; and
having composed all the Lectures I had occasion to deliver and
finding myself at liberty for any undertaking, I mentioned to Dr.
Franklin an idea that had occurred to me of writing the history
of discoveries in Electricity, which had been his favourite study.
This I told him might be an useful work, and that I would willingly undertake it, provided I could be furnished with the books
necessary for the purpose. This he readily undertook and my

other friends assisting him in it, I set about the work, without having the least idea of doing any thing more than writing a distinct and methodical account of all that had been done by others. Having, however, a pretty good machine, I was led, in the course of my writing the history, to endeavour to ascertain several facts which were disputed; and this led me by degrees into a field of original experiments, in which I spared no expence that I could possibly furnish.

These experiments employed a great proportion of my leisure time; and yet before the complete expiration of the year in which I gave the plan of my work to Dr. Franklin, I sent him a copy of it in print. In the same year five hours of every day were employed in lectures, public or private, and one two months vacation I spent chiefly at Bristol, on a visit to my father-in-law.

This I do not mention as a subject of boasting. For many persons have done more in the same time; but as an answer to those who have objected to some of my later writings, as hasty performances. For none of my publications were better received than the *History of Electricity*, which was the most hasty of them all. However, whether my publications have taken up more or less time, I am confident that more would not have contributed to their perfection, in any essential particular; and about anything farther I have never been very solicitous. My object was not to acquire the character of a fine writer, but of an useful one. I can also truly say that gain was never the chief object of any of my publications. Several of them were written with the prospect of certain loss.

During the course of my electrical experiments in this year I kept up a constant correspondence with Dr. Franklin, and the rest of my philosophical friends in London; and my letters circulated among them all, as also every part of my History as it was transcribed. This correspondence would have made a considerable volume, and it took up much time; but it was of great use with respect to the accuracy of my experiments, and the perfection of my work.

After the publication of my Chart of Biography, Dr. Percival of Manchester, then a student of Edinburgh, procured me the title of Doctor of laws from that university; and not long after my new experiments in electricity were the means of introducing me into the Royal Society, with the recommendation of Dr. Franklin, Dr. Watson, Mr. Canton, and Dr. Price.[1]

The *History of Electricity* contains an account of Priestley's experiments during this period and sets the pattern for his later scientific writing by describing the details of the experiments and the mistakes he made as well as his successes in pursuing them. Extensive as this account is, it does not, however, show his growing confidence as an experimenter nor the interplay of his ideas with those of his correspondents. Fortunately, many letters of that voluminous correspondence "with Dr. Franklin, and the rest of my philosophical friends in London" have been preserved.

No. 1.

FROM JOHN SEDDON TO JOHN CANTON

Warrington Dec. 18, 1765.

Sir

As my Friend Dr. Priestley, Tutor in the Languages and Belles Lettres here, is going up to Town, & has a great desire of being introduced to you, I have undertaken to do him this kind office; not depending so much upon the small acquaintance I have with you myself, as encouraged to it by the polite and obliging manner in which I once had the pleasure of being received by you. — You will probably have some knowledge of my Friend, as Author of a *Chart of Biography*; and of an *Essay upon Education*, in which he animadverts upon Dr. Brown. You will find him a benevolent, sensible man, with a considerable share of Learning; besides the studies which belong to his Profession, he has a taste for Natural Philosophy, wch will not render him less agreeable to you. . . .

---

[1] Priestley, *Memoirs,* pp. 50–52.

P.S. If Dr. Franklin be in Town, I believe Dr. Priestley would be glad to be made known to him.[2]

No. 2.

From Priestley to John Canton

Dear Sir

The time I had the happiness to spend in your company appears upon review like a pleasing dream. I frequently enjoy it over again in recollection, and ardently wish for a repetition of it. I wish, but in vain, that it may ever be in my power to return in kind your generous communication of philosophical intelligence and discoveries. Judge, however, of my disposition by my readiness to impart to you the very little that I have to impart.

I have made an experiment which, I think proves that *Glass when heated red hot is a conductor of electricity.* I took a glass tube about four feet long, and by means of mercury on the inside, and tinfoil on the outside, I charged about nine inches of it very strongly. This charged part (after taking off the tinfoil, and carefully pouring out the mercury) I made red hot, and upon pouring in the mercury and replacing the tinfoil, I found the glass discharged. This discharge could only have been made by the electrical fluid passing thro' the glass; for, to go round, it had a surface of about six feet to get over, the greatest part of which was very dry and cold.

That the glass was not discharged by the method of pouring out the mercury was evident, because the very same operation, without heating the glass, did not discharge it at all. This experiment I was led to make by your saying, that you had tubes charged and sealed hermetically, which gave a small quantity of their fire when they were warmed.

The professor of naturally philosophy at Glasgow says, in his syllabus of lectures, that frozen water is a nonconductor. This, as

---

[2] The source of this letter and of all others in this collection is to be found in Appendix I.

you suspected, I find not to be true. I got a large piece of ice, and insulated it in the open air when it was freezing very intensely. This I electrified, and fetched large sparks from every part of it. I also discharged a jar through it in several places, as also along a large quantity of the surface of a pond which was frozen. So that I look upon ice to be nearly as good a conductor as water.

I wrote to Dr Franklin, to acquaint him with the result of two other experiments which I desired he would communicate to you. As he may not have had an opportunity, I shall just tell you, that I have found, by experiments made with the greatest circumspection, that *air which is called mephitic*, or that in which a candle will not burn *is* (the reverse of common air) *a perfect conductor of electricity*. I have tried it with air from my lungs, and from the center of a charcoal fire. I shall soon try it with air produced by fermentation.

I have also found, that condensing air in a glass tube lessens its power of electrifying; that the addition of an atmosphere, or a little more, intirely destroys its virtue, and that it is recovered upon the readmission of the air.

I have made some of your *phosphorus* which is pretty good. Neuman in his chemistry published by Lewis says, that every selenetic earth has that property when it has been calcined. This accounts for the use of the sulphur. I wish you would read Neuman upon the subject.

We have given orders for an electrical kite, and shall make the experiments you desire with the greatest care, the first opportunity.

I mentioned to Dr Franklin the plan of a treatise I am writing on Electricity. I have brought the history of it to the year 1742 when Desaguliers wrote. I am at a stand at present for want of materials, which I expect soon to receive. Nothing I ever wrote gave me such pleasure. And I hope so full an account as I shall give of the order and manner in which the discoveries in electricity have actually been made will not be unuseful to protect discoverers. I have desired Mr Johnson to apply to you for Epinus. If you have any other books that will be of service to my design, I am sure you will not fail to communicate them.

My friends here imagine it would be a great advantage to the publication, if I were fellow of the Royal Society, and have per-suaded me to be a candidate for that honour. Dr Watson has been written to about it. I hope I need not formally ask your interest and that of Mr Price. If Ld. G. Cavendish could be prevailed upon to join you, I should think the rest would be easy. Leaving that to your conduct and friendship, I remain, with compliments to Mr Price and Dr Franklin to whom I beg you would communicate the contents of this letter! . . . .

P.S. If you think the few experiments I have made relating to Electricity would facilitate my admission to the Royal Society, I would send you a fuller account of them proper to be read before the society, and for that reason I should of a line from you or Mr Price as soon as may be convenient.

Warrington Feb. 14, 1766

No. 3.

FROM PRIESTLEY TO RICHARD PRICE

Warrington 8th Mar. 1766

Dear Sir

I have received the favour of yours, for which I think myself much obliged to you. You will by this time have received a letter I had written to you before the receipt of yours and *One Number of my history of Electricity.* I have another of them transcribed, and the quantity of two more ready to transcribe. I find I have English Materials enow, but I find a want of several foreign Articles particularly of *the method of charging other electrics besides glass said* (Phil. Trans. 57. 909) to have been first done by *Carolus Vilke* of Stockholm, and to have been published in the acts of the Stockholm Society, and also *Aepinus's first account of the Tourmalin.* If you or your friends can procure me those, or tell Mr Johnson the bookseller where to get them, you would do me an important service. I have met with materials for greatly improving the first section of the history — I know not what in the world to make of Mr Wilson's experiments on the Tourmalin, especially as I have no Tourmalin to try his experiments with. Aepinus, I find, could not repeat them after him. If they were fallacious I would not take any notice of them. Let me know Mr Canton's opinion.

I take it for granted, you have seen the letter I wrote, about a fortnight ago, to Dr Franklin. I desired he would show it to you, and Mr Canton. Writing upon a philosophical subject to any of you, I would have it considered as writing to you all. I mentioned to him an experiment I had made, and which I believe is a new one proving that there is a real current of electric matter from all electrified points, negative as well as positive. I mentioned to the Dr. the method in which I first tried it. I now exhibit the same fact in a more easy manner. I charge a vial by the inside, and place it upon a glass-stand, the outside coating in contact with a pointed wire. An inch from the point of this wire I place the flame of a candle, and then take sparks from the wire communicating with the inside. Now, according to the theory of positive and negative, for every spark of the electric fluid which comes out from the inside coating another must go to the outside, entering at the pointed wire, for there is no other way; but every time I take a spark, the flame is blown, with great violence, from the point. It is the very same, if I charge the outsides. Placing another point opposite to the former, the candle being betwixt them, the flame is nearly supported; and compleatly, if I connect that point with the wire with which I take the sparks. If I even discharge the jar, by these points, thro the flame of the candle, it is only thrown into a tremulous motion, but is not blown to one side more than another — I place wires communicating with the floor betwixt the point and the candle. These wires intercept all the electric virtue, but the current of it from the point, having begun a current in the air, that goes on, and, as far as I can perceive, as violently as before, or more so perhaps — the flame was in some measure attracted by the electric matter, and so in a small degree supported it against the current of air.

I beg you would communicate these experiments to Dr Franklin and Mr Canton, and let me know what they think of them. I shall be glad to reconcile them with the hypothesis of positive and negative electricity. At present, I own, I am rather inclined to think there are two fluids, which have strong affinity with each other, and that the action of this globe and rubber separate them, Consequently in every spark there is both a giving and taking. But I consider no hypothesis as of any use but to assist us in discovering new facts, which new facts serve in turn to correct the hypothesis; till, at length, by this method of approximating we shall have discovered all the facts, and have got a perfect theory. — I ask pardon if I was guilty of any impropriety in desiring the recommendation of Ld Ch. Cavendish. [I thought] that, if his friends Mr Canton & Dr Franklin could [not satisfy] him, from my letters (which you are pleased to supp[ose] would recommend me to the society) that I was a pers[on] properly qualified to be a member, mere personal acquaintance had been of no moment at all. My recommendation [to the] university of Edinburgh was signed by Ld Willoughby [and] Dr Chandler of whom only Ld Willoughby had the lea[st] knowledge of me. Along with that certificate, he also [wrote] to Dr Robertson in my favour, a copy of this Dr Robertson gave my friend Dr Percival, who has sent it to Dr Watson, as it may possibly be of some weight in this affair. I shall write out a full account of the new experiments I have mentioned to Dr Franklin and Mr Canton after a week or two, in which I shall have made other experiments which have a connection with them. In the mean time, my friends here think it will be best to mention them to some of the principal members, and to read the full account of them to the society about the time of election.

But I beg of you, dear Sir and Mr Canton, not to have me proposed at all (if it be not done) unless you be morally certain it will be carried. I thankfully accept the offer of your name and Mr Canton's and desire you would act in concert with Dr Watson.

No. 4.

PRIESTLEY'S ROYAL SOCIETY CERTIFICATE[3]

Joseph Priestley of Warrington, Doctor of laws, Author of a chart of Biography & Several other valuable works, a gentleman of great Merit & learning, & very well versed in Mathematical & philosophical Enquiries, being desirous of offering himself as a candidate for election into this Society, is recomended by us on our personal knowledge, as highly deserving that honour; & we believe that he will, if elected, be a usefull & valuable Member.

1	—— 13 March 1766	James Burrow	W. Watson
2	—— 20 March	Cha: Morton	
3	—— 10 April		B. Franklin
4	—— 17 April	Ballotted for	John Canton
5	—— 24 April	& Elected	Sam Chandler
6	—— 1 May		
7	—— 8 May	12 June 1766	Richd Price
8	—— 15 May	paid 25 Guineas	
9	—— 29 May		
10	—— 5th June		

No. 5.

FROM PRIESTLEY TO BENJAMIN FRANKLIN

Warrington.
25 March 1766

Dear Sir

I have received your letter, containing some remarks on my experiments, and a printed paper for the transactions which has given me very great satisfaction, and for which I think myself much

---

[3] Rutt (*Life of Priestley*, vol. 1, pp. 65–66) prints parts, at least, of three letters exchanged by Priestley and Emanuel Da Costa, Clerk of the Royal Society, about his election to the Society. While they reveal his anxiety to become a Fellow and his pleasure at his election, the letters say very little about Priestley's science.

obliged to you. I shall think myself very happy if the accounts you are pleased to permit me to send you of my imperfect experiments do but revive your attention to your once favourite study; for that seems to be universally acknowledged to be the great desideratum to further discoveries.

Immediately upon the receipt of yours, I set about pursuing the hints you gave me, and I am impatient, little as I have done, to give you an account of it. My great ambition would be to act under your auspices in the business of electricity.

I carefully repeated the experiment with *condensed air* and could perceive no more cloudiness when it could not be excited than when it could, as I have written more at large to Dr Watson, to whom I beg leave to refer you.

I have this day tried the experiment with the *vanes* and I believe I should have done it, tho not so soon, if you had not recommended it to me — I took a cork, and stuck into the sides of it (pointing directly from the center) thirteen vanes each consisting of half a common card. Into the middle of the cork I stuck a needle, by which I suspended [illegible   ] glass stand, in contact with a pointed wire projecting some inches from the jar. In this situation it is evident that for every spark that I took from the inside, one must enter at the point which communicated with the outside. — I then held the vanes about two or three inches from the point of the wire, but a little on one side, that the stream of air (if there were any) might act to advantage, on the extremities of them; and observed, that all the time I was taking sparks from the wire communicating with the inside, the vanes turned, as if strongly blown upon by a current setting from the point. In a great number of trials they never failed to turn the same way, and even if they were made to turn as much as possible the contrary way, the stream never failed to fetch them back again, and make them turn as before.

To determine whether this effect was produced by any electrical attraction or repulsion, I placed a wire communicating with the ground, between the vanes and the point, to intercept the electricity, but the vanes turned as swiftly as before. The motion was sometimes so swift, that I could hardly distinguish the separate vanes as they turned round, and the motion would continue a very considerable time.

As I never chuse to depend upon my own testimony, I called in Mr. Holt to witness the experiments, and we repeat
[ed   ]
different principles, and very agreeable to the theory of negative and positive electricity.

I shall make all the experiments you direct, and many more which I have thought of relating to *mephitic air* when my apparatus is completed, and I have finished the greatest part of my treatise on Electricity. I have sent to Mr Price *five numbers,* a quire each, and I shall send (if all be well) three more the beginning of the next week. You must only consider it as a very rough draught, but I think I have made the most of the material I have at present. I am impatient to receive the books you are so kind as to procure for me, and wish you would likewise procure me the *histoire de l'electricité* you mention. Desire Mr Canton also to favour me with his *Gilbert,* and that piece of *Otto Gueric,* if he have it, which treats of electricity. Please also to desire Mr Johnson to send me a copy of *Theophrastus,* for I have not the book, tho I rem[emb]er reading it formerly, I think, in an addition of Dr Hill's. — I have this day been favoured with a letter from Mr Price, for which I beg you would make my acknowledgements to him — After puzling myself to no purpose with some of *Mr Wilson's experiments* you will find that I have related them just as he published them, himself, with very few remarks. I thought that the most [illegible   ] directed by you what to do. . . .

[End of letter as in manuscript.]

No. 6.

FROM PRIESTLEY TO JOHN CANTON

Warrington March 29th. 1766

Dear Sir,

You will herewith receive three of the last numbers of my

history of electricity. When I wrote to Mr. Price, I seemed to desire they might be returned pretty soon, but I now beg you would take full time to peruse them, that you may give me your opinion of them at leisure, and assist me to complete them. I will let this part of the work rest 'till I have, in the same manner, drawn out a rough draught of the remainder of the treatise. In the mean time, I can keep by me a paper of hints for whatever may improve and complete the history.

I wrote to Dr. Franklin, to acquaint him with the result of an experiment, wch I made by his directions, with several vanes cut out of cards, and stuck in a cork. I have since made twenty-two vanes of pretty strong white paper, much lighter than the cards, with wch I have repeated the experiments in a variety of new circumstances; and I do assure you it is not only a very clear, but a very beautiful experiment.

I presently found, that it was not necessary to hold the vanes opposite to the end of the wire. It was sufficient to hold them within six or seven inches on either side of the wire; and I thought they turned with the most rapidity, when they were held as near as possible to the wire, and very near, but not beyond the extremity of it. Using very long wires, I found the blast far from the extremity and near the jar so broad, as to act almost equally upon all the vanes, and therefore the effect was not very certain or striking; but about half way from the extremity, the blast was very certain, and exceeding strong. And yet, when the vanes were moving with the greatest velocity, it was only removing them to the other side of the wire, and they would presently turn as strong the contrary way; and this change I could make five or six times in discharging one common jar.

When I placed the jar upon the middle of a long strait wire, the experiment was the very same at each end, and like-wise when the wire was bent, one half at right angles to the other. This experiment may easily be tried in a still greater variety of circumstances.

NB The vanes I at present use make a cylinder, three inches in diameter, and two inches and a half in length. They weigh [this space left blank in the MS]. They are sustained by a magnet as the others.

I must now ask pardon of you, and my other electrical friends in London, for troubling you too soon with my experiments on mephitic air; for, decisive as they then appeared to me, and others who were present when they were made, I found, yesterday, that they were ambiguous. In the account which you have seen of those experiments, I did not fail to mention every circumstance which appeared to me to have the least influence on them, but I did not attend to one circumstance which I now find to be of the greatest moment. The receiver in wch I made the experiments was four inches and an half in diameter, and seven or eight inches high; and I think I observed, (tho I have no copy of the former letter) that whether I filled the receiver with air from my lungs or from the centre of a charcoal fire, there was no appearance of any cloudiness in the receiver, but what might adhere to the sides of the vessel; and, in so large a space, could not affect the air in the centre, where the small charged phial was put. I think I also observed, that when I changed the air in the receiver, in order to shew that the discharge had not been made by passing the phial thro the neck of the receiver, I wiped it with a cloth on the inside, but it was with no other intention than to clear it more effectually of all the mephitic air. After this, the phial was never in the least discharged by introducing it thro the neck of the receiver, as it had been when it contained the mephitic air.

On repeating these experiments, as I have done many times, with the same success, since I wrote the account of them, and varying the circumstances; I found, that if the receiver was not wiped on the inside, and the air was only changed by moving it several times backwards and forwards in the open air, the phial was discharged in the common air now contained in the receiver, as completely as if it had been mephitic. I then took a receiver perfectly dry, and slightly moistening the inside of it with a wet spunge (but leaving all the part about the neck quite dry) I found, that the phial, let down into it by a silken thread, was presently discharged, tho it was kept as far as possible from the sides, and tho not the least cloudiness was visible, or hardly to be conceived in the middle of the receiver. Besides, it had only stood a few seconds after being wetted, before the experiment was made.

I propose very soon, to try the experiment with air produced by fermentation, and also with air that is inflammable. in which, I think, there will be no moisture or cloudiness of any kind. The vapour from charcoal is often very considerable.

I cannot yet help smiling to think how much I was confirmed in my opinion, that mephitic air is a conductor of electricity, by several new experiments I had been making upon it, just before the above discovery of this ambiguity. I had let down cork balls, suspended by silk, and found that the electricity with which they were charged was presently taken off. and I placed a coated phial, in a receiver containing mephitic air, and found it impossible to charge it in the least degree, tho', the moment before and after, it was charged in the same situation, but surrounded with common air, with great ease. But a few minutes after I found these, and all the other experiments I had made on mephitic air, to mean nothing.

However, notwithstanding this ambiguity, if one think on the subject a priori, it may not appear improbable that mephitic air (wch is so remarkably different from common air in other respects) should differ from it also with respect to electricity. Mephitic air failed, indeed, to conduct a shock but so does a wet thread, and various other pretty good conductors of common electricity.

Dr. Franklin, in his letter to me upon the subject, proposes to put equal burning candles in mephitic, and in common air, till that in the mephitic air be extinct, or for a *shorter* equal time. But it is impossible to keep the flame of a candle, for the least sensible space of time, in mephitic air. It will be extinguished in the very neck of the receiver, where there is a very considerable mixture of common air with it; as there necessarily must be in my method of collecting mephitic air, viz. by the receiver of an air pump, and a brass pipe, both which must contain some common air.

At the same time that I was repeating the experiments with mephitic air, I amused myself with making some with *hot air*, and particularly those which you mention in your answer to Mr. Deleval, and I found them in all respects the same with those before described as made with mephitic air.

[25]

I placed a lighted candle within a few inches of my conductor, and could not get one spark from it. I held a charged jar near the flame, and also near a coal fire, and, in both cases, it was instantly discharged. But I found that those effects were not owing (as I think you seemed to suppose) to the rarifaction of the air by heat. For the phial was completely discharged by being held about a second of time, within three inches off the flame of a common candle, where, by an accurate air thermometer, there was no sensible rarifaction at all. Besides, I could heat the phial itself before I charged it, much hotter than it could have been by being placed, for so short a span of time, at such a distance from the flame; when it might be well charged, notwithstanding. Also, I could bring it much nearer to a large piece of red hot glass, without discharging it in the least. The discharge, therefore, made by the candle must have been by means of some invisible conducting effluvia proceeding from it. I could draw the phial thro the thinner part of the smoke of a coal fire without discharging much of it, but I could not draw the phial thro the flame of the candle, or of the burning coals, tho in the swiftest manner that I could, without intirely discharging it.

The phial which I used for this purpose, (and which is extremely convenient for many others) is about two inches and an half in length, and a little more than half an inch in diameter, coated half way. Two or three turns of my globe will make it discharge itself. I hold it by the wire, which is very long, and always charge the outside.

Before I quit this subject, I would just observe, that when the candle was insulated the effect was always the same as when it was not insulated.

When I made the experiments mentioned above, I found an easier method of proving that *red hot glass is a conductor of electricity,* than that about wch I wrote to you before. Laying a red hot glass tube along this charged phial, so as to be opposite both to the wire and the coating, the phial was discharged, not silently, as it would have been if it had been done by the rarified air, but with two pretty strong sparks upon the glass, the one at the wire, and the other at the coating; tho the sound made by the explosion was but dull. When I discharged the same phial with a bar of red hot iron, I observed, that it was done, as if by points, the electric fire appearing like a lambent flame in the two places, and the explosion was very light. It is well known, that hot iron always takes the electric fire from a common conductor as if by points, and the electric fire may be seen very distinctly upon the red hot iron.

I thought it something remarkable, that tho the red hot glass tube discharged the phial by strong sparks, I could not make it take a strong spark from the conductor, tho I held an iron wire in my hand, wch was put within the tube, and reached to the hot part of it. It exhibited only a lambent flame tho I presented a pretty broad and smooth part to the conductor. But I intend to repeat this experiment with more care.

In drawing my small charged phial thro steam from a boiling kettle, the smoke of coal fire, or the vapour which arises from burning charcoal, it was equally discharged by them all; but it could not be charged again after being drawn thro the steam without wiping; whereas it might easily be charged immediately after being drawn thro the smoke of the fire, or the vapour of the charcoal, without wiping.

I have got a very good *kite* made of oiled silk, and shall soon have upon the top of our academy, which is pretty high a very good apparatus for collecting electricity from the clouds. With these I propose to make the experiments you desired me to make, with all the attention I am capable of. But I could wish to have a fine brass wire twisted in the string of the kite and it will require a great quantity of wire and a considerable time to prepare it. If you could send me a thermometer, barometer, and hygrometer, so constructed, as to tell what the state of the air *has been* in any interval of time, I will send them up with the kite, and by measuring the height at which it flies (which will not be difficult) perhaps some observations may be made worth your notice.

I hope you will excuse my employing an amanuensis in this long letter. Writing much in long hand is irksome to me. If writing letters be in the least inconvenient, or disagreeable to you, as it is to many persons I beg you would only give me your sentiments, as occasion may require, by Mr Price, or any other of my friends in London, who do correspond with me. I shall think myself sufficiently honoured by being permitted to transmit my imperfect experiments and projects to a person so excellently qualified to inform and direct me. I shall always reckon my late journey to London as one of the most favourable circumstances in my life, as it gained me such a valuable acquaintance.

I shall be much obliged to you for *Gilbert de Magnete,* or any other book that you may have, & that you think would be of service to me.

The numbers of the history I herewith send you do not quite finish it, but what remains is nothing considerable. Also I have deferred writing the history of experiments on the *Tourmalin,* till I can get (which I wish you could assist me in) *AEpinus's first observation* upon it, and till I can determine what to do with Mr. Wilson's strange account of it. —— I beg you would make very free with the blank page of MS. It was left for that very purpose —— I do not know which of my experiments I can draw an account of, to lay before the Royal Society. In the experiment with hot glass, I find, since I wrote to you, that I have been in some measure anticipated by Mr. Kinnersly, who could not charge a Florence flask filled with boiling water. And even the blast from electrified points upon a cand[le] I was surprized to find, mentioned by Nollet, but he did not make it with any accuracy, or with a sufficient variety of circumstances, and he argues very absurdly from it. He did not think there was any current of air at all in the [c]ase —— I should as soon think the rays of light might blow out a large candle, turn a heavy set of vanes with great velocity, as the electrical fluid, by mere impulse.

All my other experiments want pursuing, and diversifying, before they can be fit to lay them before the public. I mention them to you, as to a friend in whom I put confidence, and who will point out any circumstances I may appear not to have attended to, and thereby prevent my drawing hasty conclusions from them and imposing upon myself, or others. . . .

No. 7.

FROM PRIESTLEY TO BENJAMIN FRANKLIN

Warrington. 13 Apr. 1766

Dear Sir

I this day received your favour of the 10th instant, and the day before yesterday another letter, with several parcels of books, containing all that are mentioned in your letters. At the same time I received a parcel from Dr. Watson, containing, among others, the same history of electricity which you have sent me —— I shall immediately apply myself to the purusal of them all, with the greatest attention, and I make no doubt but from these, and other books which I hope you will be able to procure me, I shall make many valuable additions to my history. I need not tell you, that you will find it, in the condition in which it comes into your hands, very imperfect. It contains indeed every [thing] that the materials I then had by me [illegible   ], but [some] very important articles have already [come] my way. When Mr Canton sends me his *Gilbert,* [I will] not fail to inrich my work with a particular accoun[t of] all that he did in electricity. If I cannot get *Otto Gueric,* I must copy what is said of him in the history you have sent me.

I shall be very glad to hear your remarks on my experiments with the *vanes,* tho' I am quite satisfied, that it is perfectly agreeable to your general theory. You will find some additional experiments with the vanes in my letter to Mr Canton.

Since I sent my last two numbers to Mr. Price, I have neither written a line on the subject of electricity, nor made any experiments of consequence, having been wholly employed in constructing an electrical machine upon a new, and, I think, in many respects, an improved plan. I propose to give a particular description and a cut of it in the book.

I have not repeated my experiments with *condensed air* since I wrote to Dr Watson, but in a piece of Boulanger which he has sent me I find that the same experiment had been made before, and with the same success. This author adds, that the impossibility

[29]

of exciting a tube in which air is condensed cannot be owing to moisture, as some suspect; for if a drinking glass full of water be poured into the tube, and poured out again, it will not destroy its electrifying power so effectually as the condensed air. He adds, in another place, that Marcasites are incapable of being excited, chiefly on account of the condensed air that is in them. This last is certainly a very groundless supposition. I think, with you and Dr Watson, that the effect is, some way or other, owing to moisture. Mr Boulanger did not know, that when the [tube] was heated it might be excited, tho' it did contain [condensed air.] This is not the first or second time [in] which I [have found] myself anticipated in experiments which I imag[ined h]ad been originally my own. The blast from electrified [poin]ts, and even the blowing of the candle is I find mentioned by Nollet. But he did not pursue the experiment, and he argues very weakly from it. —— I am ashamed when I think of the experiment with *mephitic air,* but I made use of every precaution I could think of, and others were deceived as well as myself. ——

I was yesterday favoured with a letter from Mr Canton. Please to present my compliments to him. Tell him I thank him for the curious particulars it contains, and that I shall, with great pleasure, make the use of them that he desires, as well as strictly conform to every thing else that he requests of me. I sincerely ask his pardon for my hasty misapprehension of his observations on *hot air,* but I think he will find that I have not made that mistake in the history. When I have made some more experiments on *hot air* and on *effluvia,* I will write to him again.

I shall not forget the motto of your seal. I consider Mr Wilson's performance in the same light that you do.

If electrics naturally contain more of the electric fluid than other bodies, should not red hot glass, as it cools, draw the fluid from the bodies with which it is in contact? I placed a piece of red hot glass and let it cool upon a very smooth piece of insulated copper, without perceiving any such effect.

I hope you will be able to procure me *Beccaria.* I am sorry that *Wilke's* piece is not complete. I greatly admire *AEpinus.* —— I hope you will make very free with the blank page of my MSS. I

shall be sorry if I find but little [up]on it. — I am much obliged
to [illegible   ] his expla[nati]on of two latin terms. If
[illegible   ] take of that kind, I hope you will
[illegible   ]sometimes inclosed French words in brai
[illegible   ] doubtful of my rendering of them. . . .

No. 8.

FROM PRIESTLEY TO JOHN CANTON

Warrington. 18 Apr. 1766.

Dear Sir

I have this day been favoured with your obliging letter of the
15th in which you say you have made some experiments that
plainly show you, that the vanes in my experiments are not
turned by a blast, or current of air from an electrified point; but
by electrical repulsion. Tho' I differ from you in opinion, I
rejoice in having engaged your attention to this subject. Could
but Dr Franklin, Dr Watson, and yourself be once more seriously
engaged in these pursuits, something very considerable, I am
confident, might yet be done in electricity. Should I be nothing
more than the means of reviving this attention, I should not think
I have lived in vain.

If you will take the trouble to reperuse my letters to Dr Franklin and Mr Price, upon the subject of the flame and the vanes,
you will find that I never had any doubt of their being affected,
both by electrical attraction and repulsion; but I observed (what, I
think, you do not seem to have attended to) that, in order to take
off this effect of electricity, both with respect of the flame and the
vanes, I placed small wires communicating with the ground betwixt the electrified point and them. These wires must necessarily
take off all the effects of electricity, whatever they were, but a current of air having reached the wires must go on. So that whatever
effects were produced beyond those wires must be ascribed to that
current, and not to electricity. Beyond those wires the flame of a
candle was blown out, and the vanes turned with great rapidity.

As you advised me, I dipped my vanes in water, which, as you

[31]

say, would make them a pretty good conductor. The consequence was, that they moved faster than before. This I apprehend necessarily followed from the circulation of the electrical fluid, and consequently of the air being thereby quickened.

I also made a set of vanes of *Tinsel,* which is both thinner and lighter than the paper I had used, and a far better conductor than paper could be made by wetting. These, when they were not insulated, could hardly be supposed to retain so much electricity as to be repelled by the electrified wire, yet they turned with more velocity than the paper vanes; owing (as in the case of the wet paper vanes) to the freer circulation of the electrical fluid, and the consequent brisker current of air. These tinsel vanes, however, did not move around with the same certainty when they were held by the side of the wire, because the electrical attraction prevailed over the current of air.

When a small wire was held betwixt the vanes and the point, they turned with the same swiftness, as near as the eye could distinguish. When the wires were held very near the point, the blast was more feeble, the space through which the electricity passed being shorter, and consequently the air having less space to be accelerated in. When the wires were interposed, it was easy to perceive that no electricity reached the vanes; for whenever it did, it was visible in a spark betwixt the needle and the magnet.

I then made a set of vanes like *a smoke jack,* and held them over the point of the wire turned upwards; when no one vane was nearer the point than another, and yet the motion was as certain and rapid as before, and made a much more beautiful experiment than ever. Though the set of vanes was only three inches in diameter, they were turned more than a foot above the point. When the point was turned downwards, and the vanes held under it, they turned with as much rapidity the contrary way.

These experiments were all carefully made, in the presence of good judges, and with every variation of circumstances that we could think of, with points from positive and negative conductors, and from charged phials; with wire interposed and not, and with the vanes insulated or not insulated &c. The motion was generally so rapid that you cou[ld] not distinguish the separate vanes as they whirled, and [yet] they would often stop and turn the contrary way, when they [were] removed to a different situation with respect to the point, often in the space of about two seconds.

Presenting the flame of a candle to the point, we observed, (what I had not taken notice of before) that when held very near it was attracted much more strongly to it when it was electrified negatively than positively. Though when held about an inch from it, the current of air prevailed so much above the electrical attraction as to endanger blowing the candle out, and a very large one too.

From these experiments I have, at present, no doubt of the reality of the current of air, and a considerable one too; but I shall with pleasure attend to whatever you shall offer to show the contrary, and in this or any other case, the moment I am convinced I shall acknowledge it. Dr Franklin said he should write to me upon this subject please to show him this letter as soon as you conveniently can.

I shall be much obliged to you for the books you mention. I am writing nothing at present, being wholly employed in constructing an electrical apparatus, which will soon be a very complete one. — I had a good deal more to say to you, but have no room at present, but to conclude myself. . . .

P.S. I have this moment recd. your books frm. Mr Johnson and am much obliged to you for them.

No. 9.

From Priestley to John Canton

Warrington 30 June 1766

Dear Sir

Since I wrote to Mr Price I have heard of my election into the Royal Society, for which I think myself much obliged to your interest, and that of my other electrical friends. but if you would not have me disgrace your recommendation, you or Mr Price must write to me a little oftener, and make remarks upon my experiments. It will not be possible for me, without that, to keep up my attention to the subject — Since my letter to Mr Price, in which I mentioned the *circular spot* upon the metal knobs used in making explosions, I have examined several of them with great attention with a microscope, and upon a gold watch, have found a great number of globules, which have radiant points, and look very dazling in the sun. They are easily distinguished from the hollow places, by having the radiant point on different sides with respect to the light, when they are held in the sun-shine. I suppose the metal is first melted, then, being liquid, it is thrown forward, or rises, as water would do. This sometimes makes the bubbles above mentioned, the greatest part of which burst, and leave hollows. The hollows are four or five times as deep in the gold as the silver, which is melted very superficially. What I think most remarkable in these spots is *another external circle,* which I have observed since I wrote to Mr Price, consisting, like the former, of small spots perfectly melted, but much smaller than the other. The first of these I received upon a piece of Tin, the second on pewter, and two last (but imperfect) on brass. The most perfect is on pewter and has the following appearance, which I must delineate from my memory, being now at the house of a friend where I have not it by me. This is not far from the true size, but 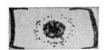 the external circle is rather fainter than I have drawn it, yet it may very easily be seen with the naked eye. All the black spots represent melted places. Qu. Can these spots be produced by a simple fluid, the particles of which do only mutually repel one another. Would not the effect in that case be greatest in the center, and vanish gradually towards the extremities? Quer 2 / Is not this appearance analogous to the case of the five men of whom the first, third, and fifth were struck dead by a stroke of lightning, while the second and fourth escaped? I have many more observations on these spots, but they are too minute for a letter. —— Thinking to enlarge my battery in the cheapest manner I got 3 *Florence flasks* but to my great surprise found them all *permeable to electricity* without breaking. It would be tiresome to go over all the experiments that demonstrate it. You will easily imagine them, and the result of them all was the same. Mr Kinnersley found one of them permeable to electricity with boiling water in it. I wonder he did not try it when cold. They hold a very small charge, and then all the rest goes through.

I have made a great number of *experiments on animals,* for some of which I refer to a letter I lately wrote to Dr Watson. Since I wrote to him, I discharged 37 Square feet of coated glass through the head and tail of a CAT three or four years old. She was instantly seized with universal convulsions, then lay as dead a few seconds, after that succeeded tremblings in different parts of the body, particularly in the sides; which terminated in a violent convulsive respiration, and that in as quick a breathing, for $\frac{1}{4}$ of an hour, as can be imagined; after about 20 Minutes she was able to raise her head, and move her fore feet, but not her hind feet in the least, though the shock did not go through these. Thinking she would probably die a lingering death in consequence of the stroke, I gave her a second, about half an hour after the first. She was seized, as before, with universal convulsions, and in the convulsive respiration which suceeded she expired. She was dissected with great care, but nothing particular was observed, except a great redness on the lungs, but no extravasation anywhere. It was impossible to bring her to life by forcing air into her lungs. —— I have been this day discharging large shocks through small wires and leaves of Iron, copper, silver and gold pressed between glass plates. But the pieces of glass have always been broken and the fragments dispersed with such violence that no large pieces can be found. They are all deeply tinged with the melted metal. However I can scrape off the tinge in all but the gold. These are exceeding beautiful. When held in one light they are of a gold colour, when held in another of a fine purple.

I beg I may hear from you or Mr Price soon, and let have your remarks upon some of my experiments. . . .

No. 10.

FROM PRIESTLEY TO BENJAMIN FRANKLIN

Dear Sir

I wrote to Mr Price last post, in which I desired him to remind you of your promise to procure me *Beccaria's work,* which you said you thought you could do of Mr Delaval. Fearing he might not see you soon, I write to desire you to get it for me, if possible, without loss of time. Otherwise, I must reserve his experiments for an *Appendix*; for, by the references I meet with to them, I find my book absolutely must not come abroad without them. I am in such haste, as we have already begun to print, and have done five sheets. The whole work will make betwixt 400 & 500 pages 4to, and we shall not have done quite so soon as Christmas. For the same reason, I must beg you would also send me, as soon as you conveniently can, the two last numbers of the work, which I left in the hand of Dr Watson, to be transmitted to you. I am now wholly employed in revising and correcting. I defer drawing up the account of my own experiments, till I have some more in puruance of them, and several others. In about a week I shall betake myself to experiments in good earnest, but I have no expectation of doing much more than I have done. Upon Mr Price's letter, I sent the mark that was actually made by a chain, when a discharge was sent thro it. I have several times since I came home got *three* and almost always *two* concentric circles, upon the metal knobs with which I make discharges. — If I verify your experiments on the *electrified cup,* and *animal fluids,* may I publish them as yours, in some proper place in my work? I shall soon go about them. — Have you procured the *list of books* written on the subject of electricity, or the remainder of *Wilkes's treatise.* — Dr Watson has sent me a curious tract of *Johannes Franciscus Cigna,* which I am now digesting. — In your note on one of my former numbers you say, you question whether Aeolipyle will turn the same way whether it draw in, or throw out the water. I had tried it before I wrote the paragraph, you may depend upon the fact. — I hope to find more of your excellent remarks upon the two numbers in your hands. . . .

Warrington. 21 Sepbr. 1766.

Since I wrote the letter, I have made a discharge, through a chain that lay on this side of it. At the moment of the discharge, the whole appeared like a bright flame. From (a) where the chain was returned, it was thrown back as far as (b). I have tried the same several times since, laying one half of a chain parallel to the other, and marking exactly how far it reached upon the table; and always found the middle part pulled back about one inch and a hal[f, as] if a sudden jerk had been given [to] it. Indeed it was manifest, by comparing the link with the mark, that every link had moved a little. Must not that have been effected by the links repelling one another, while the shock was passing? Is not the paper really *burnt?* Was not the chain made superficially hot? and does not the electric shock pass chiefly over the surfaces of bodies? so that small bodies will be melted, because they have most surface in proportion to their bulks. NB The faint marks, at a distance from the rest, are not made [by] handling. They are just as the discharge left them. Indeed you will find they are not easily effaced. NB The [wire] of the chain is not so thick as the marks.

[A note by Jared Sparks (ed., *The Works of Benjamin Franklin,* vol. 6, pp. 273–275), appended to his copy of this letter, says, "On the face of the original letter, from which the above has been copied, the marks of the chain are still distinctly visible as here described, it being seventy-one years since the experiment was performed. The marks are of a yellow green color."]

No. 11.

FROM JOHN CANTON TO PRIESTLEY

10 Jany. 1767

Dear Sir

I have this morning received your letter to Dr Franklin on the tourmaline by the penny post, and have since repeated all your experiments. I own I am quite unable to account for the difference between your tourmalines and mine, unless you so managed the tourmaline that the heat of one side of it was increasing while that of the other side was decreasing, and then indeed it must act in the manner you describe. I suspended the down with a single thread of the silk worm and when it was electrified by one side of the tourmaline it was constantly repelled by that side, and on turning the other side towards it, it was strongly attracted and would fly to the stone from the distance of about 2 or 3 inches but on withdrawing the stone the side that was last presented to the down would repel it and the other attract it, and so on 'till the stone had lost all its electricity. For my trials on two pieces of down I constantly found they would repel each other when electrified by the same side of the tourmaline but attract each other and meet when electrified by different sides. To heat my tourmaline I put it between two bars of the grate into a hollow place made in the middle of the fire of 2 or 3 inches diameter and held it there about a minute by a bent piece of brass which touches it nowhere except on 2 opposite points of its edge. If you think proper to publish your experiments on the tourmaline you may if you please mention them not succeeding with . . . John Canton. . . .

P. S. I may perhaps not have another opportunity of writing to you on this subject before your history is published but will be glad to have as many letters from you as you have time to send me without your troubling Dr Franklin with them. Mr Price called upon me while I was writing this P. S. and I showed him the experiment which convinced him that you must in some way or other be mistaken. I have lately been making experiments on the electrified cup of Dr Franklin which I find does not *contain* any mystery in electricity: I expect the Dr in a few days to see the experiments. If heat as you imagine only disposes the tourmaline to collect electricity as friction does glass pray how do you account for the following experiment which I have sent you before. Jan. 8, 1762 Having placed a small tin cup of boiling water on any end of my electrometer which was supported by warm glass and two balls suspended at the other end I dropped into the water Dr Heberden's largest tourmaline and during the whole time of its heating and also while it was cooling in the water the balls were found not to be at all electrified. In my register for Jan. 8, 1762 I also find the following observation: having placed Dr Heberden's largest tourmaline (of which see a description in the 51st vol. of the Philosophical Transactions page 316) edgeways on a heated poker when not so hot as to make the air a conductor I found while the tourmaline was heating the convex side of it was electrified minus and the plane side plus whereas when taken out of boiling water or (which is much better) from within two inches of an almost surrounding fire while it was cooling the convex side was electrified plus and the plane side minus. . . .

No. 12.

FROM PRIESTLEY TO RICHARD PRICE

Dear Sir

This day I have received your obliging letter, and some time before, those from Dr Franklin and Mr Canton, for all which I think myself much obliged to you. These letters, and those I received from you all about the *electrified vanes,* convince me, that the only method to make you have recourse to your apparatus, is to contradict you. I am sorry that I was not sufficiently aware of this before, I would have found you all work enough. At present this business is nearly over with me.

I can see no fallacy in the experiments on the Tourmalin, of which I sent you an account, and, the day after I wrote my last about it, I had a stronger appearance of the same nature; and yet, before I had heard from any of you, these appearances ceased gradually, till I now verify all Mr Canton's experiments, except one. I have exactly noted all the variations, and made no alteration whatever in my method of treating it, and yet cannot repeat the former experiments. I am sensible you will pay no regard to this account, but that I cannot help. I report what I see, you must judge of the facts, and my skill in exhibiting them. — I have since made some new experiments with the Tourmalin, which I am afraid you will find no objection to. I lay a small piece of glass on the standard bar of Mr. Ellicot's pyrometer, and upon the glass the Tourmalin; and which side so ever I lay upon the glass, I always find the both sides of the glass, and it possessed of the opposite electricities; and, upon the whole, equally strong; except that when the convex side of the T–n is laid upon the glass, they are both positive. Imagining, however, that this was owing to the Tourmalin touching it in so few points, that it derived its electricity from the air, in preference to the glass, to which it afterwards communicated it; I, this day, got an impression taken of the convex side of the T–n in Plaister of Paris, and observe, that when it is thus heated in contact with every part, the stone is negative, and the plaister positive in heating, and in cooling, the stone is positive, and the plaister as strongly negative. They affect the same thread in different ways, at the distance of 4 and 5 inches. It would be tedious to recite all the particulars of these experiments, you will see them soon. If these experiments deceive me, I shall say the stone is bewitched. Hitherto they have been exceeding striking and constant. And I have now acquired such dexterity in managing these little matters, and have my electrometers &c in such excellent discipline, that I shall hardly yield to any body in these things except, perhaps, Mr Canton. — The thing in which I differ from Mr Canton is, that I find the electricity of the two sides never fails to change, tho' the stone be not touched by my body, in heating or cooling. I do assure you I am very glad of this small difference. I hope it will make mr. Canton bring out his

T–n once more, and send me an account of the experiment from which he drew his conclusions; but I shall not say that he is at all mistaken, tho' the result of our experiments be quite different.

I have not yet done with the Tourmalin, tho' it has used me so ill. I have been busy in completing my old experiments, and drawing up an account of them; which is now twice as large as when you saw it. A few things I have done that are new, but hardly worth mentioning.

Having struck a dog blind with the discharge of my battery, I found the blindness to be an *albugo* occasioned by inflammation; and not a *gutta serena*, as I should have imagined.

I cannot find the [electrification by] *freezing*.

In sending the same explosion thro' wires of dif[ferent] metals, I find that, if I join a piece of copper [to one] of brass or iron wire, of the same length and thickness, the [brass] vanishes, and the copper is untouched; also [iron . . . is] when brass is untouched. So that these [conduct in] the following order. Copper, Brass, Iron. [I have] sent for more wire from Liverpool. I could assort [them] all in one evening, and the experiments are clear [and] pleasing. —— Disappointments with printers have made me keep continuing my experiments so long, but I must very soon give over, tho' I have almost everything in the middle but the more I do, the more I see may be done.

Hartley quotes the Essay you mention, as what gave him some hints, but it is in many respects different from his sentiments. It is not fair to charge one another with those consequences of our opinions which we disclaim. Were I to follow that rule, I could draw a much blacker picture of your sentiments than you do of mine. . . .

Warrington. 21 Jan. 1767.

[41]

No. 13.

FROM PRIESTLEY TO JOHN CANTON

Warrington. 28ᵗʰ Jan 1767.

Dear Sir

I fancy Mr. Price will have shown you my letter containing experiments on the tourmalin, and of my not being able to repeat all yours. I have since made another course of experiments on it, by which I can make either side of the stone in heating or cooling, positive or negative at pleasure, with the greatest certainty. Heating or cooling it in contact with the palm of my hands, is in all cases exactly the reverse of heating or cooling it in contact with the air. I have tried it in all the possible varieties, and can command either power, and change them several times alternately, in the course of one heating or cooling, by keeping it on my hand, or heting [heating?] it a little in the air. I have tried several of the experiments with the tourmalin in contact with quicksilver, and also with sealing wax, when it is contrary to what it would be in the open air, and the quicksilver or wax are always the reverse of the stone —— The experiments with the palm of my hand are so pleasing, that I have almost blistered my hand in making them. It would be too tedious to tell you the views I had in these experiments, and all the particulars of them.

I have made the stone cool in *vacuo* and noted the effects. I hav made Tourmalins heat and cool in contact with one another, in all varieties. But I met with nothing worth telling you.

Heated in boiling *oil* it acts very well, and when buried in a stick of sealing wax I could deceive any body with it. The positive and negative sides are as striking as in the naked stone.

I have made a number of experiments to investigate the appearances I first sent you an account of; for there could be no fallacy or mistake in them, as you all suppose. I can often make both sides positive, & till it be quite cold. But I dispair of doing with design, what I then did without any design.

I have made other miscellaneous experiments but nothing worth mentioning. . . .

They have begun to print my own experiments. The work will be almost too large for one volume. I wish I could have foreseen how large it would be.

No. 14.

FROM PRIESTLEY TO JOHN CANTON

Warrington. 21 Aprl 1767

Dear Sir

I have been so often troublesome to you, that I am almost ashamed to apply to you again so soon, but I have no friend in London, on whose judgment I can so much rely, with respect to philosophical instruments. At Warrington I have the use of a pretty good apparatus; but I am about to remove to Leeds in Yorkshire, and therefore shall have occasion to purchase several for myself, to complete my own set of instruments. Every thing that is made in plain wood, or plain brass work I can get made under my own inspection, much cheaper, and, I think, better than I could get it in London: But there are some things that cannot be done in the country, and for these I must beg leave to be, now and then, troublesome to you. I want chiefly a good *microscope for opaque objects,* and a good *telescope;* and with respect to both shall be obliged to you both for your advice and assistance. I was much pleased with the construction of your microscope in which you shewed me the small brass globules. It was a Liburkun's [Lieberkuhn's] with a *stem* and a *concave mirror:* therefore unless you know of a better, I wish you would get one of those made for me, either by Mr Nairne, or who you please. the plainer and cheaper the better, provided every part be as good as it can be made for use — I have a Wilson's for transparent objects.

As to the *Telescope* I should not chuse to go the expense of one that would show the belts of Jupiter, or the Satellites of Saturn; and therefore one by which I could with ease and certainty just see the *moons of Jupiter* would be quite sufficient; and for that purpose I think *glass* is on many accounts preferable to *metal,* for country use. Suppose you got me a *Dolland.* Would not one for

[43]

three or four guineas answer the purpose abovementioned? If not, a common one of four — five or six feet would do.

I wish you would give me your opinion of the *Globes* that Mr Adams advertises, and the price of them. I have got [illegible] 12 Inches, but can perhaps sell them before I leave Warrington.

Electricity is at present very much out of my thoughts; but I promise myself another winter's campaign when I get to Leeds, in which case I shall be glad to renew our correspondence on that subject. I shall to hear your impartial opinion of my history, now that you have the whole work before you. It is very probable that you will not approve of the light in which I have represented several of the articles, particularly some of Beccaria's discoveries, and the theory of two electric fluids; but I followed my best judgment at the time . . . .

There are no clues which satisfactorily explain Priestley's turning in late 1765 from an interest in chemistry to a study of electricity. His early possession of an electrical machine is hardly sufficient to outweigh the emphasis on chemistry revealed in his academic studies and the course in chemistry taught by Turner at Warrington, while the chemical laboratory established there would have provided him with the apparatus and chemical substances needed for experimentation.[4] Nor can the suggestion, made by Priestley in his *Memoirs* that it was the influence of Price, Canton, Watson, and Franklin that started his work on the *History of Electricity* remain unmodified. Seddon's letter (No. 1) makes it obvious that Priestley's meeting with Canton and Franklin was deliberately sought, while there are some indications that he may have commenced writing the *History* before his trip to London. It is probable that he began that trip shortly after the date of Seddon's letter of introduction (18 December 1765). On 9 January 1766 he attended a meeting of the Royal Society.[5]

[4] Priestley purchased an electrical machine while at Nantwich; see *supra,* p. 6; for his chemical studies, see pp. 6, 8–11.

[5] Record Book of the Royal Society, vol. 25 (1763–1766), p. 707; Archives of the Royal Society.

The tone of the 14 February letter to Canton being that of a first courtesy letter to a new and helpful acquaintance, it seems reasonable to suggest that Priestley remained in London from approximately 18 December 1765 at least through the early part of January 1766. To have begun the organization of his materials, performed the five sets of experiments described in his letter (No. 2), and also written the sixty-three quarto pages with their seventy-eight references to seventeen different books or journal articles — necessary to bring the *History* "to the year 1742" — all in the time remaining after his return to Warrington, seems most unlikely. His trip to London must be regarded as a search for support and assistance in a project he had already commenced.

Whatever his reasons for the change, Priestley was soon deeply involved in electrical experiments. His references to Canton's "phosphorus" and William Lewis' edition of Neuman's *Chemical Works* (No. 2), and to "mephitic air" (Nos. 2, 6) indicate that he had not entirely abandoned chemical research — as, indeed, we might expect from his comments in the *History of Electricity* that a combination of electricity, chemistry, and optics might be a fruitful path to the understanding of the nature of matter.[6] Nevertheless, the dominant topic in his scientific correspondence from 1765 through 1767 was electricity, and the span of letters written during that period shows an increasing command of his subject and, very quickly, an independence of his advisors.

In Canton, Franklin, and Watson, he had chosen as his mentors the most eminent of British electricians, while Richard Price demonstrated throughout a long career in theology, politics, and actuarial mathematics a vigorous common sense that was always useful. Although these men had not suggested to Priestley the writing of his *History of Electricity*, they had certainly supported the idea with enthusiasm. As the cor-

---

[6] Priestley, *History of Electricity*, pp. xii, 502–503.

respondence shows, they were able to supply him with many of the published materials he needed in his research and they examined the book in sections as it was written. It is also apparent that they suggested to him the earliest of his electrical experiments, "to endeavour to ascertain several facts which were disputed," but also, as in the case of the electrical kite (Nos. 2, 6), to gain new information. When his results in these and later in his own experiments failed to agree with those of his correspondents, he maintained his position, even to the point of occasionally doubting the single fluid theory of Franklin and Watson, though he mitigated his doubting by adopting Franklin's near-positivist definition of an hypothesis as a device "to assist us in discovering facts" (No. 3).[7]

Almost at once Priestley shows that ability to diversify experiments and to design new ones which was one of his most distinguishing characteristics as a scientist. As anyone knows who has tried (or watched others trying) them, exact experiments in static electricity are not easy to make. Equipment generally is crude, voltages are high, but currents are low, so that small variations in atmospheric conditions, or even in the configurations of objects in the laboratory, can vary results with seeming indiscriminateness. Yet, though electricity had excited scientists in Europe at least since the days of Stephen Gray (d. 1736) and had been almost a popular amusement since Franklin's discoveries were first published between 1747 and 1754, Priestley began to make original discoveries. The first two of these that he announced to his friends were, indeed, not discoveries at all — the conductivity of hot glass having been discovered earlier and the conductivity of mephitic air

[7] See I. Bernard Cohen, *Franklin and Newton* (Philadelphia, American Philosophical Society, Memoir 43, 1956), pp. 343–353, for a discussion of Franklin's views of scientific theories and, incidentally, of Priestley's debt to Franklin in the formulation of his philosophy of science. We may also assume that Priestley's predilection for rushing into print (see the Preface, p. vi above) derives from Franklin, whose similar views are quoted by Cohen, p. 71.

being an error induced by moisture in the gases used in the experiment. Since the time wasted. in rediscovering a previously unnoticed discovery served to reinforce the value of writing a history of electrical studies, while the mephitic air experiment led Priestley to a true discovery, the conductivity of charcoal (described in his *History of Electricity,* pp. 602–603, but not in any of the letters so far unearthed), even these abortive experiments proved useful to him.

These experiments are interesting also as the beginning of Priestley's marked interest in conductivity and comparative resistances, an interest best exemplified in this series of letters by those experiments which relate metallic conductivities to the comparative ease of melting wires by electric shock (No. 12). Priestley's contributions to the study of resistances are among his most important as an electrician.[8]

The experiments on that "real current of electric matter from all electrified points" (Nos. 3, 6, 7, 8, 12) also relate to significant work, though the Abbé Nollet may, as Priestley suggests, have hinted at it earlier, and Benjamin Wilson certainly wrote on the subject as early as 1750. Against the opposition of Canton, Price, and Franklin, Priestley supports the experimental evidence and his interpretations of it. Finally, as can be seen in the next chapter, Franklin includes the blast of air coming from electrified points as one of Priestley's discoveries, and it is now described as "the well-known electrical wind."[9] Opposition from his coadjutors, Priestley found, was not to be taken seriously. He began to insist that they experiment first before objecting to his experiments — and even that was not always sufficient. Witness John Canton's remark (No.

---

[8] See R. E. Schofield, "Electrical Researches of Joseph Priestley," *Archives Internationales d'Histoire des Sciences,* No. 64 (1963), 277–286.

[9] *Encyclopaedia Britannica,* 11th ed. (London, 1910), vol. 6, p. 886b; see Myron Robinson, "A History of the Electric Wind," *American Journal of Physics,* 30 (1962), 366–372, though Robinson is unaware of Priestley's contribution to the recognition of this phenomenon.

11): "I have lately been making experiments on the electrified cup of Dr. Franklin which I find does not *contain* any mystery in electricity." Priestley's identification of this experiment as a significant one (shown first in Letter 10 to Franklin) was not changed by Canton's opinion, and this has since proved Priestley's most memorable claim to fame as an electrician. Perhaps that electrified cup contained no mystery, but it did contain the answer first published by Priestley in the *History of Electricity* (p. 732) to the force law between electrical charges.

The other experiments reported in this section need less commentary. The physiological tests on animals reveal Priestley as an anatomist (the *Memoirs* mention that he once taught anatomy at Warrington) but otherwise are similar to the equally unrevealing tests being performed by others. Those dealing with the tourmaline, which fill so large a part of the correspondence, demonstrate only the difficulty of working with a material which had too many variables to be easily tractible until its crystalline properties were studied by Hauy in 1801. The tourmaline is a pyro- and piezo-electric crystal, which also is easily charged by friction and loses its static charge very slowly. The combination of phenomena caused by these properties confused the issue during Priestley's experiments, which do not uncover the axial character of the induced charges. Priestley's account of the tourmaline, in subsequent editions of the *History of Electricity* (e.g., 3rd ed., 1775, vol. 1, p. 374), notes, without understanding, its polarizing properties and fails to relate this to electrical phenomena. The experiments which tinged glass with melted metal (No. 9) are notable only for the indication that Priestley had made no attempt to relate this phenomenon to optics, though that was to be his next formal study.

The references to the Royal Society provide a commentary on some social aspects of eighteenth-century science. Priestley became a candidate for the honor of membership in the Royal Society because his friends believed that would help him in selling his book. Though he refers to the possibility of privately showing some "principle members" of the Society an account of his experiments, there is no clear indication that this was done, and his Certificate for membership (No. 4) mentions his chart of biography and "several other valuable works" (none of which can at this time have been on science), but does not refer to experiments. Of course, four of the seven signers of the certificate were Priestley's correspondents and their names and influence may well have been sufficient to carry the day. At any rate, there is little support in this correspondence for Priestley's statement in his *Memoirs* that his "new experiments in electricity" were the means of introducing him into the Royal Society. The Society was not alone in lightly dispensing its favours, since Priestley's cherished LL.D. seems to have been obtained from the University of Edinburgh with even less ceremony and effort at justification than was the F.R.S. (No. 3).

The last letter of this section (No. 14) presages the next phase of Priestley's career. With the *History of Electricity* successfully completed, he moved from his academic post at Warrington to become minister at Mill-Hill Chapel in Leeds. Intending to continue his interest in science, he needed the apparatus which Warrington had previously been able to provide. The list of optical instruments he planned to purchase in 1767 already suggests the work for his *History of Optics,* which was published in 1772.

CHAPTER THREE

The Testing Years, Leeds
1767-1773

THE PERIOD OF PRIESTLEY'S LIFE between September 1767, when he moved from Warrington to Leeds, and the summer of 1773, when he left Leeds to become a member of Lord Shelburne's household, was probably the most important of his life. In those six years he became a Socinian, started writing the theological works which made him the leading publicist for the Unitarian cause in England, and began his career as a polemicist in theology and politics. During this time he published some twenty-eight nonscientific works in first editions, ten in second, and three each in third and fourth editions. Nor was it a fallow period for his scientific work, for it includes the dates of publication of four of his books on science in first editions, two in second editions with revisions, and a short volume of *Additions* (the equivalent of a third edition) to one of these. He also read to the Royal Society and had printed in its *Transactions* seven papers describing scientific experiments. These are the years of Priestley's most interesting independent electrical discoveries, and they are the years during which he put aside electricity and began his work on chemistry. Scientifically, the period culminates in that classic paper of 1772 which demonstrated to Europe that a master chemist had appeared.

The scientific aspects of the Leeds period are covered in Priestley's *Memoirs* in six octavo pages:

. . . But nothing of a nature foreign to the duties of my profession [as a dissenting minister] engaged my attention while I was at Leeds so much as the prosecution of my experiments relating to *electricity,* and especially the doctrine of *air.* The last I was led into in consequence of inhabiting a house adjoining to a public brewery, where I at first amused myself with making experiments on the fixed air which I found ready made in the process of fermentation. When I removed from that house, I was under the necessity of making the fixed air for myself; and one experiment leading to another, as I have distinctly and faithfully noted in my various publications on the subject, I by degrees contrived a convenient apparatus for the purpose, but of the cheapest kind.

When I began these experiments I knew very little of *chemistry,* and had in a manner no idea on the subject before I attended a course of chemical lectures delivered in the academy at Warrington by Dr. Turner of Liverpool. But I have often thought that upon the whole, this circumstance was no disadvantage to me; as in this situation I was led to devise an apparatus, and processes of my own, adapted to my peculiar views. Whereas, if I had been previously accustomed to the usual chemical processes, I should not have so easily thought of any other; and without new modes of operation I should hardly have discovered any thing materially new.

My first publication on the subject of air was in 1772. It was a small pamphlet, on the method of impregnating water with fixed air; which being immediately translated into French, excited a great degree of attention to the subject, and this was much increased by the publication of my first paper of experiments in a large article of the Philosophical Transactions the year following; for which I received the gold medal of the society. My method of impregnating water with fixed air was considered at a meeting of the College of Physicians, before whom I made the experiments, and by them it was recommended to the Lords of the Admiral (by whom they had been summoned for the purpose) as likely to be of use in the sea scurvy.

The only person in Leeds who gave much attention to my experiments was Mr. Hay [Hey], a surgeon. . . . we always conversed with the greatest freedom on philosophical subjects, without mentioning any thing relating to theology. When I left Leeds, he begged of me the earthen trough in which I had made all my experiments on air while I was there. It was such an one as is there commonly used for washing linnen.

Having succeeded so well in the History of Electricity, I was induced to undertake the history of all the branches of experimental philosophy; and at Leeds I gave out proposals for that purpose, and published the *History of discoveries relating to vision light and colours*. This work, also, I believe I executed to general satisfaction, and being an undertaking of great expence, I was under the necessity of publishing it by subscription. The sale, however, was not such as to encourage me to proceed with a work of so much labour and expence; so that after purchasing a great number of books, to enable me to finish my undertaking, I was obliged to abandon it, and to apply wholly to original experiments.

In writing the History of discoveries relating to vision, I was much assisted by Mr. Michell, the discoverer of the method of making artificial magnets. Living at Thornhill, not very far from Leeds, I frequently visited him, and was very happy in his society, as I also was in that of Mr. Smeaton, who lived still nearer to me. He made me a present of his excellent air pump, which I constantly use to this day. Having strongly recommended his construction of this instrument, it is now generally used; whereas before that hardly any had been made during the twenty years which had elapsed after the account that he had given of it in the Philosophical Transactions.

I was also instrumental in reviving the use of large electrical machines, and batteries, in electricity, the generality of electrical machines being little more than play things at the time that I began my experiments. The first very large electrical machine was made by Mr. Nairne in consequence of a request made to me by the Grand Duke of Tuscany, to get him the best machine that we could make in England. This, and another that he made for Mr. Vaughan, were constituted on a plan of my own. But afterwards Mr. Nairne made large machines on a more simple and improved construction; and in consideration of the service which I had rendered him, he made me a present of a pretty large machine of the same kind.

The review of my history of electricity by Mr. Bewley, who was acquainted with Mr. Michell, was the means of opening a correspondence between us, which was the source of much satisfaction to me as long as he lived. I instantly communicated to him an account of every new experiment that I made, and, in return, was favoured with his remarks upon them. All that he published of his own were articles in the *Appendixes* to my volumes on air, all of which are ingenious and valuable. Always publishing in this manner, he used to call himself my *satellite*. . . . His letters to me would have made several volumes, and mine to him still more. . . .

While I was at Leeds a proposal was made to me to accompany Captain Cook in his second voyage to the south seas. As the terms were very advantageous, I consented to it, and the heads of my congregation had agreed to keep an assistant to supply my place during my absence. But Mr. Banks informed me that I was objected to by some clergymen in the board of longitude, who had the direction of this business, on account of my religious principles; and presently after I heard that Dr. Forster, a person far better qualified for the purpose, had got the appointment. As I had barely acquiesced in the proposal, this was no disappointment to me, and I was much better employed at home, even with respect to my philosophical pursuits. My knowledge of natural history was not sufficient for the undertaking; but at that time I should by application have been able to supply my deficiency, though now I am sensible I could not do it[1] . . . .

[1] Priestley, *Memoirs*, pp. 61–67.

Fortunately we have available a large number of his letters, referring to his scientific work, written to an increasing number of correspondents. Information to be learned from these letters supplements the biographical details to be read between the lines of Priestley's published scientific work as well as those sketched in the *Memoirs*.

No. 15.

FROM PRIESTLEY TO JOHN CANTON

Dear Sir

I wrote to Dr Watson a post or two ago, to give him an account of some experiments I have made on Mephitic and inflammable air, and I desired him to acquaint you with them. I have since made a few more, which I beg you would communicate to him.

The colour of a red rose, fresh gathered, and plunged in mephitic air is perfectly discharged in a day or two and becomes white or yellowish, exactly as it is made by the electric sparks, as in a leaf I inclose —— I put a mouse into a receiver full of inflammable air (after it had stood 8 days in a receiver plunged in water). It lived an hour and about five minutes, the same time that another lived in the same receiver filled with common air. The inflammable air was converted into mephitic —— Gunpowder not only explodes, but explodes with a bright red flame in air strongly mephitic —— I have made several other observations on this subject but I can only write upon everything in general. By the way, I make most delightful *Pyrmont Water,* and can impregnate any water or wine &c. with that spirit in two minutes time.

I am not sure whether I mentioned to Dr Watson the *lateral effect of explosions.* I was under a mistake when I wrote to you about it. The repulsion is from the *flask* & not the *wire,* but it is the same in vacuo —— and also behind pieces of paper, and tinfoil interposed between the light bodies and the explosion. I can affect small bodies at the same distance, about 2 inches, with a few small jars as with the battery. The distance I find depends upon the height of the charge, but the weight of the bodies to be removed, and the distance to which the same body can be thrown, depend upon the quantity of coated surface. By making the explosion of the battery pass visibly over the surface of green leaves, &c, and laying large corks &c. all along the path, a fine experiment is made. The corks are driven with great violence from all parts of the path.

You will see by the inclosed leaves, that I now make perfect *fairy circles* without any central spot. They are made by presenting the point of a wire to a leaf fresh gathered. The first appearance is a small purple spot opposite to the point. This spot keeps enlarging and by degrees the center resumes the colour of the leaf. This new central spot also grows larger, the longer the electrification is continued, and the outer circle extends farther, and turns from purple to yellow. This conversion is quicker in proportion to the freshness of the leaf. Some times I leave the circle purple, and next morning find it yellow. I have noted several other circumstances relating to this experiment, but they are too minute to relate at present. I have also tried the electrical spark on other vegetable colours, with various results, which I shall give you an account of when I have continued them a little farther.

I have made farther experiments on the circular spots by explosions. When I make it pass thro the finest needles, the fire at the distance of about the $\frac{1}{10}$ of an inch, opens, and marks a circle in proportion to the quantity of coated surface, and does not enlarge with a greater distance. At less than $\frac{1}{10}$ of an inch the circle is smaller and more confused.

Upon a piece of brass, with which I took a number of explosions, I find a perfect circle with all the colours of the rainbow, the diameter of the violet is about $\frac{1}{4}$ of an inch and of the red $\frac{1}{2}$ an inch. The colours are indelible. The stages in the progress of the formation of this circle are too minute to be described here.

Neither mephitic nor inflammable air are in the least degree conductors of electricity. . . .

Leeds. 27 Sepbr. 1767.

P.S.   I desired Mr Nairne to consult you about a Micrometer to my Microscope. Please to hasten him for I am in want of it.

No. 16.

FROM PRIESTLEY TO JOHN CANTON

Leeds. 12 Novbr. 1767

Dear Sir

I must ask your pardon for not sending your *battery* before this time, but this day I have been fitting it up, and proving it, when it answered perfectly well. The greatest part of the jars are the same that composed my battery in my former experiments, and they have all been tried again and again. I shall send it by Monday's Waggon.

Mr Price supposes that bodies, which are driven off by the lateral force of an electrical explosion, are suddenly charged with electricity. I omitted in former letters to mention some experiments, which seem to prove the contrary, for I give you only the heads of things. Suspecting what Mr Price does, I insulated an iron rod, with a brass knob at each end, and fixed one of them, at different times within an inch, half an inch, and a quarter of an inch above the explosion of the battery, passing over the surface of a green leaf; while the cork balls were suspended at the other end of the rod; but not the least motion was perceived in them. I then still kept the rod insulated, and made the explosion pass thro' the knob of it, but still no motion was given to the balls. So that I think, in neither of these cases, did the rod either acquire any permanent electricity, nor was the equilibrium of the fluid within it sensibly disturbed. These experiments were repeated several times with the greatest care, and by the help of an assistant observer.

When I wrote to you last upon this subject, I think I had not found that this lateral force of the explosion could affect bodies thro' glass interposed between them and the flash; but I have since found that it can. I put some pieces of cork in a thin glass phial closely stopped, and held in the hand of an observer, about a quarter of an inch, or half an inch above the explosion of the battery, passing over the surface of a green leaf; when they were seen to be agitated with a violent motion; tho' when it was held at the distance of an inch, no motion was produced. This lateral force appears to me very extraordinary. I have, on a late occasion, observed it to act with amazing quickness and force. A small wire put thro' a quill filled with gunpowder, the ends of which were hand rammed, and held in hand vises, has been several times totally exploded, the quill has been burst, and the powder dispersed about the room, without any or, at most, only a few grains of it taking fire. If the powder be laid at some distance, where the sparks of red hot iron can fall upon it, and where it is out of the reach [of] the lateral force, it explodes at once.

I have lately been amusing myself with a set of experiments, to ascertain the practicability of firing mines by an electrical battery, from whence have resulted some observations, which I should not have conjectured a priori. I took a quantity of the smallest steel wire that is used for harpsichords, and found that, with a moderate charge of just such a battery as I shall send you, I could effectually melt 9 or 10 inches of it, so that it should be driven by its own lateral force three or 4 feet every way, which is a fine appearance. This I could do when the steel wire was fastened at each end to a small piece of brass wire of about 4 times its thickness and placed close to the battery. If I use only three yards for a half circuit of the same wire (which, however, is so thick that I am sure 10 times the force I use would not sensibly affect it) I can melt only three inches of it, even when it is insulated. When I insulate 15 yards of a half circuit of iron wire, the thickness of a crow-quill, I can melt thro 9 inches, but at 20 yards, cannot melt 6. It is evident, therefore, that the force of an explosion is weakened both by the length and the smallness of the wire thro which it passes. I imagine, however, that if I had rods as thick as the diameter of the circular spots made by any battery, they would transmit the explosion without any diminution of its force, at the greatest distance, and a coating of tallow would sufficiently insulate them, tho' they were laid thro ditches &c. filled with water; and there is no occasion to insulate more than one half the circuit, and it is indifferent which half.

I have made several experiments to ascertain, if possible, the *momentum of the electrical matter in explosions.* If it passes over the surface of a cabbage leaf, you may see the track very distinctly afterwards. I, therefore, cut one with a sharp angle as to make the fire pass from *a* to *b*; thinking that, if the fluid was any substance, as it went with such inconceivable velocity, it must be driven a little out of its direct path, and make a small curve at the c: but no such [curve] could I ever observe. It turns at the sharpest angle, without being carried, by its *impetus,* ever so little beyond it. Again, I take a brass wire, about 6 yards long, and observe what length of the small iron wire can be melted, when it is insulated, in two straight lines and the wire in the middle of it. I afterwards take the very same wire, and, upon a board of baked wood, I twist it backwards and forwards, in a great number of very acute angles thus and find I can still melt the very same quantity of the small wire, in the middle of it. The force of the explosion, therefore, is not weakened by its being obliged to turn short so very often. — You will think I talk strangely, but I own, that these experiments, together with that of the insulated hot glass, mentioned p 716 of my book and others too long to recite here make me inclined to think, there is no electric fluid at all, and that electrification is only some [new] modification of the matter of which any body consisted before that operation. . . .

P.S.   I wrote to Dr Watson on the subject of *Mephitic air,* and desired he would send the letter to you & Mr Price. Please to send this to him.

No. 17.

From Priestley to John Canton

Leeds. 17 Novbr. 1767

Dear Sir

Yesterday I sent the battery by the Waggon, packed up as secure as I could contrive it. All my batteries stand in open boxes, covered with a cloth or paper cover, and I sent you the best that I have, in the same manner. If you chuse a better and neater case, with a wooden cover, you may soon get it made to your own fancy. In order to pack this, I first got a cover for the tops of the jars and wires, and then a very strong packing box to receive the whole. I think your best way of unpacking it will be to take off the top first, and then one of the sides of the outer box, for it fits so close, that you will not be able to draw it out without running a risque of doing some damage. When the battery is out, and the white wooden cover taken carefully off, you will pick out all the tow; and I think, if you then only warm it well by a good fire, it will take a charge immediately. It takes the strongest charge of any battery I ever had of the size. The waxed strings are to support the wires in the middle of the jars. It is sufficient if they do not touch the sides. Perhaps you will think of a better contrivance for that purpose, but this is ready & effectual. In about five minutes I can take out every jar wipe the mouth of them, and replace them; but this I have not occasion to do once in a month —— As to the price, I cannot tell you till I see you, which I expect will be the latter end of January.

If writing be the least inconvenient to you, I beg you would not give yourself the least trouble about it. I shall not take it in the least amiss. It is quite sufficient if Mr Price give me, in as few words as possible, your opinions of my experiments. I should think myself greatly honoured if Dr Franklin would give me a line upon the subject of my last to you.

You must not expect much more from me till I see you. I have long been teized by Mr Johnson to dispatch an *English Grammar,* about which we have made an agreement, and the materials of which have been ready some years, and I have promised to carry it finished to London —— I am, likewise, printing a *Theological tract,* and may possibly print [a] *treatise on Civil and religious liberty* which I have written since I came hither. I have besides the *High Dutch Language* to learn, and at my time of life, tho I am not old, it is irksome to learn languages, but I must and will do it. I hope to have made it pretty easy to me before Christmas. —— You will receive with this my *Familiar Introduction to the study of electricity.* I was persuaded to write it by Mr Aikin, and

[59]

also by some of my friends here. Do you and Mr Price look it over, and if you think it will be of use, it shall be printed, otherwise it shall be suppresed. The composition of it cost me very little —— Tell Mr Price I have quite given up the scheme of selling any machines in London; but not my design of writing the *general history of experimental philosophy,* but I think I had better apply to it about a year, before I think of subscriptions. I shall then be a better judge of the extent of the work, and it can be but one year's labour lost, if the scheme do not take. . . .

No. 17a. Advertisement on verso of Half-Title page,
Familiar Introduction to the Study of Electricity, first edition
(London, 1768)

ADVERTISEMENT.

About the middle of March will be ready for sale, *Electrical Machines,* with a proper apparatus, of a new construction, strong and elegant, equally proper for philosophical purposes, or for entertainment, made under the direction of Dr. Priestley. A copy of this *Familiar Introduction to the Study of Electricity* will be given with each machine, and the most particular printed directions will be added, if necessary. He assures the public, that he will himself particularly attend to the construction of these machines, and every improvement that hath occurred to him. Orders may be given either to himself at Leeds, or to his brother, the Rev. Mr. Priestley, at Manchester, under whose immediate inspection a considerable part of the machines and apparatus will be made, and who will take care to send them, carefully packed up, to any part of England. Remittances may be made to Mr. Johnson, bookseller in Pater-noster Row, London, to whom orders may also be directed.

N. B. The price of the machines, and of each part of the apparatus, will be distinctly advertised in the public papers. . . .

No. 18.

From Benjamin Franklin to Lord [Morton]

[*1767*]

My Lord

In Obedience to your Lordship's Commands I have look'd over that Part of Dr Priestly's Work that contains an Acct of the Experiments made by him. I find There are a great Number of them, mostly quite new, and some I think very curious and important, well deserving for that Reason and for the great Pains & Expence he has been at in making them, the Honour of the Society's Medal. But I do not see that his Account of them can well be abridg'd and as the Book has been long publish'd, and probably is in the Hands of all those of the Society who from their Acquaintance with the Subject are the best Judges of the Merit of such Experiments, I apprehend that any other Account is hardly necessary. I am however so engag'd at present that I could not possibly prepare any thing of the kind fit to be laid before the Council on Thursday, & hope your Lordship will be so good as to excuse me. . . .

No. 19.

From Benjamin Franklin to John Canton

Friday, Nov. 27. [*1767*]

Dear Sir

After the Society was gone, my Lord Moreton said, (when I offer'd him the Paper) that it ought to have been delivered before & read to the Society: he however desir'd me to produce it to the Council. There the Reading of it was oppos'd as not being referr'd to them by the Society. — But this was at last got over by Dr Moreton's proposing that the giving a Medal to Dr Priestly should be taken into Consideration, & that in order to judge the better of the Propriety of that Proposal, the Paper should be read.

It was accordingly read. I was then desired, as the best Judge present, to give my Opinion of the Merit of the Experiments as to the Medal; which I did in plain Terms, declaring it as my Judgment that the great Pains & Expence the Doctor had been at in making them, & the Importance of the Experiments themselves, well deserv'd that Encouragement from the Society: and that it was a Mark of Distinction justly due to so much philosophical Industry & sagacity, &c. —— One that sat near me told me he was surpris'd at the Acct I had given, as he had been assur'd the Medal was intended to be bestow'd on the Doctor only for writing a History, which was thought wrong; but it now appear'd he had made many valuable new Experiments, &c. Then a Question arose how far it was proper to give a Medal for Experiments that had not been sent to the Society till they were published; and this occasioned a Search for Sir Godfrey Copley's Will which could not be found; but an Agreement was found recorded between the Society & his Executors, that the 5 £ should be given for the best Experiment within the Year, proposed & directed to be made by the Society, & made in their Presence: —— This not having been the Practice of late Years, it began to be whisper'd that most of the Medals had been irregularly given, and that no more could be so given. —— A subsequent Resolution was however found, to print the Clause of Sir Godfrey's Will in every Number of the Transactions for the Encouragement of Foreigners to endeavour obtaining the Reward, as there was Reason to fear a Failure of Experiments on the former Plan. By this Time it grew late; and it was concluded that the Books should be searched, to find all the Steps that had been taken in disposing of this Prize whether in Money or in Medals from the first Instance in 1717 to the last; with the Reasons & Grounds on which the Council had proceeded; and that a Copy of that Part of Sir Godfrey's Will should be obtained from the Commons; when at the next Council the Matter might be re-considered, & the Medal then given to Dr Priestly if the Council thought fit, and it should be found not contrary to the Will so to do. —— Thus the Business ended for that time; and how it will conclude at last seems an Uncertainty; for I think some Persons are busy in an Opposition to the Measure.

But I hope it will end in favour of Merit, in which case I think our Friend cannot miss it. . . .

P. S. I return the Dr.'s letter.——I imagine his Difficulty has arisen partly from his Supposition that the Electric Matter goes in a Ball with a projectile Force, which I think is not the Case; but that it is a Constant Stream from the Inside to the outside of the Bottle thro' the best Conductor and in such Direction as it can best pass, and in which Path strait or crooked it actually begins to pass as soon as the Conducting Wire begins to approach in order to make the Discharge, which would be done silently or with only a hissing Noise if the Conducting Wire were kept a little farther off than the striking Distance. . . .

No. 20.

From Priestley to Richard Price

Leeds. 16 Jan. 1768

Dear Sir

As I had intended to have set out on my journey to London the next week, I thought I would not give you the trouble of a letter relating to any experiments; but as the weather obliges me to put it off to another week, and may oblige me to delay it still longer, I shall mention an appearance or two, that you may be thinking of them against the time that I shall have the pleasure of seeing you.

I think I acquainted you before, that I had observed a piece of brass, on which I had happened to take a number of explosions, to be marked with [a] circle, containing all the colours of the rainbow. This experiment I have lately diversified, and the result has been much more pleasing than I could have imagined, but the operations are very laborious each experiment requiring 30 or 40 explosions of the battery. I make the fire to pass from a pointed wire upon a polished plate of metal, generally steel. After a few discharges, I perceive a *circular space* marked out, of about 1/2 an inch or 3/4 in diameter, like a shade the whole of which is afterwards filled with *coloured rings*. These, however, begin at the melted circle, and spread outwards with every explosion. The first colour is *violet* or *purple,* it then changes into all the intermediate colours, til it becomes *red.* As this ring expands, another comes up in its place, and in this manner I have sometimes procured 3 or 4 distinct rings. There is, however, a considerable variety in them, in several respects —— Beyond the coloured rings, the steel shows a fine *shade,* not sensibly coloured, which is sometimes near an inch in diameter. It is very visible after 8 or 10 explosions —— I generally place the needle perpendicular to the polished surface, and the rings are nearly circles. When I make the needle point obliquely, The circle made by the fusion is properly and exactly a circle, the center being in the perpendicular let fall from the point upon the surface; but the colours extend in an *oblong form,* as if the matter that formed them had been thrown directly from the point —— I have made a great number of other observations on these coloured rings, the account of which would fill several letters. I shall, therefore, refer you to my *book of minutes* which I shall bring along with me, and read to you.

My experiments on *Air* I find will run out to a great length, several new circumstances have occurred, which I cannot yet ascertain, and some of the operations require several weeks before they are completed. The late frost broke me 4 or 5 Jars, in which I had several processes, which had been going on above a month. I shall not renew them till I return from London.

Inflammable air fresh made, from steel filings and diluted oil of vitriol, kills animals as suddenly as any mephitic air. At the same time the smell of it is extremely offensive. Afterward, it sometimes deposits a quantity of red matter, which I believe is the calx of the iron, and then it is quite sweet, and a mouse will live in it as well as in common air —— I want to find a method of facilitating the mixture of mephitic and inflammable air, and have tried *heat, cold, condensation, rarifaction* &c without any effect —— In a few minutes a narrow necked phial filled with inflammable air, and suspended, with its mouth downwards, or with mephitic air, and placed with its mouth upwards, will in a

short time be found to contain nothing but common air, tho'
[the air] when they are exposed be ever so still[. The] air of a
phial filled with inflammable a[ir] suspended in mephitic air
changes in half [the time] it doth suspended in common air.
Y[et both] kinds put in a bladder require about [illegible] incorporate. I once made up two equal mi[xtures] in two bladders.
I tried one of them after three [weeks] when the explosion of it
burst a glass and had like to have done me a mischief [I had] the
other a week longer, and it was but [com]mon air. A candle
neither made an[y] explosion [nor] was extinguished in it ——
Before I see you, I shall endeavour to ascertain whether the *reflection, refraction,* or *inflection* of light be affected by *electrification,* or *charging* ——

The *colour of an electric spark* in inflammable air, is a beautiful
purple or bright red, in mephitic air it is uncommonly white ——
I am obliged to Mr Canton for his letter, and the curious experiment it contains. . . .

No. 21.

PAPER BY BENJAMIN FRANKLIN

[*Endorsed: "Read March 10, 1768."*]
A brief Account of that Part of Doctor Priestley's Work on
Electricity, which relates the new Experiments made by himself.
—— This part is divided into thirteen Sections. ——
Section I. contains Experiments on the Excitation of Glass
Tubes fill'd with compress'd Air, whereby he discover'd that the
compress'd Air does no[t], as had before been thought, prevent
the Excitation, provided the Glass be warmed. ——
Section II. contains a Number of new and curious Experiments
to prove that a Current of *real Air* proceeds from the Points of
Bodies electrified either positively or negatively, which had been
deny'd or disputed by some preceding Electricians.
Sect. III. contains Experiments on Mephitic Air, and on Charcoal. By the latter the Doctor discover'd a Property that was not
before conceived to be in that Substance, viz. that it is, equally

[65]

with Metals, a good Conductor of Electricity. Wood is, in its common State, but an indifferent Conductor, & when perfectly dry it was known not to conduct at all. Therefore, as all Water was suppos'd to be expell'd from it when reduc'd to Coal, it was not suspected that Charcoal would become a better Conductor than moist wood; but the Doctor found it would perform the Office of the best Conductors, in conveying a Shock of the Leyden Bottle. ——

Sect. IV. contains Experiments on the conducting Power of various other Substances, viz. Ice, hot Glass, hot baked Wood, the Effluvia of flaming Bodies, melted Tallow, Oil of Olives, essential Oils of various Sorts, saline Substances of various kinds, black Sand, black Lead (which was unexpectedly found equally a good Conductor with Metal or Charcoal) various Stony Substances, Spars, &c. which afford a Number of Observations that are new & curious.

Section V. contains Experiments on the Diffusion of Electricity over the Surface of Glass Tubes, & showing a new Method the electric Shock. These Experiments were partly made on new Flint Glass, which was found to differ greatly from Glass some Months old in regard to that Property ascrib'd to Glass of its being absolutely a NonConductor. The Experiments are many and varied very ingeniously, particularly those relating to the new Method of giving a Shock, and tend to throw new Light on this Part of the Science. ——

Sect. VI. contains a Number of Experiments tending to verify several Particulars of P. Beccaria's theory concerning the electric Matter carrying into its Path light Substances to assist its Passage. To which are added sundry ingenious Experiments to discover if possible the direction of the electric Fluid in an Explosion. ——

Sect. VII. contains various Experiments relating to charging and discharging Glass Jarrs, & Batteries. In these experiments the Doctor appears to have raised and applied, at a considerable Expence of Time & Money, a much greater Force of Electricity than any one had done before him; and the Observations that arise on the use of that Force in several Instances are very curious & useful. ——

[66]

Sect. VIII. contains Experiments on Animals struck by these powerful Discharges; and give a particular Account of the Effects and Appearances upon them while they were dying and after their Death.—— Animals larger and more difficult to kill, appear to have been killed by the Doctor's Apparatus, than by any other before used; and the Facts & Circumstances are in several of the Instances very surprising.

Sect. IX. contains Experiments on the circular Spots made on Pieces of polish'd Metal by large electrical Explosions. Three concentric Circles were sometimes made by one Explosion. —— From this Experiment the Doctor endeavours to explain some extraordinary Effects of Lightning, and particularly what are called the Fairy Rings. ——

Sect. X. contains Experiments on the Effects of the electric Explosion discharged thro' a brass Chain and other metallic Substances. —— A black Smoke or Dust was found to be constantly thrown off from the Chain upon the Paper on which it lay, so as to mark the Paper strongly with a black Stain distinguishing the Links. —— This seems a Fact very curious, as are the Observations made by the Doctor upon it; and the subsequent Experiments he made in pursuance of it. ——

Sect. XI. contains new Experiments on the Passage of the Electric Explosion over the Surface of some conducting Substances without entring them. ——

Sect. XII. contains new Experiments on the Tourmalin; and

Sect. XIII. contains a number of miscellaneous Experiments, all very curious with regard both to the Views with which they were made, and the Success of the several Variations in making them ——

Upon the whole Dr. Priestly appears to be a very intelligent, ingenious, & indefatigably diligent Experimenter; and to have contributed considerable Materials for the Improvement of the Electrical Branch of Natural Philosophy.

No. 22.

FROM PRIESTLEY TO JOHN CANTON

Dear Sir

With this you will receive a corrected copy for the *second edition of the history of electricity*. I send it to you, that you and Mr Price may see what additions I have made, and especially that you may insert the sentence you mentioned to me, relating to some of your experiments, as I have forgot the passage. If I have omitted anything else that you observed to me, I wish you would note it. You will excuse my making no greater alterations with respect to *earthquakes* —— If you turn to p 541, you will find, I think, that I had not given a wrong account of the phenomena of the balls. I have now only added a few words by way of explanation. If I had made the mistake in any other place, I wish you would point it out to me —— I would gladly make this edition as correct as possible —— There are some of the additions, which, I fancy, you will be pleased with. I am sure it has cost me a great deal of labour to collect them. Several of the Dutch books proved very tiresome and very empty —— let Dr Franklin know, that he may have those I had of him whenever he pleases, but I would like to keep them as long as I can, lest I should have occasion to consult them again before the extracts I have made from them be printed —— I shall be obliged to you, if you could get me the paper I gave in to the society, or a copy of it, to print with the *additions*. If I compose it again, there will be too much variation in the manner, &c. The other large additions, of my own experiments, I shall draw up at my leisure, and when I have carried them a little farther.

Tell Mr Price, I hope I have satisfied all his scruples by the manner in which I have introduced his, and all the names, in the preamble to the *Theological Repository;* three copies of which he will receive of Mr Johnson. The words I have printed are exactly his own. He may yet make any alteration that he chuses; but I cannot do without his name, and I cannot mention one in a light different from the rest.

I shall be glad to hear from you or Mr Price when you have perused my additions. If you have made any new experiments I hope you will communicate them to me. . . .

Leeds. 24th May. 1768.

No. 23.

FROM PRIESTLEY TO JOHN CANTON

Leeds 11 Augt. 1768

Dear Sir

I am much obliged to you for your last favour, and should have acknowledged it sooner, but I have been removing to another house and various other things have likewise happened to engage my attention. You surprise me by your account of the extreme lightness of pith of elder. With your leave, I shall take notice of that circumstance in the new edition of my history, as also of your having suggested, that electricity may be the cause of the phenomena of *falling stars.*

I have been told, upon pretty good authority, of a storm of thunder and lightning in the Orkneys, in which of 12 Cows, standing in a line, in a Shed, Exactly every other was killed, the 6 in the intervals not being hurt, and I am referred for farther particulars to *Edward King Esq in Bedford Row.* As all the essential circumstances will be more easily come at by enquiring of him personally, I wish you or some of our friends, would give him a call for the purpose, and send me the account, for my 2d edition. Let him know, that Mr Walker of Yarmouth referred me to him.

Tell Mr Price I am much obliged to him for his letter —— I am about to make a journey of a fortnight into Lancashire, and soon after my return propose to resume my experiments. Those on *air* have been interrupted by an accident, which has rendered useless 8 phials, which had been kept some time, with different mixtures of air —— If you look into the preface of my grammar, you will see a reason why I make no *future tense* in English. ——

If the account from Mr King can be procured in less than a

week, I wish it may be sent to me at *the Revd Mr Aikin's in Warrington,* where the book is printing, and where I shall be some time to attend to it. . . .

P.S. My wife has brought me a son —— I see *Mr Mitchel* pretty often, we are neighbours. I am very sorry for the difference between you and him, But perfect harmony cannot be expected on earth —— When will Dr Franklin's book be published?

[The story of the cows struck by lightning appears in Priestley's *History* — see, for example, 3rd ed., vol. 2, p. 274 — but without reference to King. The citation is to a book by Wallace, and relates to a storm of 1680.]

No. 24.

From Priestley to Benjamin Franklin

[*Leeds. 1 November 1768*]

[Dear Sir]

I take the opportunity of giving you [a letter by] Mr Lee of Lincoln's inn, a very worthy [and s]ensible man, a friend of mine, who wishes to [be] introduced to you. If you will please to deliver to him the *plates* belonging to your last work, he will have many opportunities of transmitting them to me.

I can hardly say that I have begun to make any experiments, having been busy in fitting up a battery or two; but I have one observation, which confirms another that has often puzzled me, and is mentioned in the account of my experiments published in *the history of electricity.* I was amusing myself with making a pretty large common jar explode between two brass balls, fixed at as great a distance as I could make the jar to discharge; when, after several explosions, it broke (a hole being made thro it as usual) tho the spark between the balls was of precisely the same length, and to all appearance, in every other respect the same that it would have been, if no other communication had been made

between the inside and outside of the glass. The fact mentioned
in the history is, that a silver wire [illegible] the battery I was
using could melt, [illegible] at the same time that two of the
[jars were bro]ken. In this case, tho' there are several [paths]
opened for the fluid, its whole force seem[s to have] been exerted
in each of them —— If your [present] business will now admit
of your giving me your thoughts on this subject, you would oblige
me by your observations on it. In the mean time I shall be con-
triving a few experiments to illustrate it —— I also propose to
make a few to refute what Mr L'Epinasse has advanced in the last
volume of Transactions, concerning the great loss of force occasioned by interruptions in the electric circuit. I remember his
telling me, when I was with him in London, that he did not doubt,
but he could do as much by his three jars, each of which was but
about a square foot, as I could with my batteries, tho' he had only
screwed their wires into one common conductor. —— I shall also
soon draw up another paper of original experiments, for the Royal
Society. They are those I have mentioned to you, but I must repeat
some of them, with a little variation of circumstances. . . .

No. 25.

FROM PRIESTLEY TO BENJAMIN FRANKLIN

Dear Sir

According to my promise, I send you the other paper, containing an account of experiments, which I desire you would lay
before the Royal Society. I have materials for another short paper
of *Miscellaneous experiments,* but I think it better to wait till I
have enlarged it, and completed some of the courses, particularly
that concerning Magnetism. I made use of *one needle* for a few
days, and the eye turned North, when it was suspended, but its
strength was very small. I have now three to collect the fire, but
I have not tried them. Indeed, I make but little use of my machine
now, in comparison of what I used to do, and without using a
machine very much, little can be expected of such an effect as this.

[71]

I hope that our American affairs have rather a better aspect than when I had the pleasure of hearing from you last. . . .

Leeds. 28 Novbr. 1768.

No. 26.

FROM PRIESTLEY TO JOHN CANTON

Dear Sir

I sent you by the coach yesterday a paper containing *Experiments and Observations on Charcoal,* to be laid before the Royal Society by Dr Watson; but I would have you and Dr Price, and Dr Franklin see it first. Let it, however, be presented the first opportunity, that it may be read while I am in London. I must now shut up my experiments till my return from London, and sit down to the recomposition of the MS that was consumed at Mr Johnson's. I have materials for a good part of another paper on *Air,* but the processes in this course of experiments are often very slow, so that it may be some years before I complete them, and Philosophy is now only an *occasional object* with me; tho' I do think to undertake the *history of Experimental Philosophy* and I keep your two books with that view. I am, indeed, ashamed to have kept them so long, but have a little more patience with me, and I will set to them in good earnest.

Along with the paper I sent a parcel, directed to Mr Goode at Needham in Suffolk. I wish you would take it to Mr Johnson, and desire him to put to it *My Answer to Mr Venn,* and then forward it by the coach. I hope he will find a copy of that pamphlet some where, and I will replace it with another when I come.

I have given orders to cancel the paragraph at the conclusion of the preface to my *Perspective,* according to your advice, received this day from Dr Price, and I have inserted a recommendation of Mr Nairne's composition (as he calls it) Tell him that I think it is fair, that he should be at the expence of the alteration. If he sell half as many of his cubes, as I shall copies of my book, he will get much more than I shall. However, he is very welcome to what I have done.

I wish you would desire Mr Johnson to get impressions of the two plates of which he sent me prints, for 300 books of Perspective, which I shall send to London in a few days. The books will be in boards, and guards will be left to paste these two cuts in the end. They should be printed off immediately, that they may be dry, ready to put into the books as soon as they arrive.

I am sorry to give you this trouble, but it will save me the expence of a letter to him on the subject.

I shall be at a loss for a lodging in London. Could you be thinking of a place for me? I intend to take the liberty to be Dr Kippis's guest for a night or two, till I can dispose of myself.

As my brother has some thoughts of selling *electrical machines in London,* I bid him send one to meet me there; and not knowing where to bid him send it, I took the liberty to bid him direct to you. It shall not trouble your house long. Mr Dolland, he says, has applied to him to sell machines for him, so that it will probably be soon ordered thither.

I expect to set out on my journey on monday next, to be with you on Wednesday. I shall meet you at the Royal Society.

Having, I think, put your friendship to a pretty fair test, I now conclude. . . .

Leeds 28 Feb. 1770.

No. 27.

Copy of Memorandum

[No date, no address, no signature; *c.* 1770]
Dr. Priestley, having written the *History and Present State of Electricity,* would willingly undertake to write the history of all the other branches of *experimental philosophy* upon the same extensive plan. He apprehends that a work of this kind, exhibiting a view of all that has been done already, would, on several accounts, greatly facilitate future discoveries in science; but he has

hitherto been discouraged from undertaking it by the expences in which it would necessarily involve him, and which he is not able to supply; particularly in procuring the books to which he cannot have access in his present situation. In order to execute this work with advantage, he will also be under an immediate necessity of considerably enlarging his *philosophical apparatus,* both to ascertain many disputed facts, and to pursue the hints for farther discoveries, which the consideration of those that have been made by others will unavoidably suggest. His history of electricity was very expensive to him on this account, but he thinks himself well repaid by the many *original experiments* he was thereby enabled to make, most of which are now before the public.

Dr. Priestley would think himself greatly honoured, if his Grace the Duke of Northumberland should think this work worthy of his patronage.

No. 28.

FROM PRIESTLEY TO BENJAMIN FRANKLIN

Dear Sir

I inclose a few copies of my *Proposals,* with the catalogues much enlarged. I therefore beg you would destroy the former, and dispose of these as you shall think most conducive to the design. I shall send a greater number soon to Mr Johnson from whom you may have whatever you want. In the mean time, I am obliged to take the liberty to inclose a small parcel for him in a cover to you

I hope you received Beccaria safe. . . .

Leeds. 2 June 1770.

No. 28a.

PRINTED PROPOSAL, &c.

LEEDS, Feb. 1, 1771.

PROPOSALS
for
PRINTING by SUBSCRIPTION,

The Histories and Present State
Of Discoveries relating to

VISION, LIGHT, AND COLOURS.
By Joseph Priestley, LL.D. F.R.S.

CONDITIONS

I.   This Work will be comprised in one large volume, quarto, and will be illustrated with a great number of copper-plates. Care will be taken that it be correctly and elegantly printed, and that the plates be well executed.

II.   The price will be One Guinea in Boards, to be paid on the delivery of the book.

III.   It is now ready for the press, and, if no unexpected hindrances intervene, will be delivered to the Subscribers about the beginning or middle of next winter.

IV.   The Names of the Subscribers will be printed, unless orders be given to the contrary.

SUBSCRIPTIONS are taken in by the AUTHOR at Leeds, by J. Johnson, No. 72, St. Paul's Church-Yard, London, and by all other Booksellers in Town and Country.

An Advertisement

DR. PRIESTLEY takes the opportunity, of this second Publication of his Catalogues, to thank those of his friends who have contributed to the enlargement of them; and particularly the anonymous person, who supplied him with the books that are marked with an *asterism,* to whom he has no other method of making his acknowledgements known.

As he promised that, with the next copies of his catalogues, he would endeavour to give his friends some idea of the probable extent of his work, he now informs them that, having carefully examined, and made distinct references to all the original matter in the books of which he is already possessed, he imagines that he shall be able to reduce all the philosophical knowledge they contain into the compass of about *six or eight volumes in quarto;* and he does not suppose that the books he still wants can make any considerable addition to the bulk of his work, though they may contribute to its accuracy and perfection.

He has already made such progress in writing *The History and present State of Discoveries relating to* LIGHT AND COLOURS, that he flatters himself, that, if he meet with no unexpected hindrances, he shall be able to deliver it to the printer about the beginning of the next summer. This part of his work will make one volume in quarto; but perhaps not quite so large as his *History of Electricity.* He chose to begin with this branch of experimental philosophy, for no other reason, but because the books he had collected furnished him with more materials for it than for any other. The next subject he proposes to give his attention to is MAGNETISM, which, he conjectures, may make another volume. Beyond this he has no distinct views himself, and therefore he can give no farther information to others.

Notwithstanding the generous assistance he has met with, in the *books* that have been sent to him for the use of this work, he could not avoid being at a very considerable expence himself; but, being now engaged, he is determined not to be retarded by any expence for which he can possibly provide; confiding, for his indemnification, in the encouragement he promises himself from the liberal-minded friends of *science,* which is of no particular party, either in politics, or religion; and in his attachment to which, he is as sincere, and as zealous, as he is with respect to any other subject, which he imagines to be equally interesting and useful to mankind.

N.B. In this second publication of the *catalogue of books wanted,* he has inserted those volumes of the *Philosophical Transactions* which have been abridged; because, though there can be no doubt but that the *Abridgments* may be depended upon as much as the originals themselves, these contain many articles which have not been abridged, and particularly accounts of *foreign books,* with the contents of some of which he may have no other opportunity of getting acquainted.

Those who desire to have a particular account of this undertaking may see DR. PRIESTLEY's *Proposals,* which he drew up for that purpose, at Mr. Johnson's, Bookseller, No. 72, St. Paul's Church-Yard, London.

LEEDS, December 1, 1770.

To the P U B L I C

This work is one part of *The history and present state of all the branches of Experimental Philosophy,* which Dr. Priestley has undertaken to write, upon a plan similar to that of his *History and present state of Electricity,* which has been some years before the public. At present, philosophical knowledge is so dispersed in various books and languages, that it is in the power of few persons to make themselves acquainted with every thing that they would wish to know, relating to any branch of it; and on this account, the progress of this valuable kind of knowledge is much retarded. Indeed, the very reading and comparing of the books that are absolutely necessary for this purpose, would take up more time and attention than any person would ever think of bestowing upon it, who did not make it his business to digest all the materials into such a history as this; not to mention the expence of purchasing so many books, which would be several hundred pounds for any one branch of the science; since, for this purpose, he must be possessed of the periodical publications of all the philosophical societies of any note in Europe.

Dr. Priestley, being encouraged by his friends, and by the favourable reception which his first essay of this kind has met with, has been induced to carry his original design to its just extent, and he promises that nothing shall be wanting on his part in point of fidelity and care. But he finds himself under an absolute necessity of having recourse to the public, to enable him to prosecute the work; as it cannot be supposed that booksellers should be able to give any person an equivalent, even for the *expences* in which it will necessarily involve him, without considering the value of his *time* and *labour*; which, with all the assistance he can derive from method and experience, cannot but be conceived to be very great.

The historical method, adopted in this work, has many obvious advantages over any other, being particularly calculated to engage the attention of the reader, and to communicate useful knowledge with the greatest ease, pleasure, and certainty; and the subject of the present volume, which will contain the discoveries that relate to *vision, light,* and *colours,* will, perhaps, be as generally entertaining as any thing within the compass of philosophy. This part of the work will exhibit a number of the finest gradations in the discoveries of different persons, a view of the greatest and happiest exertions of human genius, and the labours of those who are the most celebrated for their philosophical pursuits. The appearances in nature which these discoveries explain are constantly before our eyes, and must be perpetually exciting the curiosity of all thinking persons; the instruments to the construction of which they led, are in daily use; and every thing relating to Opticks is capable of the most perfect illustration by figures, in which no expence will be spared.

That the generality of readers may not be discouraged from purchasing this work, the Writer undertakes to make every thing, at least every thing of much value in it, perfectly intelligible to those who have little or no knowledge of Mathematicks, provided they give a proper degree of attention to the subject. He will, also, endeavour to avail himself of every circumstance or incident, that can contribute to render his narration pleasing and interesting to the reader; at the same time, that he will be careful never to lose sight of his principal object, which is to bring into a moderate compass, and to digest into an easy method, an account of every real improvement or discovery in science, in such a manner as shall enable the philosophers of the present age to resume, and pursue the inquiries of their predecessors, to the greatest advantage.

At the close of each part of this history, the Author will give a comprehensive view of all the discoveries that have been made in that branch of science to which it is appropriated, pointing out their natural connection, noting what he shall imagine to be the principal *desiderata,* and giving hints for the extension of it. To each volume he will also subjoin an explanation of all the *technical terms* that occur in it; and, in order to give a clearer view of the progress of the science, he will, whenever it can be done conveniently, exhibit a view of all those persons who have made the greatest figure in this history, in the manner of his *Chart of Biography.*

Those who chuse to be informed more particularly concerning the whole extent of Dr. Priestley's present undertaking, may see his *Proposals for writing* it, dated June 1, 1770, and the second publication of his *Catalogues of the Books he was possessed of, and those that he wanted* for that purpose, dated Dec. 1, 1770, at Mr. J. Johnson's, Bookseller, No. 72, St. Paul's Church-Yard, London.

[I have omitted the three quarto pages which followed: two of "A Catalogue of the Books, of which Dr. Priestley is already possessed, or to which he has Access, for compiling *The History of Experimental Philosophy,*" listing some one hundred and fifty titles, including, as single items, sets of scientific journals; and a one-page list of "Books Wanted," including some fifty-eight titles.]

No. 29.

FROM PRIESTLEY TO THEOPHILUS LINDSEY

Dear Sir

I thank you for your obliging invitation to Catterick, but it will hardly be in my power to make any more journeys this summer.

If I have the pleasure of seeing you, it must, I believe, be at Leeds, Where you will be a very welcome guest. I have sat down very closely to my *History of Experimental Philosophy*. I make a point of giving six hours a day to it, which in six years, I hope, will do a good deal of business. I am afraid, however, of being much retarded for want of books, for I can, at present, only common place the materials I have. I should be certain to lose a great part of my labour, if I were to begin to compose any part of the work till I have nearly all the books that would be of any use to me relating to it. Notwithstanding very considerable assistance, I find I must be at very great expence myself. I have already expended about £ 100, and now that I am in for it, shall risk a good deal more. I have had a large hamper of books sent me from a person unknown.

Please to give my compliments to his Grace, and tell him that I think myself greatly obliged to him for his *Encyclopedia;* but as I do not find it contains any original experiments, it will be of little or no use to me; and therefore he may depend upon my returning it before winter, along with the other books I received with it. *Kercher* [Kircher], the most useful of them, I had purchased before his arrived.

Some of my friends talk of making a subscription, to assist me in defraying the necessary expence of this work, but I do not know what they have done. I believe the first application will be made to the Duke.

My Ansr to Mr Enfield is now printed off, and I hope I have quite done with controversy. All I intend to do along with the *History* is to finish the *Harmony of the Evangelists,* and write small pieces for the *Repository,* another No. of which is nearly printed.

I am sorry to hear that several friends to the Warrington Academy intend to withdraw their subscriptions, on account of Mr Enfield's sentiments, expressed in his late pamphlet. I have written to those with whom I have any influence, to prevent it, if possible, and hope to succeed. Mr. Aikin will be exceedingly distressed. He is alarmed at every thing. . . .

Leeds 30 July 1770

No. 30.

FROM PRIESTLEY TO BENJAMIN FRANKLIN

Dear Sir

I took the liberty to trouble you with a line the last post, and being but just able to finish my letter in time, I recollect a mistake in the catalogue of books wanted, which I beg you would rectify as follows,

Vitellione's Optica   best edition   1572
Kepler's Paralipomena in Vitellionem

I also very much want *De la Hire's differens Accidents de la vue.* But I should think it might be got without a public advertisement. I have already collected from that writer as much as will make a considerable section. I cannot well do without *Du Hamel's History of the French Academy,* and tho' it is inserted among books I have got, it is only in the library at Manchester, and I cannot, without great loss of time, and expence, go and study there. Many other books I foolishly inserted in the catalogue of those I had access to; which are only there, particularly the *Petersburg Memoirs* which I must absolutely purchase, tho they will cost me, I believe, above £20. I shall give Johnson orders for them this post. I have not yet got *Boyle's Works,* and I find a tract of his on *colours* quoted, but I believe it relates to the chymical production of colours. However, it is within my subject, but Johnson tho he has had my order for *Shaw's Boyle* several months, has not yet been able to get it.

I have just dispatched the discoveries of Newton and his Co-temporaries, and from his time to the present have such a number of *Memoirs, dissertations, tracts,* and books on the subject of Light and colours to read, compare and digest, as, I think, would make any person, not practised in the business of arrangement, absolutely despair. Till I had actually taken a list of them, I did not think there had been a tenth or a twentieth part so much upon the subject. And other subjects, I see, will be much times more embarrassing than this.

[81]

If you be obliged to advertise for the books, I think it would be better not to mention my name, but only say *A Person being employed &c.* . . .

Leeds 21 Novbr 1770.

No. 31.

FROM PRIESTLEY TO THEOPHILUS LINDSEY

Dear Sir,

I thank you most sincerely for your remarks on the *Free Address,* which I have sent to the printer, corrected in every place as you would have it, and improved in other respects, in such a manner as, I flatter myself you will not dislike. The conclusion of the section I troubled you with is now more serious than the beginning, and has no reference to the publication you now have in your hands. The close of it was dictated by the warmth of my affection for you, and your friends. I will say nothing more till you see it, but it will not be very soon, as our printers will not do much work in the holidays.

I shall take your advice with respect to my *Lectures,* tho' I really want printed copies for the use of my class. I shall, however, go on composing, as soon as I resume the lectures, in the summer-time, and may perhaps publish them without my name, when they are all completed. I am fully convinced that, if I would make any thing of my *philosophical work,* I must make the world believe what is by no means true, that I mind nothing else. But there are many ways of imposing upon the world, as well of being imposed upon by it.

I can now inform you that I must dispose of fifty more sets of this volume of the Repository, at the full price of *six shillings,* before I shall be indemnified for the expence attending the publication. For I am a loser rather more than fifteen pounds. But I hope that the work will be so established in time as to need no assistance of the kind that I am now obliged to ask.

I look upon my History of Discoveries relating to *Vision Light* and *Colours* to be as good as finished, as little remains to be done besides *transcribing* which however, is necessarily slow and tedious. There will be a great number of *plates* in this volume; but as I have spared no expence in the purchase &c for it, and no pains in the composition of it, I will not be sparing of anything that may contribute to the *elegance* or *dignity* of it. I think it will appear to more advantage than the *history of Electricity*. It is a much finer subject for history, and I can assure you it was full as much *wanted*. I am satisfied that few, or no person, have any idea of the discoveries that have been made in this branch of science. Indeed nothing but this undertaking would have brought me acquainted with it, and no person could purchase the books in which the knowledge is contained under several hundred pounds. I think myself very fortunate in happening to begin with this subject. But after all so capricious is the public taste, that tho it be ever so well executed, it may not be well received; and then I shall go no farther with the undertaking. If I have tolerable success, and meet with no hindrances, I think I can dispatch the whole work in much less time than is imagined, and yet do it in the best manner that I am capable of. But indeed, I have no reason to complain of the reception of my philosophical works. My Piece on *Perspective,* I believe, is generally liked, and I hope will be useful. But I am sensible I have made myself many enemies by my *Theology* and *controversy*; which however I would [not] recall.

You are the best judge whether Mr Mann has anticipated your design with respect to the harmony — I expect, however, the sequel of *Patrobas* and the Remarks on the *Intermediate state* from the Archdeacon's friend — I long to see *Mr Jebb's harmony*. I ordered it as soon as ever I saw it advertised, but have not received it yet — I hope you will not have occasion to keep my *lectures* much longer, but do not hurry yourself in the perusal of them, I want your opinion both of the *plan* and *execution*. . . .

Leeds 23 Decbr. 1770

No. 32.

FROM PRIESTLEY TO BENJAMIN FRANKLIN

Leeds. 19 Apr. 1771

Dear Sir

I am glad that you have received your *Comm Bonon*: safe. I thank you for the use of them, and think myself [fortunate] in having an opportunity of doing you the smallest favour. I told you I either had or expected very soon to be possessed of the memoirs of all the philosophical societies, *of note,* in Europe, and the following account of the price of them will, I fancy, be sufficient for your purpose.

A complete edition of the *Memoirs of the Royal Society at Paris* cannot, I imagine, be bought for less than 120 £. My Amsterdam edition 2d hand will cost about 30 £. NB The *Memoires Anciennes* are 11 Vols, and comprehend the *Ouvrages Adoptés.*

Memoires de Mathematique et de Physique 5 Vols 4to, about £ 5.5s. 0. These are generally quoted by the name of *Memoirs Presentées* or *Memoires de Savans Etrangers.*

Miscellanea Berolinensia 3 Vols 4—— £ 1.11s.6d of the modern *Berlin Memoirs,* 23 Vols 4to have been published. The last is for the year 1767. They may perhaps cost 15 Sh at a medium, which is 17.5.0.

Commentaria Bononiensia 6 Vols 4to. I am told there are three or four more, and I think they will not be less than a pound a piece —— 10.00.0

Miscellanea Taurinensia 3 Vols 4to. 2.5.0

Of the *Acta Helvetica* I have 5 Vols 4to. the last for 1762. I believe there are four or five more. They may perhaps cost half a guinea a Vol. 5.5.0.

The *Dantzig Society* in High Dutch, 3 Vols 4to. Mine, I think, cost me 18 Sh a Vol, at Hamburgh. I remember I thought them very dear. —— 2.12.0.

Of the *Drontheim Society* in High Dutch 8vo I have three volumes. I think Mr Heydinger told me there are 3 more. He charged me 5 Sh a Vol. —— 1.10.0.

Of the *Royal Society in Sweden* I have 17 Vols. 8vo the last for 1757 (A translation into High Dutch) I expect the remainder to the present time every day. They will then cost 5 Shill a Vol —— 6.15.0.

The *Petersburg Memoirs* I have not yet received, but I remember I expected that they would cost me 30 £.

The *Acta Hafniensia* I have not yet got, and want much. They are 2 Vols 4to, and may perhaps be had for £ 1.10.0

The *Acta Naturel Curiosorum Caesariensia* have been published, with some change of title, for, I believe, near a century, a Vol. 4to every year. The *Acta Nova* are 4 Vols. perhaps 15. I have 9 Vols of the title preceding these, but they are not the whole, and contain very little philosophical knowledge, consisting almost wholly of Medical articles. The Acta Nova and the 12 Vols (I think there are) of the title preceding them will probably cost — — 12.00.0.

Of the *Acta Upsaliensia* I know nothing.

Of the *Acta Chymica Holmiensia,* by Nierne, I have 2 Vols in 12mo. I believe no more are published —— 0.6s.0

Essays Physical and literary of a Society at Edinburgh, 2 Vols 8vo. 12.0

Of the Philosophical and Medical Society at *Breslau* I know nothing

Of our *Philosophical Transactions* I need not say any thing.

This, Dear Sir, is all the intelligence I am able to give you concerning these Societies, and the price of their publications, omitting the *Acta Eruditorum,* or *Acta Lipsiensia, Journal Des Scavans,* and several others, which are chiefly accounts of books, tho' they contain several Original Essays.

All the sums I have mentioned, you will find amount to £ 216. 16.6. Taking in the Philosophical Transactions, and those of which I have no information; together with the old *Acta Curiosarum Casariensia,* 300 £ will, perhaps be about the sum requisite for your purpose.

Commentaria Societatis Gottingensis 4 Vols 4to at 15/ —— £ 3.0.0.

You give me pleasure by your account of the success of my

subscription. If it indemnify me for what is past I shall be very happy; but that, I am afraid, is more than I can expect. We begin to print this week. I expect the first proof every hour. I print a thousand —— You say nothing of the patronage of the King, which you thought it possible to procure. . . .

No. 33.

FROM BENJAMIN FRANKLIN TO JOHN CANTON

Augt. 15. —— *71* ——

Dear Sir,

I have just received the enclosed from Dr. Priestley. And as it contains an Acct. of a new Discovery of his, which is very curious, and, if it holds, will open a new Field of Knowledge, I send it to you immediately.—— Please to communicate it to Dr. Price when he returns. I am just about taking a Trip for a few weeks to Ireland. I hope I shall find you well at my Return. . . .

No. 34.

FROM PRIESTLEY TO RICHARD PRICE

Dear Sir

You may depend upon the account I sent you of my experiments on the restoration of air made noxious by animals breathing it or putrefying it, which I sent to Dr Franklin. Air in which candles have burnt out is also restored by the same means. In some instances, however, this method has failed to restore the two former kinds of air. Perhaps it may be owing to the plants not having the same vigour at the close of the year.

But I have just suceeded in a method of restoring these kinds of noxious air in a more certain and expeditious method; viz by mixing with it, with certain precautions, a quantity of air from lime stone, or fermentation, which is equally deadly when separate. I have had seven decisive proofs of this, without the least variation in the event.

I have been making many experiments on *putrefaction,* which is a most important process in nature, and which is little understood. The putrid effluvium is neither *fixed air,* as Macbride supposes, nor *inflammable* as Mr Cavendish thinks it partly is, but a thing *sui generis,* which diminishes the bulk of any quantity of common air to which it is admitted, disposing it, I believe, to deposit its fixed air. Had not Macbride been mistaken concerning the putrid effluvium, his own experiments would have led him, as they did me, to this discovery.

We have printed 530 pages of the History of *Light* &c. I shall send on to Mr Canton as far as 400, with the plates the next coach. I hope you will give so much attention to this work, as to read the printed sheets, and let no great mistake escape me. Also note the more considerable *Errata* of the press.

I send you a copy of the paper that was given me containing an account of the Inhabitants of Leeds,

In the Manor of Leeds,

Inhabitants		12690
Families	3023	
Kirkgate,		
Inhabitants		2491
Families	618	
St Johns Land,		
Inhabitants		1199
Families	258	
	——	——
	3899	17300

Leeds 3 Oct. 1771

No. 35.

FROM PRIESTLEY TO JOHN CANTON

Dear Sir

I send you, rather later than I promised Dr Price, the printed sheets of my work, as far as p. 400, with the plates. I also send you a book, which I beg you would return for me to the Royal Society. I shall draw up an account of my experiments as soon as I possibly can, to lay them before the Royal Society.

I shall be glad to hear from you, to acquaint me with the safe receipt of this. . . .

Leeds. 9 Oct. 1771

No. 36.

From Priestley to Richard Price

Leeds. 12 Oct. 1771

Dear Sir

In my last I mentioned my having restored air made noxious by putrefaction, and the breathing of animals by a mixture of fixed air. I had several more seeming proofs of it afterwards, particularly in air which was generated solely from putrefying mice, which I have been collecting some months, than which nothing can be more deadly, and which I made a mouse to breathe, for a considerable time, without shewing any sign of uneasiness. And yet some air tainted with putrid cabbage, and another quantity that animals have breathed baffle all my efforts, so that I see there is something in this subject that I am by no means master of, and I must suspend my conclusion respecting it some time longer. If I were to tell you how much time I have spent upon this subject, you would hardly believe me. I believe I must desist for the present. . . .

I hope you have received the printed sheets I sent you.

No. 37.

FROM PRIESTLEY TO RICHARD PRICE

Manor of Leeds, Inhabitants	12690	Families	3023
Kirkgate	2491	. . . .	618
St John's Land	1199	. . .	258
	16380		3899

Dear Sir

The above is an exact copy of the paper that was given me, respecting the number of people and families in Leeds. I fancy you had mistaken some of my figures, and I had cast it up wrong. I have no doubt but that the number of Inhabitants was taken for the same district for which I sent you an account of the burials and baptisms before. However, I will make particular inquiry, and if it be not so, will not fail to let you know the next week, when I shall send you 200 more pages of my work. I this day corrected p. 600. We shall have about 200 more —— I thank you for your animadversion, tho' I have not yet seen it.

I rejoice exceedingly in the success of your work, both on your own account, and that of the public, which, I think, cannot but receive great benefit from it.

I thank you for your condolance on the failure of some of my experiments. This day I made few, seemingly decisive ones, in favor of my first conclusion. I took, to a public brewery, a quantity of air made highly noxious by mice putrefying in it; and, dividing it into several parcels, in phials, I hung them, with their mouths downward, in the fixed air, generated in the vats; but, tho' they hung, some of them, near half an hour, they were not mended. I put mice into them, and they would have died almost instantly; but, leaving about ⅓ of the phial full of water, and letting it out, when they were hung over the vats (that a quantity of fixed air might mix with it) mice lived in it, and seemed to be perfectly at their ease. I let one continue, in a drinking glass full of it, five minutes, and it was taken out as vigorous as when it was put in. The same mouse, as well as some others, was exceedingly convulsed, and would have died in a minute or two, in the place from which the fixed air had been taken. Had it been very strong, they would have died much sooner. I propose to repeat these experiments several times, and shall reexamine those that failed.

Plants have in no instance yet failed to restore air in which wax candles have burned out, whereas air of the same parcel, kept in a phial, extinguished a candle, when the experiment was tried, and I have no doubt will do so some years hence. This process, however, has no effect on air in which brimstone has burned out. It is remarkable, also, that lime water does not become turbid in this air, whereas it is instantly so in air in which most other kinds of bodies have burned. The *diminution of the bulk* of air is much the same in all the cases —— The diminution of the bulk of air by putrefaction is a constant, and remarkable fact. I believe it precipitates the fixed air it contains, as it makes lime water turbid —— You will hardly believe me, but it is a fact, that I have spent more time on this tedious and puzzling course of experiments then I have bestowed on the Volume I am printing; but they have not been very expensive, whereas the other work is exceedingly so. When it is printed off, I shall not be worth a groat, except my *books,* and the *copies* of the work; and I have no reason to think that I shall have 300 subscribers —— My two papers in the Transactions are very incorrectly printed, and so I see is a former paper of mine which I did not attend to till lately.

Mr Walker I am told will contrive to meet me in London which will be some time in March. . . .

Leeds 19 Oct. 1771

I have made inquiry and find that what I said is right. The manor of Leeds includes a small village about a mile from the town, but all the Inhabitants bury here.

No. 38.

FROM PRIESTLEY TO JOHN CANTON

Dear Sir

You may depend upon it that I shall either reprint those leaves that contain any considerable errata, or correct them with a pen. It cannot but give me pleasure to have the approbation of such persons as you are, in a work of this kind, and I am sure you have so much friendship for me as to point out any thing that you think would discredit the work or me. I am not quite sure how much I sent you the last time, but I hope you will find these pages begin where the others ended. You will please to make what dispatch you conveniently can in perusing these sheets, and return all the three together. In two months the whole I hope, will be printed off so that I must send you the remainder in smaller parcels; but I believe you must do without the *plates*.

I wish you would acquaint Mr Johnson, and any of my friends who have collected subscriptions for me, to send me the names as soon as they can. Get me the Names of Dr Harris and Mr Rice at full length; but first inform yourself, if you can, whether Dr Harris gave me his name or not. I am not quite sure of it. . . .

Leeds 22 Oct. 1771

No. 39.

FROM PRIESTLEY TO JOHN CANTON

Dear Sir

Your letter, which I have this moment received, inclosed in one from Mr Johnson, gives me great concern, especially as I have given just the same attention to every article. I can never write every thing myself. But to prevent mistakes, my general custom is to make my amanuensis pronounce all the figures as he writes them, or to look over them myself; and all tables are printed directly from the originals, which I carry to the printer, unless they be abridged; and then I have never failed to have them read, and compared with the original. Besides myself a very intelligent clergyman always corrects the press, and I have two persons in the country besides you in the city to find in the sheets after they are printed off. You may depend upon it that the mistakes shall be effectually rectified.

I have this day corrected for the press as far as p. 704 and shall send you to this place some time this week, but I shall dread opening your letters, after they have gone through your hands. However, find all the faults you can. I had see them now than afterwards.

I very much question whether I shall proceed any farther with this work. Most of the subscriptions are now come in, and they will not even purchase the books I have bought for the purpose; and I had better drop it at once, then not go on with proper spirit. If I could afford to do it, I should not mind the money; but I ought, in common prudence, to make something of my time if possible. If I do work for nothing, it shall be upon theological subjects.

I defer drawing up my papers for the Royal because I keep getting farther light into the subject I am upon. I can pretty well account for the doubts I mentioned to Dr Price, but some of my experiments can hardly be repeated till the next summer. . . .

Leeds. 18 Novbr. 1771

[The "very intelligent clergyman" was most likely John Michell, Rector of Thornhill.]

No. 40.

FROM PRIESTLEY TO RICHARD PRICE

Leeds 23 Nov. 1771.

Dear Sir

I have just received the *printed sheets* of my history, and the view of the margin makes me regret exceedingly, that the work could not have the benefit of your revisal before it was printed.

The most considerable of your remarks, I observe, relate to my objections to *Newton's fits of easy reflexion and transmission,* as you think he doth not suppose that the rays are in those fits in the whole of their progress. At p. 257 8°, you will find these words. "Light is in fits of easy reflexion and easy transmission before its incidence on transparent bodies. And probably it is put into such fits at its first emission from luminous bodies, and continues in them during all its progress. For these fits are of a lasting nature &c." I therefore think that all my objections must be well founded. Boscovich, also, Mr Melville and Mr Michell understood him in that sense.

It was absolutely necessary to abridge Newton; but I never ventured to do it, unless I imagined, at least, that I did not make his sense less clear; but I may be mistaken in that imagination. I am sure I spared no pains to understand him myself, or to make his meaning intelligible to others.

I own that the more I consider the experiments of *Mazeas* on thin plates, the less I see in them. All your remarks will be useful to me, if ever there be a second edition of the work; but I think it will hardly be worth the while to cancel the leaves for the sake of them —— I beg you would continue your remarks with the same, or greater freedom. In about a month we shall finish the whole, and it must take its chances with many imperfections about it, but none, of much consequence that I could have obviated. *I have really done my best.* To strangers, I hope you will speak as favourably of my work as you can.

I do not think that I have made less than 20 seemingly decisive experiments in favor of the curing of putrid air by fixed air. In those that failed nothing was wanting, I now believe, but more time. Air that kills instantly after being kept in water three or four months, is made wholesome by this means; but it generally requires longer time than fresh made putrid air. The reason why lime water does not grow turbid when brimstone is burnt over it, is that the fixed air in the common mass unites, with the oil of vitriol, and together with the lime, makes a selenite, soluble in water. This I have found by evaporating the water. Air in which candles have burnt out, tho seemingly greatly reduced in bulk, is, I think, rather lighter than common air.

I find the most astonishing diminution of air in which I put a mixture of steel filings and pounded brimstone, even tho the whole process is in quicksilver and there is nothing that I can see to absorb it. That air is also of a most noxious quality.* It kills instantly, after keeping near a month, whereas air in which brimstone only has burnt out presently becomes breathable.

I think I have lately found a remarkable difference in the putrid effluvium in different stages of putrefaction, and that its noxious quality is by no means in proportion to its offensiveness to the nostrils.

It is evident that in airs that kill instantly (or that in which animals have before breathed and died) other animals do not die from want of any *pabulum vitae;* but it contains something of a stimulating nature, by which the animal is thrown into convulsions, and which when sheathed or neutralized by some other substance is fit enough for breathing again.

Missing a post. I have since I wrote the above made that very noxious air mentioned above* perfectly wholesome by fixed air in several trials but with this remarkable circumstance the mass of air not miscible with water is doubled or nearly tripled after the mixture — I have just found a plant of a proper size that grows very well in water at this time of the year, and am renewing my experiments with them. I, this day, send more printed sheets, by the coach, to Johnson.

Two of the passages you have censored are in the words of Mr Michell. What you say is *by no means rightly expressed,* is his variation of Motte's translation of Newton, which I had before used. I have not so often departed from Newton's own words as you imagine, hardly ever except to make his phrase more modern. . . .

No. 41.

From Priestley to [William Eden]

Dear Sir

I think myself very greatly honoured by Mr Banks's desire of my accompanying him in his second voyage, in so respectable a capacity as that of Astronomer; and, to be as frank and explicit with you as the friendship you have shewn me requires, I will at once acknowledge, that the proposal will not be disagreeable to me, provided a suitable provision can be procured for my family; and this I shall be perfectly easy in leaving to your management, and that of my friend Mr Lee.

Had Mrs Priestley been extremely averse to the scheme, I should not have thought of it; but she is happy in a considerable degree of strength of mind, and if she think it right upon the whole that I should go, she will, I doubt not, make herself not unhappy whatever be the consequence. No person can have a more domestic turn than myself, or be more happy in his family connections. I shall leave an affectionate wife, and three children, at an age which is, of all others, the most engaging; but a regard to their advantage, and, I will add, the ardour I feel for promoting natural knowledge will induce me to forgo my domestic satisfaction for a time. Other considerations, which you and Mr Lee have hinted, have their weight with me, especially the pleasure I shall promise myself from the company of so intelligent, so worthy, and so amiable a man as, by all accounts, Mr Banks is. Mr Lee will be able to tell him what kind of a man I am; and I flatter myself that we shall not be disagreeable to one another.

The sooner I am informed of the terms you can procure for me the better, that, if I think them worth my acceptance, I may be preparing myself for so important an undertaking. I shall be exceedingly solicitous to acquit myself to advantage in my province, and shall not fail to be attentive to every thing that may occur to me, as a proper object of attention, so as to make the most of so great an opportunity.

I have mentioned these expeditions into the South seas with

a degree of enthusiasm, which, if Mr. Banks should see it, will not be displeasing to him, in the preface to my History of Electricity; but little did I then think of ever being engaged in them myself.

I am truly grateful for your obliging notice of me, and am, with great respect, and most respectful compliments to Mr Banks. . . .

Leeds 4th Decbr. 1771

No. 42.

FROM PRIESTLEY TO RICHARD PRICE

Dear Sir

I cannot help communicating to you a proposal that Mr Banks has just made to me, to accompany him in his second voyage, in the character of *Astronomer,* with a handsome provision secured to me and my family. I have so far listened to it, as to desire to know what terms can be procured for me. I wish to have your real thoughts, and that of some other of my friends on the subject, as I am far from being determined. My favorite employment is that of a minister, but I doubt not my place would be supplied till my return, and retirement will be necessary to the execution of my schemes, which I could resume with peculiar advantage after my return. I wish you would see Mr Vaughan or Mr Lee on the subject. The proposal came to me through the hands of Mr Lee and Mr Eden.

Since I wrote to you I have had undoubted proofs of inflammable air losing its inflammability, extinguishing flames, and killing animals, and afterwards being made breathable by fixed air. I can also render fixed air not miscible with water, but permanently elastic, and wholesome to breath, by another most noxious air, but have not time to mention the particulars. . . .

Leeds. 5 Decbr. 1771

No. 43.

FROM PRIESTLEY TO WILLIAM EDEN

Dear Sir

I see your friendship and esteem for me, whether merited or unmerited, in every line of your letters; and this makes me overlook the disagreeable situation into which I have been brought, by seeming to jump at a proposal which was never made to me, and so many days of painful anxiety, which my friends and family have suffered on this account.

I can hardly bring myself to think so very meanly of Dr Blackstone, and his friends in the board of longitude, as to suppose they would have any objection to my services as a philosopher. If this be the case, you must allow me to think and speak of them with proper contempt. It is very possible that the recompence you mentioned to me was never intended to be given to any person; but if the board of longitude consist of such characters as you and Mr Banks represent them, I should not be surprised at them giving twice as much either to a high churchman, or a known atheist, tho' his reputation for philosophy or virtue should stand very low.

Mr Lee has written to me, but only in ten lines, and without mentioning either Mr Banks, or you, or any other person —— You will do me great injustice, if you suspect that I think you in the least to blame in this affair; but it is a pity that the thing had not been better considered by Mr Banks, before he requested you to write to me upon the subject.

I find, by letters from London, that the thing was no secret there, presently after you first wrote to me, so that my enemies, I expect, will rejoice not a little upon the occasion. . . .

Leeds 10 Debr 1771.

No. 44.

From Priestley to Sir Joseph Banks

Leeds, Dec. 10, 1771

Dear Sir

After the letter which I received about a fortnight ago from Mr. Eden, who informed me that he wrote at your request, I cannot help saying that your's, and his, which I have now received, appear a little extraordinary. In the former letter, there was far from being the most distant hint of any objection to me, provided I would consent to accompany you. You now tell me that, as the different Professors of Oxford and Cambridge will have the naming of the person, and they are all clergymen, they may possibly have some scruples on the head of religion; and that on this account you do not think you could get me nominated at any rate, much less on the terms that were first mentioned to me. Now what I am, and what they are, with respect to religion, might easily have been known before the thing was proposed to me at all. Besides, I thought that this had been a business of philosophy, and not of divinity. If, however, this be the case, I shall hold the Board Of Longitude in extreme contempt, and make no scruple of speaking of them accordingly, taking it for granted that you have just ground for your suspicions. I most sincerely wish you a happy voyage, as I doubt not it will be greatly to the emolument of science; but I am surprised that the persons who have the chief influence in this expedition, having (according to your representation) minds so despicably illiberal, should give any countenance to so noble an undertaking. I am truly sorry that a person of your disposition should be subject to a choice restricted by such narrow considerations. . . .

No. 45.

FROM PRIESTLEY TO ALESSANDRO VOLTA

Monsieur,

Your letter to me was very welcome, and I am happy to have there certified your beautiful discoveries in *Electricity,* and you may be sure that I will render you justice in future editions of my work. At present I will attempt to procure the two pamphlets of which you speak.

There are many ingenious men, as well as yourself, Monsieur, who have wasted much good time and work on the discoveries of others. It is the purpose of my work to prevent this grievous business in the future. In this connection, I have already written the history of electricity, and I have published this month the *history of discoveries about vision, light and colours,* a work larger than the first; and provided my labours are well received, I intend to write the history of all Experimental Philosophy.

The idea of your machine, made of pasteboard surprised me. Therefore I had one made and I was much surprised to see its performance, although this was considerably worse than that of glass globes. Nevertheless, I can well suppose that if one constructed it in better manner, its force would be greater; especially if one introduced many plates of pasteboard, or of wood (of which it would be still easier to make [them]) while one rubber will suffice for two plates.

You send me, Monsieur, the first news of the French translation of my history, and I have not yet seen it. . . .

Leeds 14 March 1772

No. 46.

FROM PRIESTLEY TO THORBERN BERGMAN

To the distinguished Thorbern Bergman

Most worthy man, it was most pleasing to receive your answering letter, in which you inform me of the Swedes' accomplishments in electricity.

I acknowledge, indeed, that foreign discoveries were not enough known to me when writing the History of Electricity. Now, however, I am about to write a history of all experimental philosophy. I have collected with the greatest care and at much expence all the philosophical books I could, for scarcity of which, the work which you have so graciously praised, has attained by no means the perfection that I could wish. With this assistance, your help and that of others, I hope to bring out a future edition richer and more completely accurate.

I had not yet [when I received your letter] seen the French translation of which you saw a copy, nor have I heard if a more recent one has been made. I am entirely ignorant as to what [translations] have been made.

I published recently a History of Optics showing the properties of vision, light, and colour, a somewhat larger work than the History of Electricity, and am proceeding, God willing, to describe the properties of air in the same historical manner.

Whether you apply your celebrated genius to studies of chemistry or electricity, we will all, without doubt, seize upon the results. . . .

Leeds 14 March 1772

No. 47.

FROM BENJAMIN FRANKLIN TO PRIESTLEY

London, May 4, 1772

Dear Sir,

I think with you that there cannot be the least Occasion for my explaining your Method of impregnating Water with fix'd Air to Messrs. Banks & Solander, as they were present and I suppose are as well acquainted with it as myself; however I shall readily do it if they think it necessary. I am glad you intend to improve and publish the Process. ——

You must go half an Inch farther with your Spark to exceed what I show'd here with my Philad Machine in 1758 to Lord Charles Cavendish & others, who judg'd them to be nine Inches. —— My Cushion was of Buckskin with a long damp Flap, and had a Wire from it thro' the Window down to the Iron Rails in the Yard; the Conductor of Tin 4 feet long & about 4 Inches Diameter. So powerful a Machine had then never been seen in England before, as they were pleas'd to tell me. A Machine was made from mine for Mr Symmer & was afterwards in the Possession of Lord Morton. A more convenient Construction I have never since seen, except that of yours.

I intend soon to repeat Barletti's Experiments, being provided with the Requisites, & shall let you know the Result.

I should be glad to see the French Translation of your Book. Can you conveniently lend it to me when you have perus'd it? I fancy it was translated at the Request of Abbé Nollet by a Friend & Disciple of his; as I know there was one (whose Name I have forgotten) that us'd to translate for him Extracts of English Electrical Books. —— The Abbé's Machine was a very bad one, requiring three Persons to make the smallest Experiment, one to turn the great Wheel, & one to hold Hands on the Globe. And the Effect after all but weak. Delor had a similar one, and invited me to see him exhibit to the Duchess of Rochefoucault, but the Weather being a little warm, he could perform nothing, scarce obtaining a Spark. This Inconvenience must have occasioned their

Making fewer Experiments, & of course his not being so easily convinced. —— M. Le Roy, however, got early possession of the Truth, & combated for it with Nollet; yet I think the Academy rather favoured the latter. Le Roy will I suppose now confute this Translator, for I have just seen a Letter of his to Mr Magelhaens, thanking him for sending so excellent an Electric Machine to France; (it is one of the Plate ones) which he has improv'd so as to produce the positive & negative Electricities seperately or together at the same time, de façon (says he) qu'on peut faire toutes les Experiences possibles sur l'une ou l'autre de ces deux Electricités. —— Enfin on etoit si eloigné de connoitre les Phenomenes de ces deux Electricités ici, faute de Machines commodes de les demontrer, que beaucoup des Gens ont été étonnés de voir avec quelle évidence ils etablissent la distinction de ces deux electricités. &c. This Letter is of the 5th Instant. . . .

No. 48.

FROM PRIESTLEY TO BENJAMIN FRANKLIN

Leeds. 13 June 1772.

Dear Sir

You make me very happy by the near prospect of seeing you and Sr John Pringle at Leeds. I shall be intirely at liberty to receive you, and I hope you will contrive to stay as long as possible in this town and neighbourhood. I thank you for the *Native of New England*. I had casually seen the same paper, and was particularly struck with it, without having any suspicion of *Poor Richard* being the author of it. I am obliged to you for your advice with respect to the *dedication*, and shall comply with it, but some other alterations, besides what you noted, must be made in it, if it be addressed to Lord Sandwich only.

I am intent upon the prosecution of my experiments on *air;* and since I wrote to you have observed several remarkable appearances. That very extraordinary kind of air, which Dr Hales got from Walton Pyrites, and which I had despaired of procuring, I get from all the metals I have yet tried by means of spirit of nitre. It is quite transparent; but a mixture of it and common air is red for a considerable time, in which the whole quantity is greatly reduced in bulk. A mixture of this and fixed air is not turbid. This air alone is reduced above one half by a mixture of iron filings, and brimstone standing in it, whereas common air is diminished only about one fifth by the same process. When I have the pleasure of seeing you I shall acquaint you with some other remarkable properties of this new kind of air. In the mean time, you will do me a very important service by procuring me, and bringing along with you a little of highly concentrated *marine acid.* There is none to be got here; and using a weaker sort in the solution of gold (in order to observe what kind of air came from it) I was obliged to apply a considerable degree of heat, the consequence of which was that the acid menstruum suddenly boiling, my hands, face, clothes, and the walls of the room have been great sufferers by it, as, I am afraid, I shall be able to shew you. A pennyweight of gold, which I had bought for the purpose, was also lost. As a reward for this damage, I preserved about three ounce measures of *air* extracted from gold, which, I believe, was never seen before, and have the prodigious satisfaction of finding that it has the very same properties with that which is produced from copper. If I had studied *poor Richard* in time, I should not have indulged myself in these expences, but bad habits are not easily corrected. If, however, the passion be not kept up by considerable success, frugality, and an attention to a growing family will, at length, get the better of experimenting, and then I shall write nothing but *Politicks,* or *Divinity,* to furnish the Bishop of Landoff with more quotations for his future invectives against the Dissenters.

The French translation of my History of Electricity I borrowed of Mr Walsh; but, as it will be of some use to me in a future edition of my work, I think to purchase it. In the mean time, Mr Walsh will have no objection to your having it for what time you please, and I can give it you when you are here.

I am surprised that the French electricians should not have been able to provide themselves with better machines. I am confident that plates will never answer so well as globes or cylinders. . . .

I wish you could bring Dr Price with you.

No. 49.
FROM PRIESTLEY TO BENJAMIN FRANKLIN

Leeds. 1 July 1772

Dear Sir

I presume that by this time you are arrived in London, and I am willing to take the first opportunity of informing you, that I have never been so busy, or so successful in making experiments, as since I had the pleasure of seeing you at Leeds.

I have fully satisfied myself that air rendered in the highest degree noxious by breathing is restored by sprigs of mint growing in it. You will probably remember the flourishing state in which you saw one of my plants. I put a mouse to the air in which it was growing on the saturday after you went, which was seven days after it was put in, and it continued in it five minutes without shewing any sign of uneasiness, and was taken out quite strong and vigorous, when a mouse died after being not two seconds in a part of the same original quantity of air, which had stood in the same exposure, without a plant in it. The same mouse also that lived so well in the restored air, was barely recoverable after being not more than one second in the other. I have also had another instance of a mouse living 14 minutes without being at all hurt, in little more than two ounce measures of another quantity of noxious air in which a plant had grown.

I have completely ascertained the restoration of air in which tallow or wax candles, spirit of wine, or brimstone matches have burned out by the same means.

The nitrous air, which I shewed you, I find to be an admirable test of air that is fit for breathing. It makes this air red and turbid, but no other that I have tried. I took air in which a mouse had putrefied, which was in the highest degree noxious and fetid, and also a quantity of fixed air. The nitrous air admitted to each of these kinds of air separately made no sensible alteration in them but when they were mixed (which I discovered to make a wholesome air) the nitrous air made the mixture turbid and diminished the bulk of it, as in common air, tho not in the same degree. A

[104]

mouse put to this mixture lived five minutes without uneasiness, when, if it had been put to either of them separately, a few minutes before, it would have died in a few seconds.

Air that has passed thro' hot charcoal has many, perhaps all the properties of air that has been diminished by other processes. It extinguishes flame, kills animals, and is not diminished or made turbid by a mixture of nitrous air.

But the observation that pleases me more than any I ever made, is the diminution of air by the crystallization (I believe) of quicksilver and the nitrous acid. This effect both precedes and follows the generation of nitrous air from the same mixture. This I suspect to be the case with other crystallizations.

I have observed many other things, which I have not room to mention at present. . . .

No. 50.

From Priestley to Richard Price

Leeds. 21. July 1772.

Dear Sir

I think myself exceedingly honoured by the very favorable opinion which Lord Shelburne's proposal implies that he has entertained of me, as, both from your account, and that of others, I conceive him to be, for ability and integrity together, the very first character in this kingdom. But I really think it would not be in my power to render his Lordship any services equivalent to the recompence which, in prudence I ought to expect, if ever I leave Leeds; and I could not satisfy myself with receiving a salary, without rendering what should appear to myself an equivalent service.

My salary exceeds that of most Dissenting ministers, and I may say that the whole of my time is at my own disposal, so that I can pursue what studies I please without interruption. Indeed, my place is such, that, according to present appearances, the only motive I can ever have to remove is, that, agreeable as my situation is with respect to myself, it affords me no prospect of making any provision for a growing family. I have therefore thought that, if ever I do remove, it must be to America, where it will be more easy for one to dispose [of] my children to their advantage.

I flatter myself, indeed, that I might render his [Lor]dship some service with respect to the education of [his] children, as that is a subject to which I have given [some] very particular attention, and with respect to which I have had a good deal of experience; but every thing of this nature I consider as superseded by the tutor his Lordship will chuse for them; and whoever he be, it is not probable that he will submit to be directed by another.

It is true that my reading and studies have had as great a range as, I believe, those of most people, but I imagine that the information which his Lordship might occasionally want would relate chiefly to things of a *political* nature, which I have not particularly studied, and require more acquaintance with modern history than I can pretend to.

But supposing that, by changing the course of my studies, I could become whatever his Lordship wishes me to, I am so habituated to domestic life, and am so happy at home, that it is not possible I should receive any compensation for not living in my own family. Or, if it could be compatible with his Lordship's views to compromise this article with me, his living partly in London and partly in the country would make it impossible for me to take any advantage of officiating as a dissenting minister, if any society in London should make choice of me; which, however, I do not think very probable; nor do I see from what other source I could benefit myself, except, perhaps, from reading lectures, either in Natural Philosophy, or the subjects on which I used to give lectures at Warrington.

Please to represent to Lord Shelburne my sentiments on the general view of his Lordship's proposal. If he should think that the obstacles I have mentioned may be removed, in a manner consistent with his own views, he shall find me very ingenuous and explicit on the subject.

You want to know what I am doing about AIR. I have lately resumed my experiments on that subject with considerable success. I have perfectly ascertained the restoration of air injured by respiration putrefaction or by the burning of candles, spirit of wine or brimstone matches by the growing of plants. For this purpose I have made use of mint balm, groundsel, and spinage, and have found that this effect depends upon the vegetating state of the plants. I have also discovered that air receives, in a great measure, the very same *kind* of injury from flame, as from respiration &c but only about one third in *degree*.

To ascertain this I make use of a new and accurate measure of the fitness of air for respiration, viz a mixture of air [genera]ted by spirit of nitre from all metals, I believe, except zinc. [I] get it from iron, tin, copper, silver, quicksilver, and gol[d (in] aqua regia). One third of this kind of air mixed with two thirds of common air makes it hot, red, and turbid for some time, and is so far from making any addition to the bulk of it, that it considerably diminishes it. By this means I have a very large scale of mensuration. It has no sensible effect on air unfit for respiration, on whatever account it be so. I have [no] occasion, therefore, to make use of mice &c to ascertain the fit[ness of any] kind of air for breathing —— This is the same kind of air that [Dr Hales] got from the Walton Pyrites and which I never expected to [see. It has] other remarkable properties. Mixed with inflammable air it [makes it] burn green, even tho' it has been extracted from silver or go[ld. By a] mixture of iron filings and brimstone it is reduced from [10 to 2½] whereas common air is only reduced ⅕ in the same circumstan[ce.]

By making the process in quicksilver, I have made [farther] observations on that very remarkable kind of air which Mr Cavendish got from copper by the marine acid, and find about ¼ of it to be inflammable. The very same curious appearances arise from the solution of lead, and in a small degree from that of iron and tin with the same acid.

These are but few in *number,* but I think the principal with respect to *importance* of the observations I have lately made —— The pamphlet I have printed only contains directions for making Pyrmont water. I can make better than you import, and what costs you 5 shillings will not cost me a penny. I might have turned quack —— Several of my observations relate to air that has passed thro' burning charcoal. These and many others I am pursuing farther, and should oftener write to you on these subjects, but that I consider every correspondence as an additional burden to you. . . .

No. 51.

FROM PRIESTLEY TO RICHARD PRICE

Leeds. 27 Sepbr. 1772

Dear Sir

You think much too well of me, and are too much concerned about me. I am truly sorry for the trouble you have given yourself on my account, as it is not now likely to answer the friendly design you had in it —— I thought it right to send you Mr Johnson's letter. It was the first remonstrance I received upon the subject. After that Mr Lee talked to me in much the same strain, except that upon the whole, he seemed inclined to think favorably of the Earl of Shelbourne's character. I also find that Sr John Pringle and others are of opinion that the state I should be brought into would be too dependant and humiliating, and not leave me sufficiently master of my own conduct.

For my own part, I do think that, if I be capable of doing any good in the world, exclusive of my own private interest, I can do it to the most advantage in my present situation. It is true that my schemes lead me into a variety of expences, and put it out of my power to do much for my family; but my children, by the favour of a good providence, may do as I myself have done who had not a single farthing, besides my education, to set out with.

As to the *history of experimental Philosophy*, it does not appear, from Mr Johnson's last account of the sale of my *History of Vision* &c that it will be worth my while to prosecute it any farther. I may, perhaps, indeed, at my leisure, write the history of discoveries relating to *air*, because I shall have particular advantage in doing it, in consequence of having made so many observations of my own on the subject. I mean, however, to prosecute my *experiments* as I have opportunity, keeping off such as would involve me in much expence.

I have been long bewildered with a multiplicity of new appearances of an extraordinary kind, but I think that I now begin to see a little into the nature of them, and am not without hopes that, after another summer's course, I shall be able to give a much better account of them than I can at present. I have been improving my electrical apparatus with a view to some experiments of that kind this next winter. From a globe, which I fitted up this day, I can make a dozen, or twenty pencils fly off at a time, a sight which, I fancy, was never seen before.

My air pump, in Mr Smeaton's construction, is now complete, with the syphon gage, to shew the degree either of condensation or exhaustion. It has sometimes exhausted above $\frac{1}{1000}$, whereas the best common pumps scarce go beyond $\frac{1}{100}$. Mr Canton, I remember, said that his went to $\frac{1}{120}$ when it was in its best order. This pump is also much easier to work than any other. I expect to derive great advantage from this instrument in many of my experiments. I wonder they are not in general use; but as far as I can learn there are but two, that are good for anything, in being, my own and Mr Smeaton's, both of his making. I am making use of it at present to ascertain the specific gravity of different kinds of air, and think it rather remarkable that when air is diminished above $\frac{1}{3}$ I can find no constant differences in the specific gravity of about 3 pints of it.

I am desiring of getting subscriptions to the first volume of the *Repository,* as the reprinting of it might make more sets go off. At present I lose near 50 £ by that work. Myself and a few [of] my friends wrote the greatest part of it. It was a favorite scheme of mine, but I was obliged to give it over. . . .

Can you tell me any news of [Dr.] Harwood. I hear he left Bristol, and is in London.

No. 52.

FROM PRIESTLEY TO THORBERN BERGMAN

To the distinguished Thorbern Bergman

Your information about the properties of fixed air is certainly most worthy of my attention and, indeed, all your observations will be most welcome. But, most learned man, I could wish your descriptions had been more concise, lest this correspondence become burdensome to you.

My observations on the origin of separate airs are many and the long history of these observations has been presented to the Royal Society and will be published in the next volume of their Transactions. In the meantime, to gratify your eagerness (which does me great honor), I will attempt to describe briefly a few of my experiments. Common air was diminished by one-fifth by means of respiration, putrefaction (which process also poisons the air), calcination of metals, burning of carbon and other similar processes.

Air, once diminished by any of these causes, will permit no further diminution by any other cause and in this state is most noxious to animals breathing it. It is restored, however, by long agitation in water, or if you prefer, by plants growing in it. Plants likewise restore air corrupted by fire.

Inflammable air, much agitated in water, is at first rendered innoxious to breathing, then loses all its inflammability, and at length puts out fire. Common air, agitated much in water, likewise puts out fire.

I impregnate water with fixed air by agitating it as briskly as possible and in this manner imitate the water from the Pyrmont springs. I published a sufficiently exact description of this process in a little pamphlet which, as you hear, has already been translated into French.

I extract a certain remarkable air from several metals by means of spirit of nitre. Two parts of common air, mixed with one part of this nitrous air, becomes hot, reddish, and undergoes a sudden diminution into a smaller space even than it previously occupied.

However, this nitrous air least affects air which, for whatever reason, is unsuitable for breathing. Nitrous air also, in some miraculous manner, preserves flesh from putrefying and even restores putrefied meat. A mixture of sulphur and iron filings in water diminishes nitrous air to a fifth part of itself.

By means of spirits of salt [hydrochloric acid] in addition to the air which vanishes on contact with water, as observed by Mr Cavendish, I extract from copper and lead inflammable air.

If, by writing with the same brevity, it should not be excessively burdensome to you, you would do me a great service by describing your particular observations to me. I would, on the other hand, have described these few selected observations more adequately had they not been about to be published very shortly. . . .

Leeds 21 October 1772

P.S. I beg that you will arrange for Dr. Carolus Wilcke to read this letter.

No. 53.

FROM PRIESTLEY TO RICHARD PRICE

Dear Sir

Please to transmit the inclosed papers to Mr Pickard. The ministers in this neighbourhood are a very mixed body, many of them rigid calvinists, and much influenced by Mr Hitchin. They came to oppose and wrangle; but by judicious and fair management, they were brought not only to make no opposition, but to acquiesce in every thing we proposed. We were obliged, however, to divide, subdivide, and distinguish, as you will perceive by our minutes.

I still continue inclined to accept of Lord Shelburne's proposal, notwithstanding I have heard more said against it than I have yet communicated to you; and I cannot help thinking that it will put me more in the way of being useful both to my family, and the world, than I can be in my present situation. This I observe, that those who are acquainted with Lord Shelburne encourage me to accept of his proposal; but most of those who who know the world in general, but not Lord Shelburne in particular, dissuade me from it. All of them also greatly overrate my present situation, of which myself only can be a judge, and by comparison with which I must estimate any other situation. I hope to see you the first week in December, having agreed to take part of a chaise in company with Mr Lindsey, and another petitioning clergyman. We expect to be in London on the tuesday night or Wednesday morning, and on that day I propose to wait upon you.

I intend to send Mr Johnson and you, by the first coach, copies of the second volume of my *Institutes,* and if you have time, could wish you would give it a perusal before it goes into the world.

I sent my papers for the Royal Society by a first load on tuesday last (this day sennight) to be delivered by Mr Johnson to Dr Franklin, and by him to be sent to Dr Maty. I hope they are arrived, tho' I have this day received a letter from Dr Maty, desiring me to send them as soon as I can get them ready.

I am still making a few experiments, the account of which I propose to bring with me. They will be a kind of Appendix to the papers I have sent up; containing an account of all the kinds of air got by all the acids from all the metals and semimetals, most of which I have got from Mr Michell. Bismuth and Nickel give nitrous air, and regulus of Antimony, part nitrous air, and part that which shrinks up at the contact of water. Platina is very intractable.

I have just found, to my great surprise, that a quantity of air, which I got about a year ago from salt petre, and which was then quite wholesome, and in which a candle burned perfectly well, is now become in the highest degree noxious, and makes no effervescence with nitrous air. It stood in water; and common air in the same circumstance, I find not to be injured at all, [in] the same time. . . .

Leeds. 11 Nov. 1772.

No. 54.

From Priestley to Richard Price

Dear Sir

I give you this line to inform you that I do not now expect to be in town before Wednesday, and probably late at night. Being disappointed of Mr Lindsey's company, I think to take the York stage coach. I shall be engaged to dine on Thursday, and if I do not see you on the morning of that day, I shall depend upon seeing you in the evening, at the Royal Society.

There was, I recollect, an omission in the copy I sent you of our letter to Sir G Savile. After the first paragraph, ending with, *Articles of the church of England,* add, *and to procure relief for dissenting tutors and schoolmasters.*

The last course of experiments I mentioned to you, I have pursued considerably farther, but the results are too particular to be recited in a letter. I propose this day to draw up an account of them, together with a supplement to my chapter on nitrous air, and that of the miscellaneous experiments, for the Royal Society. I shall only inform you, that I have found, to my great surprize, that this vapour of spirit of salt, which is always reckoned the weakest of all the mineral acids, has never failed to dislodge the other two, and seize upon their bases. It decomposes alum and nitre; and, joining itself to the phlogiston of sulphur, becomes inflammable air. It also extracts phlogiston from the rust of iron, and the precipitate of copper, and by that means also becomes inflammable air.

I think I told you that the air which I extracted from nitre, and which was, at first, wholesome and good, had, in the course of a year, become highly noxious. By washing it in rain water a few minutes, it became again, as good as any air in the world, and a candle burned in it perfectly well. This fact appears more extraordinary to me than it can do to you, or anybody else. I cannot help flattering myself that the prosecution of these experiments will lead me, or others, to a farther insight into the constitution of the atmosphere, and also to a farther knowledge of the nature of metals and acids, &c.

Upon looking over this letter, I think it will be in vain to send it to any of our friends, as I think they will not be able to read it. If you can do it, who are more used to my hand, I shall be very glad. . . .

Leeds. 26 Novbr 1772.

No. 55.

FROM JOHN WINTHROP TO BENJAMIN FRANKLIN

Cambridge, New England, 4 March, 1773

Dear Sir,

I received your favor of September 18th. I return you many thanks for Dr. Priestley's piece on impregnating water with fixed air. If this should prove an effectual remedy for the sea-scurvy, it would be indeed a most important discovery. I am extremely concerned to hear that Dr. Priestley is so poorly provided for, while so many are rolling about here in gilt chariots, with very ample stipends. I admire his comprehensive genius, his perspicuity and vigor of composition, his indefatigable application, and his free, independent spirit, and wish it were in my power to do him any kind of service. It would give me great pleasure to see him well settled in America; though indeed I am inclined to think he can prosecute his learned labors to greater advantage in England. A man of his abilities would do honor to any of the colleges. At present there is no vacancy among them; but if there were, I believe, Sir, you judge perfectly right, that his religious principles would hardly be thought orthodox enough. Indeed, I doubt, whether they would do at the Rhode Island College, any more than in the others. That college is entirely in the hands of the Baptists, and intended to continue so, and I never understood that Dr. Priestley was of their persuasion. However, I cannot but hope that his great and just reputation will procure something valuable for him, and adequate to his merit.

I have just looked over his treatise of Optics, which you were so good as to present to our library, with great satisfaction, and met with many articles, especially from the foreign publications, which were new to me. It is indeed a most noble collection of every thing relating to that science.

In my last I ventured to mention a little slip concerning the satellites of Saturn. It would be miraculous, if, in so large a work collected from such a number of books and on such a variety of matters, there should not be many such. I noted the few that occurred to me in the chapters taken from those authors I was most acquainted with, and beg leave to enclose a list of the principal of them. There are not above two or three of them that are of any consequence; however, such as it is, the list is at Dr. Priestley's service, if you think it worth sending to him. It may help to remove a few trifling inaccuracies from that valuable work.

I have enclosed the newspaper you mention, that gave an account of the thunder-storm we had here a few years ago. As you are collecting facts on this subject, I looked over my old Almanacs where I had made some memoranda relating to your admirable lightning bells. I think it would not be worth while to transcribe them all, nor can I collect any thing from them but what is commonly known. In general, it seems that the bells hardly ever ring in the summer without a shower; they sometimes ring when there is no thunder or lightning, but do not always ring when there is. When there is a thunder shower, they generally ring most briskly while the cloud is yet at some distance, and cease as soon as it rains hard. In winter they frequently ring briskly in snow-storms, and twice they have do so after the weather was cleared up, and while the new-fallen snow was driving about with the wind, as you have done me the honor already to publish.

In looking for the newspaper before mentioned, I met with another, which gives an account of damage done by lightning in some places in Connecticut in 1771. As perhaps you have not seen it, I enclose it with the other; also, a letter sent me with another account. In my Almanacs I found also a few minutes relating to some uncommon appearances of the Aurora Borealis. I do not know that they can be of any use, but if they will afford you the least amusement I will readily transcribe them.

In addition to my newspaper account, I would mention that besides the strokes of lightning on the College and the elm tree, July 2d, 1768, there was another discharge that afternoon on a cornfield, at a little distance from the College towards the southeast. It spoiled the corn, which was of some height, in a circle of about twenty feet diameter. That near the centre was burnt down to the roots, as I was informed by the owner. I did not hear of it till some days after, and when I saw the place it had been replanted with cabbage. The corn near the circumference of the circle was only scorched, and I saw the leaves withered and drooping. The place struck was about midway between a tree on one side, and the well-pole and chimney of the house on the other, and, as I judge, about eighty feet distant from each; and there was nothing near so high on the other side for a considerable distance. Hence, their protection did not extend eighty feet. If a person had been standing in that corn, I suppose there is no doubt that he would have been killed. And therefore a person in the midst of an open plain is by no means secure from the stroke of lightning. The best security seems to be to have something high, as a tree for example, near him, but not too near; perhaps from thirty or forty to ten or fifteen feet, or rather to be near two such trees. . . .

No. 56.

FROM PRIESTLEY TO REV. JOSEPH BRETLAND

Leeds, March 7, 1773

Dear Sir,

An excursion which I have made into Lancashire has prevented my making so early an acknowledgement as I could have wished to have done of your favour, by which I think myself much honoured. I promise myself much satisfaction from your correspondence, and hope we shall have a tolerable easy communication when I come to reside in Wiltshire.

The objections you make to the hypothesis of the penetrability of matter are very ingenious, and not easily answered; but do they not equally affect the common hypothesis of the constituent particles of all bodies being prevented from actually touching one another by some power of repulsion, which however seems to be absolutely necessary to account for their condensation by cold, and dilatation by heat.

Mr. Michell supposes that wherever the properties or powers of any substance are, there is the substance itself, something that we call *substance* being necessary to the support of any properties; but what any substance is, devoid of all properties, we cannot, from the nature of the thing, have any idea whatever; since all the notices that we receive of any substance are communicated to us by means of its properties, and such as bear some relation to our senses, which are the inlets to all our knowledge. And any property may be ascribed to any substance that does not necessarily imply a contradiction, that is, that does not suppose the absence of some other *known* property.

Boscovich seems to suppose that matter consists of *powers* only, without any substance; but this differs from the theory of Berkeley, which excludes all space as well as matter.

I do not suppose that the experiment which you mention of Newton's was ever made, except by himself; and if you consider the nature of it, you will be sensible that it must require the greatest attention, the concurrance of many circumstances, and a very great expense, to make it properly. I do not believe that it could be exhibited, as he did it, for less than 50 or perhaps 100 pounds.

I thank you for your *theological hints,* and should have been glad to have had them inserted in the Repository. If I had had any thing worth your notice to observe concerning them, I should have mentioned it, but I really have not. I shall probably consider some of the subjects in the Institutes, of which I propose to publish a volume every year. The last part (concerning the Corruptions of Christianity) will grow, I believe, into two volumes.

I think myself much obliged to you for the distribution of the Appeal, &c. I hope to print all the pamphlets in one, some time before the next winter. It would have been done before this time, but that I wait for the corrections and remarks of some distant friends. I shall be glad to receive any thing that may occur to you. . . .

P.S. I am sorry that a person of your disposition and qualifications should decline the ministry, at a time when there seems to be very great want of such persons.

With the publication of his *History of Electricity*, Priestley was committed to a role in science which had little if anything to do with his own experiments. As Franklin's letter to Canton (No. 19) shows, there were many people who were unaware that he had made any experiments, and this reaction of members of the Council of the Royal Society supports the suggestion that experiments were not a significant element in Priestley's election to fellowship in the Society. In any event, Franklin's recommendation, first to the President and Council (Nos. 18, 19) and later (No. 21) to the Society as a whole, that Priestley be given the Copley Medal of the Royal Society was ignored. It would be several years before people were to think of Priestley as an experimental scientist and when this happened, it was his chemical discoveries, not his work on electricity, which achieved recognition.[2]

This is not to say that Priestley stopped experimenting, but a large part of his time during this period was devoted to his peripheral activities in education and public relations in sci-

---

[2] The Copley Medal for 1767 went to John Ellis for his work identifying the corallines as animal in nature; that for 1768, to Peter Woulfe for his experiments on the distillation of acids, volatile alkalies, and other substances. Some of Priestley's electrical discoveries, notably the inverse-square force relationship of electric charges, the experiments on relative conductivities, and the ingenious series (mentioned later in this chapter) on the oscillatory discharge of Leyden jars, perhaps deserved the Copley Medal. Since Franklin's recommendation, with singular infelicity, fails to note any of these, it would have been hard to justify a claim for Priestley that would be superior to either Ellis' or Woulfe's.

ence. Of the persons added to his list of advisors and correspondents, there were many from all over Europe who wrote
correcting, supplementing, or adding later information to
what Priestley had written in his *History* on their own work
or that of their countrymen (e.g., Nos. 45, 46, 52). Priestley
therefore felt compelled to prepare a second and then a third
edition (published in 1775; the fourth edition of the same year
is the same in content though differing in format) of that
work incorporating new material from his correspondents and
from his continued reading in newly acquired works.

Having successfully tapped the vein of popular-science
writing, Priestley expanded his efforts in that direction. No
doubt this was partially to please his not inconsiderable vanity
and because he believed that it would bring him money. A
more important motive, however, was his quite genuine belief
that in science this was his *métier*.[3] Nothing in his training or
experience, and nothing yet in the reception given his work
could have told him that he had more to contribute to science
than a talent as an educator. Moreover, nothing in his entire
career casts doubt on the sincerity of his conviction, expressed
in the prefaces to both the *History of Electricity* and the *History of Optics,* that the more people knew and the more work
they did in science the better the world would be.

Before the end of 1767 Priestley had completed the writing
of his *Familiar Introduction to the Study of Electricity* (first
edition, 1768), directed to readers for whom the *History* had
been too advanced. Having made several of the drawings of
electrical apparatus which appear as illustrations in the *History* and in the *Study of Electricity,* Priestley followed the

---

[3] As late as the second edition of Priestley's *Description of a Chart of Biography* (Warrington, 1765), pp. 1–2, he wrote in a footnote: "Few are qualified
to make new discoveries of importance . . . but when discoveries have been
made, and the principles of science have been ascertained, persons of inferior
abilities . . . are sufficient to digest those principles into a convenient
method." Obviously Priestley had cast himself in the latter role.

latter with *A Familiar Introduction to the Theory and Practice of Perspective,* to recommend to aspiring scientists the utility and techniques of good draftsmanship. The publication of the *Perspective* in its first edition was enlivened by the request of his friends that he include a recommendation of "Mr. Nairne's composition" for erasing pencil marks (No. 26). The conclusion of the preface was changed to read:

Since this Work was printed off, I have seen a substance excellently adapted to the purpose of wiping from paper the marks of a black-lead-pencil. It must, therefore, be of singular use to those who practise drawing. It is sold by Mr. Nairne, Mathematical Instrument-Maker, opposite the Royal-Exchange. He sells a cubical piece, of about half an inch, for three shillings; and he says it will last several years.[4]

This may well be the first published recommendation of the use of rubber erasers; interestingly, the second edition of the *Perspective* (1780) does not retain this recommendation, but returns to the older usage of bread-crumbs as erasers.

The education project which commanded his enthusiasm, however, was the production of a series of volumes on the history of all the experimental sciences, though he had rather suggested in the preface to the *History of Electricity* that such a project was too great an undertaking for one person. His experience with the *Electricity* had taught him the necessity of access to the literature of the field before he commenced writing, and much of the early correspondence of this chapter deals with the difficulties and the expense of amassing so large a scientific library. His success in book collecting, either by borrowing or purchase, is indicated by the extraordinary "Catalogue of the books, of which Dr. Priestley is already possessed or to which he has access" appended to the *History*

[4] Joseph Priestley, *A Familiar Introduction to the Theory and Practice of Perspective* (London, Johnson and Payne, 1770), p. xv.

of Optics. That these more than two hundred and sixty-five volumes made Priestley something of an expert in scientific bibliography is indicated by the advice he gives Franklin (No. 32) on important scientific journals and their cost.

After some initial hesitation, Priestley decided to make the next volume of the series (after the *History of Electricity*) a history of discoveries relating to light and colors. This choice was determined in part by the selection of available references (No. 28a), though surely the intimate relationship between Newton, the *Opticks,* and "experimental philosophy," which all eighteenth-century scientists believed to exist was a contributing factor; so also must have been Priestley's own conviction that electricity and chemistry, in which he was even then experimenting, and optics were related as a means of studying the nature of matter.[5]

The History and Present State of Discoveries relating to Vision, Light and Colours was published in 1772. In spite of Priestley's optimism (No. 31), the work was not a success; it had only one English edition and was translated only into German. Part of the trouble was surely in execution. Unlike electricity, the subject was not one which immediately led to original experiments, and Priestley includes none.[6] Nor was the attempt, described by Priestley in his preface (p. viii), to make *Optics* "perfectly intelligible to those who have little or no knowledge of mathematics" likely to be successful in a subject so eminently mathematical.[7] What was needed was a

---

[5] See Cohen, *op. cit.,* pp. 177–198, *passim.*

[6] He does not even refer to the experiments (mentioned in No. 20) on the influence of electrification on *"reflection, refraction,* or *inflection* of light," and it would appear that these were, in fact, never performed.

[7] In this connection, the comment of Thomas Young in his *A Course of Lectures in Natural Philosophy* (London, Taylor & Walton, 1845), vol. i, p. 381, is revealing: "The late Dr. Priestley rendered an essential service to the science of optics, considered as a subject for the amusement of the general reader, by an elegant and well written account of the principal experiments and theories, which had been published before the year 1770. But this work is very deficient in mathematical accuracy, and the author was not sufficiently a master of the science to distinguish the good from the indifferent."

sophisticated interpretation of the work of others, and for this Priestley was not equipped, though he had the assistance of John Michell and made use of the theoretical views of Roger Joseph Boscovich. Both Price and Canton were sharply critical of the state of the text and even more so of many of his interpretations (Nos. 38, 39, 40), and the published version contains a page of twenty-one errata and some twenty-four quarto pages of "Additions," which do not, however, add significantly to the work nor indicate the nature of Price's and Canton's objections. The letter to Joseph Bretland (No. 56), and subsequent correspondence and published writing suggests, however, that much of the argument centered about the introduction of those concepts of Boscovich (so influential with Davy, Faraday, Kelvin, and Maxwell in the nineteenth century), which Priestley introduced to the serious attention of British scientists.[8]

It may be doubted that the *History of Optics* was of vital interest to Priestley by the time he had set to writing it. This is somewhat confirmed by the circumstances of its composition. In a letter of 4 November 1770 to his friend and theological correspondent, Theophilus Lindsey, Priestley wrote: "I am just beginning to compile the history of discoveries relating to *light and colours.*"[9] He may have done still more after he announced that it was as good as finished except for the transcribing (No. 31), but the fact that less than two months' work at arranging his materials had satisfied Priestley did not promise well for a work which was to fill over eight hundred quarto pages. There is, however, another factor in the "failure" of the *Optics*. The topic was not, and has not been, a popular one for historical studies. There have been many histories of electricity since Priestley's day, and many histories

---

[8] See Lancelot Law Whyte, ed., *Roger Joseph Boscovich S.J., F.R.S., 1711–1787*. London, George Allen & Unwin, 1961.

[9] Priestley to Theophilus Lindsey, 4 November 1770; Dr. Williams's Library, London.

of chemistry, but Priestley's *History of Optics* remained the only book on that subject available in English until Ernst Mach's *The Principles of Physical Optics, an historical and philosophical treatment,* was translated from the German in 1926; and Wilde's *Geschichte der Optik,* the first to follow Priestley's in any language, did not appear until 1838.

The failure of the *History of Optics* meant the end of Priestley's project to write a history of all the experimental sciences, but the reasons for his decision are not as simple as Priestley makes them seem. His complaint that the sale of the *Optics* was insufficient to pay for his purchases of books and journals (No. 39 and *Memoirs*) is almost irrelevant, for these were bought for the entire series, one part of which could hardly be expected to return the capital expenditure for the whole. It may well be doubted that Priestley ought to have made so considerable an investment at this stage of his career, but, having done so, only failure to pay the production costs of publication would have required discontinuing the series if he were otherwise willing to use his time in that way. The work was published by subscription (Nos. 28, 28a), which suggests that the attempt to obtain the patronage of the Duke of Northumberland (Nos. 27, 29) failed, but surely that nobleman must have done something to deserve the handsome dedication of the volume. Over five hundred copies were taken by subscribers and, though Thomas Cooper reports that "by far the majority" of these defaulted payment, at a price of 1£. 11s. 6d., the sale should still have paid production costs.[10]

The critical factor was the failure of the work to compensate (financially or intellectually) for the time spent in preparing it. He had already commenced the far more interesting study

[10] Thomas Cooper, in "Appendix, No. 1," p. 286, *Memoirs of Dr. Joseph Priestley.* The published price of the *Optics* is given in most of the catalogues of "Books written by Dr. Priestley" appended to his subsequent works; the difference of 10s. 6d. between this price and that advertised in the "Proposals" (No. 28a) tends to excuse the defaulters, if they were assessed the increase.

of pneumatic chemistry (p. xi of the preface of the *Optics* announces that he had made several "original observations" relating to noxious airs), and he rapidly discovered the "embarrassing" wealth of recent materials to be organized for any subject he might have chosen as his next topic (No. 30). Furthermore, as he wrote to Canton (No. 39), if he was to work for nothing, he preferred to do so in theology. But Priestley could not afford to work for nothing. His move from Warrington had been dictated by financial considerations, and, although he boasts of the advantages of the Leeds situation (No. 50), his family responsibilities kept increasing, and he was soon involved in a number of expedients designed to raise his income. One of these, obviously, was by writing; another seems to have been to exploit that knowledge and interest in instrumentation described in his *Memoirs*. Whether the battery of Leyden jars was supplied to Canton (Nos. 16, 17) at a profit is not clear; there is no doubt, however, that Priestley went beyond the merely casual consideration of selling electrical machines (presumably those of his own design), (Nos. 17, 26, 7). That neat device of advertising "Mr. Nairne's composition" in the preface to the *Perspective* had a precedent which speaks well for Priestley's commercial instinct. The first edition of the *Study of Electricity* which contains the advertisement of electrical machines on the verso of its half-title page (No. 17a), also includes the specific statement: "But I would advise all persons who propose to understand the subject of Electricity . . . to provide themselves with an electrical machine, or at least desire some of their friends to show them the experiments. Without this, I should dispair of making any person whatever a master of the subject."[11]

---

[11] Priestley, *A Familiar Introduction to the Study of Electricity* (London, J. Dodsley, T. Cadell, Johnson and Payne, 1768), p. viii. This phrase is repeated in all subsequent editions, while the advertisement is transferred to a note following the text for the second (1769) and third (1777) editions, and then disappears entirely.

The advertisement seems to have been successful, for all Priestley's indecision. Timothy Priestley writes:

When we had each a small family, finding I could work in either brass or wood, and turn his work in a lathe, though I never had been taught, he proposed a partnership, for making electrifying machines; for though he had such natural abilities, he could scarcely handle any tool. Then having a child added to my number almost every year, and but 60£ *per ann.* he wished to help me, more than himself. . . . Many electrifying machines were made, and sold to his friends.[12]

Against the background of financial pressures, it is easy to see why the invitation to accompany Banks as astronomer on Cook's second voyage, with its "handsome provision" for Priestley and his family (Nos. 41, 42, 43, 44), should have been so attractive, purely apart from its intrinsic appeal as a scientific and adventurous opportunity. It is not so easy to see why the invitation was delivered in the first place. He was obviously unacquainted with Banks and, though he was known to John Lee (later attorney-general in the Portland administration; see No. 24), only his work in electricity and perhaps some part of that in chemistry could have recommended him as a scientist. However much might have been known previous to its publication of the *History of Optics,* it could hardly have been supposed that this would make an astronomer of him. Actually, the general function of this astronomer was to compare techniques in measuring longitude, specifically by checking the accuracy of the new chronometers lent Cook by the Royal Society. This would make few theoretical demands on the person involved, but the astronomers who finally accompanied Cook had previously served the Royal Society on expeditions to observe a transit of Venus,

---

[12] Timothy Priestley, *A Funeral Sermon,* pp. 42–43. This, of course, may be another of Timothy Priestley's exaggerations.

and they later published an account of the extensive observations they made on the voyage with Cook which Priestley would have found it difficult to match.[13] In any event, clerical opposition (or rather, Banks' suggestion of the possibility of clerical opposition) closed the opportunity, leaving Priestley behind to perform the experiments and write the paper that made him famous as a scientist.

The prospect of clerical opposition also halted Priestley's inquiries into the possibility of settling in America (Nos. 50, 55). His financial difficulties were finally ended with his move from Leeds to become the companion of Lord Shelburne (Nos. 50, 51, 53). With his money problems solved, Priestley might have continued his series of histories, had there not been reasons other than financial for ending it. By 1772, when the *History of Optics* was published, he was no longer to be regarded simply as an educator and popularizer. His experiments had changed the emphasis of his scientific career; henceforth he was to contribute directly to science, rather than describe the work of others.

Naturally, part of his experimental investigations involved a continuation of his studies in electricity. Though most of these were published, first as separate papers in the *Philosophical Transactions* and then in later editions of the *History of Electricity* or in various volumes of his *Experiments*

---

[13] The astronomers were William Wales and his assistant William Bayly; see their *The Original Observations, made in the course of A Voyage towards the South Pole, and Round the World, In his Majesty's Ships the Resolution and Adventure, in the Years MDCCLXXII, MDCCLXXIII, MDCCLXXIV, and MDCCLXXV, published by Order of the Board of Longitude, at the Expence of Which the Observations were made* (London, by W. and A. Stratian, 1777). None of the observations differ in kind from those that Cook himself had made on his previous voyage, but in number, precision, and variety they bespeak the skill and experience of professional astronomers. Like Priestley, Banks and his assistant Daniel Solander ultimately did not make the trip either, and their posts as naturalists were filled by Johann Reinhold Forster (the Dr. Forster of Priestley's *Memoirs*) and his son George, at the "handsome provision" of £ 4,000.

and Observations, little notice was taken of them by his contemporaries and even less has been given them since.[14] Much
of this work is at least mentioned in his correspondence.

Letters 15 and 20 describe the discovery of what is sometimes called "Priestley's Rings," that variety of "Newton's
Rings" produced when thin films of metal are oxidized by
spark discharge onto a metallic plate. The published account
of these experiments shows an acquaintance with Newton's
optical work which antedates Priestley's avowed concentration on optics for his series of histories.[15] Another course of
experiments relate to the so-called side-flash, included in the
phenomena which Priestley called "lateral discharge" (Nos.
15, 16). Price's conjecture that the effect was one of electrical
repulsion of bodies suddenly charged by induction was partially correct, though some of Priestley's observations do suggest, as he supposes in his published account of these experiments, that the rapid expulsion of air from the path of the
discharge must be included in a complete explanation of the
phenomena he observed.[16]

The particular observations which had caused Priestley to
doubt Price's explanation led to one of his most significant
(and most neglected) electrical discoveries. Mentioned only as
"a new and curious appearance in electricity" in a letter otherwise devoted to theology and politics, no further discussion of

---

[14] Sir Philip Hartog, the best of Priestley's biographers, wrote of the experiments in his "Newer Views of Priestley and Lavoisier," *Annals of Science,* 5
(1941), 1–56, calling Priestley's electrical studies the "key to Priestley's scientific mind." A more recent notice is R. E. Schofield, "The Electrical Researches
of Joseph Priestley," *op. cit.;* and the "Introduction" to the new edition of
the *History of Electricity* (New York, Johnson Re-print Corporation, 1966)
which also collects, for the first time, all Priestley's separate publications on
electricity.

[15] Joseph Priestley, "An Account of Rings consisting of all the Prismatic
Colours, made by Electrical Explosions on the Surface of Pieces of Metal,"
Philosophical Transactions, 58 (1768), 68–74.

[16] Joseph Priestley, "Experiments on the lateral Force of Electrical Explosions," *Philosophical Transactions,* 59 (1769), 57–62.

the work has been found in his correspondence.[17] The published account of the "curious appearance" shows, however, that his investigation originated in the experiments on "lateral force" and in his belief that bodies in the vicinity of the electrical spark did not "acquire any permanent electricity nor was the equilibrium of the [electric] fluid within . . . [them] sensibly disturbed" (No. 16). Pursuing the course of his experiments, he was led to what can only have been the discovery of the oscillatory discharge of a Leyden jar, years before this was to be noticed by other investigators.[18]

Included in Letter 16 and also in a second published paper of 1769 is a discussion of some experiments "to ascertain, if possible, the momentum of the electrical matter in explosions." Unfortunately, the published paper does not contain that interesting speculation which denies existence to electric fluid. On the other hand, the paper — but not any of the correspondence — describes Priestley's second method for determining relative conductivities, by comparing the lengths of the circuits of various wires through which an electric discharge would choose to pass rather than jump an air-gap.[19]

In the same year (1770) in which his last significant work on electricity, the "oscillatory-discharge" paper appeared, Priestley published what amounts to his first paper on chemis-

[17] From Priestley to Theophilus Lindsey, 21 February 1770, in Rutt, *The Life of Priestley,* vol. 1, pp. 112–114.

[18] Joseph Priestley, "An Investigation of the lateral Explosion, and of the Electricity communicated to the electrical Circuit, in a Discharge," *Philosophical Transactions,* 60 (1770), 192–210.

[19] Joseph Priestley, "Various Experiments on the Force of Electrical Explosions," *Philosophical Transactions,* 59 (1769), 63–70. The first method for relative conductivities is that described in the previous chapter (*supra,* footnote 8) and employed in the experiments of Letter 16; still a third method is suggested in Priestley's paper of 1770, in which he writes: "These experiments . . . may possibly be of some use in measuring the conducting power of different substances; since the greater is the interruption in the electrical circuit, occasioned by the badness of its conducting power, the more considerable, *caeteris paribus,* is the lateral explosion."

try, "Experiments and Observations on Charcoal."[20] Although the avowed purpose of the paper is electrical — i.e., he wished to examine the circumstances on which the variation in conductivity of different charcoals depended — references in the correspondence relate the work to chemistry at least as closely as to electricity, his citations in the paper are to the work of "Macquer and other chemists," and his specific conclusions relate electrical phenomena to chemical concepts. Of particular relevance to his later adherence to the theory of phlogiston is Priestley's idea that, metals and charcoal agreeing in their composition of earthly base plus phlogiston, their conductivity must depend on the presence of phlogiston and the "completeness of the union that is produced between the inflammable principle and its base."

Although this paper is the first public indication of Priestley's chemical studies, one of the remarkable aspects of this series of letters is the evidence (Nos. 15, 16) that his chemical experiments were resumed within the month of his settling in Leeds. Most of the early references relate to mephitic air (carbon dioxide), but it is not until October 1771 (No. 37) that any notice is taken of his visiting that public brewery which in the *Memoirs* looms so large as the agent directing Priestley's attention to studies of air. This development, it should be noted, occurs after he had "removed" to another house (No. 23). Moreover, the first letter also mentions experiments on inflammable air, while the letter to Lindsey of 21 February 1770 talks of "taking up some of Dr Hales's inquiries concerning air."[21] These with the references to "Macquer and other chemists" (in the paper on charcoal), and to the work of Macbride and Cavendish (No. 34) suggest an early familiarity with the important literature of chemistry quite at variance with the scientific naiveté implied, at least, in the

[20] *Philosophical Transactions*, 60 (1770), 211–225.
[21] See footnote 17.

description of his chemical work at Leeds that Priestley gives in the *Memoirs*.

Priestley's first public recognition as a chemist came through the publication in 1772 of his pamphlet, *Directions for Impregnating Water with Fixed Air: in order to Communicate to it the Peculiar Spirit and Virtue of Pyrmont Water, and other Mineral Waters of a similar Nature.* Sir John Pringle's address, on presenting Priestley with the Copley Medal in 1773, includes this invention of artificially carbonated water as one of the reasons for that award. It is therefore of interest to see how the correspondence supports and amplifies Priestley's historical résumé of that discovery.[22] The letters do not, however, suggest any reason for Priestley's return to chemical studies, nor why these should first have focused on fixed air and its possible uses in an antiscorbutic. His historical résumé, first published in 1775, does no better, for it refers to Brownrigg's work on fixed air in Spa water and introduces that famous "neighboring" brewery as having provided the means for his experiments, without saying why he should have read the article or performed the experiments in the first place. There exists one reference to the medical uses of fixed air which may, however, have particular relevance to this question. William Bewley, author of a very laudatory three-part review of the *History of Electricity,* wrote in the third part:

> We shall take this occasion of observing, for the honour of philosophy, that there is reason to hope that the *catalogus medicamentorum* will ere long be enriched with another promising article, the pure result of philosophical researches: we mean

---

[22] See Sir John Pringle, *A Discourse on the Different Kinds of Air, Delivered at the Anniversary Meeting of the Royal Society, November 30, 1773* (London, for the Royal Society, 1774), and appended to *Philosophical Transactions,* 64 (1774); and Priestley, *Experiments and Observations on Different kinds of Air,* 2nd ed. (London, 1776), vol. 2, pp. 269–275.

fixed air; a subject successfully investigated by the late excellent Dr. Hales, and which appears in a fair way of being soon happily applied to the relief of putrid disorders, and particularly of the sea-scurvy, in consequence of the ingenious experiments of Dr. Macbride, and his very natural practical deductions from them.[23]

This part of the review appeared in December 1767, while Priestley's first reference to artificial Pyrmont Water was dated 27 September (No. 15). The first part of the review, however, had appeared in August, and the review occasioned a lengthy correspondence between Priestley and Bewley that lasted till the latter's death in 1783. Bewley was an apothecary and was therefore the more likely to have known of Brownrigg's work and of the medical applications of fixed air. The timely appearance of fixed air in Priestley's interests was far less likely as a coincidence than as a result of an early (pre-27 September) letter from Bewley, though this cannot be verified, as the letters seem to have disappeared, except for the few published in Priestley's *Experiments and Observations* commencing in 1774.

This investigation provides an ironic commentary to the abortive negotiations regarding Cook's voyage. In a letter to Lindsey, estimated as of April 1772, Priestley wrote, "Yesterday I sent my papers and drawings to the Lords of the Admiralty, having been requested by them to make the communication to the commanders and surgeons of the Resolution and Adventure, in which Messrs. Banks &c., are to make their voyage."[24]

---

[23] [William Bewley], "Account of Dr. Priestley's History of Electricity," *Monthly Review*, 37 (1767), 453.

[24] Rutt, *The Life of Priestley*, vol. 1, pp. 167–170; see also Letter 47. Cook's second voyage was notable for the extremely low incidence of illness among the sailors, but his report to the Royal Society, "The Method taken for preserving the Health of the Crew of His Majesty's Ship the Resolution during her late Voyage round the World" (*Philosophical Transactions*, 66 [1776], pp. 450–475), for which Cook won the Copley Medal in 1776, does not refer to the use of Priestley's artificial Pyrmont water, and it may be assumed that none was administered.

Most of the chemistry briefly discussed in this part of the correspondence is repeated in detail in Priestley's paper, "Observations on different Kinds of Air," published (in 1773) in the *Philosophical Transactions* for 1772.[25] This was a magisterial paper, which richly entitled Priestley to the award of the Copley Medal for 1773, but a careful reading of it in conjunction with these letters shows that it is deceptive, for all its detail. Although written in a characteristically discursive and quasi-chronological style, it fails to convey any sense of Priestley's lengthy apprenticeship in chemical experimentation which led to these results. Thus, for example, it virtually conceals the fact that, of the three major discoveries for which the paper is famous, only the one that introduces the phenomena of photosynthesis was made prior to the published date of the reading of the paper.[26] The letters trace Priestley's growing command of his subject, from the halting reconsideration of known substances with established techniques of 1767 and 1768 (Nos. 15, 20), through the journeyman experiments with meliorating plants of 1771 (No. 33), to the mastery of the summer of 1772 revealed in the work on nitrous air (nitric oxide) and its uses in eudiometry and in that on acid air (later marine acid air, our anhydrous hydrochloric acid) (Nos. 48, 49).

For all their artless prolixity, Priestley's letters and papers, however, are frequently useless as a guide to what he was

[25] *Philosophical Transactions*, 62 (1772), 147–264. For a discussion of the date of publication, see Henry Guerlac, "Joseph Priestley's First Papers on Gases and their Reception in France," *Journal of the History of Medicine and Allied Sciences*, 12 (1957), 1–12.

[26] The paper is headed, "Read March 5, 12, 19, 26, 1772," and although there is no attempt to conceal that it contains material dated as late as November 1772, only an examination of the manuscript or a reading of the correspondence will show the extent of the additions and interpolations made as a result of the supplementary paper of late November 1772, which Priestley mentions in Letter 48. Douglas McKie gives a detailed analysis of the original manuscript in his "Joseph Priestley and the Copley Medal," *Ambix*, 9 (1961), 1–22.

doing specifically in any course of experiments, or why. Some of this obscurity can be traced to the unique circumstances of much of his work. The map of a trail-blazer is seldom as complete as that in a school atlas, and only a person who has never ventured to experiment in a completely unknown area with untried methods and materials would expect the precision of detail in all those variables where the experiments of Priestley and others have subsequently taught us information is necessary. Hindsight and imagination can, for example, inform us of impurities in his reagents which Priestley does not recognize (e.g., sulphur in the iron of his experiments in No. 20), or of details in experimental circumstances (e.g., concentrations and temperatures of acids) which Priestley does not specify.

More open to criticism is the apparent general nature of his experimenting, for nowhere in his discussions does he reveal that analytical interplay of observation and theory which characterizes the superlatively great scientist. This should not be taken as adding fuel to the persistent accusation that Priestley's experiments were haphazard and his discoveries accidental. On 23 August 1771, he wrote to Lindsey that "I have discovered what I have long been in quest of, viz., that process in nature by which air, rendered noxious by breathing, is restored to its former salubrious condition."[27] No person following his work through the multitude of parameters to his considerable share in the understanding of photosynthesis can doubt Priestley's ability to analyze experiments if he chose. Nor does the train of discoveries of one new "air" after another leave open the possibility of simple accident. Obviously, Priestley was deliberately creating circumstances which deliberately produced new gases. Nevertheless, our understanding of his work is hampered by Priestley's public acceptance of a Baconian synthetic view of science.

[27] Rutt, *The Life of Priestley*, vol. 1, pp. 144–147.

Throughout his scientific publications and correspondence there runs an expressed disdain for theory and an exclusive appreciation of "facts." This never meant (as it never does) that he had no theory, but it certainly means that we are never explicitly informed of it and of its relationship to his program of experiments.

Now, it is well known that throughout his life Priestley adopted phlogistic explanations for experimental phenomena. Yet in spite of terminology, the "theory of phlogiston" was never of itself a complete theory. For Becher and Stahl, who had invented phlogiston, it had been but part of a more basic theory of matter and chemical action, also involving related concepts of atoms, elements, simple and compound mixtes, affinities, etc. Whether subsequent chemists adopted any significant part of this entire theory is not clear, but certainly Lavoisier's "disproof" of phlogiston involved new fundamental criteria for matter and its chemical behavior.[28] In any event, phlogiston can hardly have provided that "inlet" into the internal structure of bodies for which Priestley began looking as he commenced his scientific career. His later writings in metaphysics and theology show that he was to develop over the years a general theory of matter based on components taken from Newton, David Hartley, and Boscovich.

It may be that this development had already begun by the period covered in this chapter and that it was accentuated through his reading of Hales (described by J. R. Parting-

[28] J. R. Partington and Douglas McKie, "Historical Studies on the Phlogiston Theory" (Parts I, II, III, and IV, *Annals of Science*, 2 (1937), 361–404; 3 (1938), 1–58; 4 (1938), 337–371; 5 (1939), 113–149) give the most detailed account of the various changes in phlogiston during the eighteenth century; but Hélène Metzger's *Newton, Stahl, Boerhaave et la Doctrine Chimique* (Paris, Librarie Félix Alcan, 1930) remains the most penetrating study of the philosophical context of phlogiston. For some of the material assumptions of the Lavoisian revolution, see R. E. Schofield, "Joseph Priestley, the Theory of Oxidation and the Nature of Matter," *Journal of the History of Ideas*, 25 (1964), 285–294.

ton as paying too much "attention to Newtonian staticks")[29] and through his writing the sections of his *History of Optics* relating Newton's work to Boscovichian atomism. If so, few specific signs of this are apparent.

Perhaps his continual emphasis on such physical properties as heat, cold, condensation and rarefaction, and their effects on gaseous mixtures or on electrification as a means of influencing the reflection, refraction, and inflection of light (Nos. 20, 34) constitute indications of such a theory. His belief in the mechanical restoration of "bad" air may well be another. In spite of widely varying results from frequently repeated experiments, even in spite of his own observations on gaseous diffusion and the differential solubilities of gases (which, along with faulty manipulation, today explain his "erroneous" results), Priestley maintained that agitation in water, prolonged standing over water, or mixing with fixed air restored "bad' air to its former salubrious condition. Such persistence, in the face of contradictory data and conflicting opinion, suggests the existence of theoretical preconceptions which were at least consistent with this belief, if not responsible for it.

The possession of such a theory, unfortunate though it may have been in this respect, would also help to explain Priestley's talent as an observer — as providing the necessary preparation of his mind for "chance" to favor. The most obvious characteristic of Priestley's work is his extraordinary ability to note new phenomena, not only in the major instances which resulted in recognized discoveries, but also in so extensive a range of less obvious appearances as to make his books, in Sir Humphry Davy's opinion, those most likely "to lead a student into the path of discovery."[30] But no person is so blind

[29] J. R. Partington, *A History of Chemistry* (London, Macmillan & Co., Ltd., 1962), vol. 3, p. 123.

[30] Sir Humphry Davy, *Collected Works* (London, Smith, Elder & Co., 1840), vol. 7, p. 117.

as he who expects to see nothing. To have made such observations requires as a precondition that Priestley should have been looking for something.

What that something was is impossible to define, particularly at this stage of his career, without considerably more information on his theory of matter than we as yet possess. We can only note with admiration that within five years of his beginning experiments on gases, amidst the manifold other activities described earlier, and in addition to the discovery of photosynthesis, acid air, and nitrous air, Priestley made: (1) those early observations on gaseous diffusion (No. 20) which, with his later experiments on the same subject, were to influence Dalton's studies; (2) the beginning observations on flame and electric-spark colors in different gases (Nos. 20, 50), so suggestive of spectral phenomena; (3) the gas-density observations (No. 40) which he ignored, to his subsequent confusion, as he characteristically did gravimetric data; and (4) his volumetric observations on the diminution of common and nitrous airs over iron and brimstone (Nos. 40, 48, 50) — these last two demonstrating his capacity for quantitative experimentation, if he wished.

Among Priestley's early "additional observations," the most interesting, particularly in view of his recommendation to Bergman and Wilcke that they read his *Philosophical Transactions* paper (No. 52), were those relating to the air obtained by the heating of nitre. Mentioned both in the correspondence (Nos. 53, 54) and in the published paper, the results are confused by that persistent error involving changes in gases held over water, but they still make it obvious that here for the first time Priestley has prepared oxygen. His published comment was:

This series of facts, relating to air extracted from nitre, appear to me to be very extraordinary and important, and, in able hands, may lead to considerable discoveries.[31]

[31] *Philosophical Transactions*, 62 (1772), 246.

This was a signal to ambitious chemists that here was an observation to be followed up. Characteristically, Priestley was not to do so himself, and his discovery of oxygen took place under different conditions and by a different method. The two-year delay, which permitted Scheele to anticipate Priestley's discovery though not his publication of it, was at least partially the consequence of his changed circumstances, when the negotiations with Shelburne were satisfactorily concluded, and he moved from Leeds to join Shelburne's household.

CHAPTER FOUR

Time of Achievement London and Wiltshire 1773-1780

A FTER SIX YEARS AT LEEDS, Priestley left in the early summer of 1773 to become librarian–companion to William, Lord Shelburne, later Marquis of Lansdowne. For the next seven years he was to remain with Shelburne, summering at Calne, near Bowood, the family estate in Wiltshire, and wintering in Shelburne's town house in London. During this period Priestley's official duties were few. He appears to have given some general direction to the education of Shelburne's sons, though there was also a full-time tutor; he catalogued the books and manuscripts and indexed the personal papers in the Shelburne library; through his religious and personal connections he undoubtedly served as a channel by which Shelburne could be informed of the political views of the dissenting Whigs — but essentially his position was that of resident intellectual and protégé. Priestley was in fact one of the earliest beneficiaries of Shelburne's role as a patron of ideas.

Seldom can patronage have been more opportune. Not

only did it solve Priestley's financial worries, it did so just at the time that he had reached his peak as a scientist. The creative period for most scientists is a short one; for Priestley as a chemist, it was essentially limited to the years between 1772 and 1780. In all these but the first, because of Shelburne, Priestley had the leisure to exploit his time more or less as he wished. During 1774 he traveled with Shelburne in Europe, including a month's stay at Paris, where he met Lavoisier and other French chemists. Throughout the period he continued his writing on nonscientific subjects, publishing at least seventeen works in first editions, on politics, religion, education, and metaphysics — including his most important philosophical study, *Disquisitions Relating to Matter and Spirit* (1777). But for the first and perhaps only period of his life, it was science that dominated his activities and, by that most obvious of criteria, new discoveries, he proved worthy of his opportunities. This was the most fruitful period of Priestley's scientific career, as the momentum of those months of the summer of 1772 carried him on into a continuing series of experiments through which he isolated and identified ammonia, sulphur dioxide, oxygen, nitrous oxide, and nitrogen dioxide. The description of this and his other scientific work provided by the *Memoirs* is, even for Priestley, extraordinarily curtailed.

. . . When I went to his Lordship, I had materials for one volume of *experiments on air,* which I soon after published, and inscribed to him; and before I left him I published three volumes more, and had materials for a fourth, which I published immediately on my settling in Birmingham. He encouraged me in the prosecution of my philosophical enquiries, and allowed me 40 £. per annum for expences of that kind, and was pleased to see me make experiments to entertain his guests, and especially foreigners. . . .

About three years before the dissolution of my connection with Lord Shelburne, Dr. Fothergill, with whom I had always lived on terms of much intimacy, having observed, as he said, that many of my experiments had not been carried to their proper extent on account of the expence that would have attended them, proposed to me a subscription from himself and some of his friends, to supply me with whatever sums I should want for that purpose, and named a hundred pounds per annum. This large subscription I declined, lest the discovery of it (by the use that I should, of course, make of it) should give umbrage to Lord Shelburne, but I consented to accept of 40 £. per annum, which from that time he regularly paid me, from the contribution of himself, Sir Theodore Jansen, Mr. Constable, and Sir George Saville.

On my leaving Lord Shelburne, which was attended with the loss of one half of my income, Dr. Fothergill proposed an enlargement of my allowance for my experiments, and likewise for my maintenance, without being under the necessity of giving my time to pupils, which I must otherwise have done. And, considering the generosity with which this voluntary offer was made by persons who could well afford it, and who thought me qualified to serve the interests of science, I thought it right to accept of it; and I preferred it to any pension from the court, offers of which were more than once made by persons who thought they could have procured one for me.

As it was my wish to do what might be in my power to shew my gratitude to my friends and benefactors that suggested the idea of writing these Memoirs, I shall subjoin a list of their names. Some of the subscriptions were made with a view to defray the expence of my experiments only; but the greatest part of the subscribers were persons who were equally friends to my theological studies.

The persons who made me this regular annual allowance were Dr. Watson and his son, Mr. Wedgwood, Mr. Moseley, Mr. S. Salte, Mr. Jeffries, Mr. Radcliffe, Mr. Remington, Mr. Strutt of Derby, Mr. Shore, Mr. Reynolds of Paxton, Messrs. Galton, father and son, and the Rev. Mr. Simpson. . . .

Mr. Parker of Fleet street very generously supplied me with every instrument that I wanted in glass, particularly a capital burning lens, sixteen inches in diameter. All his benefactions in this way would have amounted to a considerable sum. Mr. Wedgwood also, besides his annual benefaction, supplied me with every thing that I wanted made of pottery, such as retorts, tubes, &c. which the account of my experiments will shew to have been of great use to me. . . .[1]

The published record of his years with Lord Shelburne must also include the major part of Priestley's original chemical publications. All three volumes of *Experiments and Observations on different Kinds of Air* (London, 1774, 1775, and 1777) and two of the three volumes of *Experiments and Observations relating to various Branches of Natural Philosophy, with a Continuation of the Observations on Air* (London, 1779; Birmingham, 1781) were prepared during those seven years, as well as three papers in the *Philosophical Transactions* for 1774, 1775, and 1776.[2] These more than sixteen-hundred pages provide so substantial an account of the scientific work of the period that neither the *Memoirs* nor the letters could be expected to add much to the picture given there. The latter can, however, provide a personal dimension adding depth to this portrait of the prototype of an eighteenth-century amateur scientist during his most fruitful years.

No. 57.

FROM PRIESTLEY TO BENJAMIN FRANKLIN

Dear Sir

With this I return you *Mr Winthrop's letter*, according to your desire, thanking you for your endeavours to serve me in America,

---

[1] Priestley, *Memoirs*, pp. 77–78, 91–94.

[2] Something more than half the earliest volume is a rewriting of the 1772 Royal Society paper, other volumes reprint other early *Philosophical Transactions* papers, while the last volume, on inspection, may be seen to contain accounts of some work done in Birmingham, but the vast majority of the work described in these publications was completed between the summer of 1773 and that of 1780.

though I find, as I was apprehensive, that the scheme would not answer. Please to return my thanks to the professor for his candid and judicious remarks on my *History of Opticks,* which will be much improved by them, if it should come to a second edition.

Dr Price will have informed you, that I have resumed my experiments on *air,* and with a good prospect of success. Since that I have been much more successful; but in a letter I can only confine myself to the heads of things.

The most important of the observations I have made lately is of an *alkaline,* corresponding to my *acid air,* of which an account is given in what I have already printed. This I get by treating a volatile alkali in the same manner in which I before treated the spirit of salt. As soon as the liquid begins to boil, the vapour arises, and being received in a vessel filled with quick silver, continues in the form of *air,* not condensed by cold.

I imagined that a mixture of this alkaline with acid air would make a neutral, and perhaps a common air; but, instead of that, they make a beautiful white salt, of a very curious nature. It immediately deliquesces, and even wholly disappears upon being exposed to the open air, and if it be in a dry and deep vessel, where moisture cannot easily come at it, it wholly evaporates in dense white clouds, occasioning a very strong smell.

This Alkaline vapour, like the acid, is quickly imbibed by water, which thereby becomes Spirit of Sal Volatile.

Nitrous air makes this alkaline vapour turbid, and perhaps generates a different salt; but I have not yet made a tenth part of the experiments that I propose to do with this new kind of air.

I have just found that spirit of wine yields air also, which is probably pure phlogiston, but I have not yet made one experiment with it.

If volatile alkali, liquid or solid, be exposed to nitrous air, during its effervescences with common air, the vessel is presently filled with beatiful white clouds; and the salt is tinged blue. This explains the constitution of nitrous air, but I have no time for reasoning.

This experiment appears to great advantage when a vessel, no matter how large, containing the smallest portion of volatile alkali, fluid or solid, is opened in a quantity of nitrous air, for the whole is filled almost instantly with dense white clouds.

Report says that you are about to leave us, at least for a time. If this be true, I shall be very sorry; as it will deprive me of one of the greatest satisfactions that used to make my annual visits to London agreeable. If you should leave England before winter, I should think myself very happy in an opportunity of seeing you before your departure. As I cannot conveniently come to London, I should be peculiarly happy in seeing you and Sir John Pringle, in my new situation, and I flatter myself that I could amuse you with some of my new experiments. If you can oblige me so far, give me a line to acquaint me with your intention, that I may be sure to be at home when you come. . . .

Calne 26 Sepbr 1773.

No. 58.

From Priestley to Benjamin Franklin

Dear Sir,

If I had had a frank for Mr Johnson, I should not have given you this trouble; but Ld Shelburne is not at home, and my covers for him are expended.

I hope you received my letter, in which I gave you some account of my discovery of an *alkaline air,* tho' I have not had the ple[asure of] hearing from you since. I am still busy in examining its properties and affinities, some of which are curious enough. The most remarkable observation I have made is of the manner in which it affects *alum* put into it. This substance absorbs it very fast, and then comes out perfectly white, and altogether unlike what it was; but I have not yet examined it any farther.

I have also found that this alkaline air is slightly *inflammable.* This is not observed without attention, for a candle dipped into it goes out several times before there is much appearance of its inflammability. This, however, agrees with the opinion of chymists, that volatile Alkali contains phlogiston.

[143]

As you have not written to me, I hope you are planning an excursion to Calne, along with Sir John Pringle, or some of our friends. This would make me very happy. . . .

Calne 14. Oct 1773

No. 59.

FROM PRIESTLEY TO ALESSANDRO VOLTA

Monsieur,

I received your *two treatises* only last week. M. Guaita had placed them in the hands of one Sandoli, an Italian singer, where they have remained until this time. I will read them at once, and I am persuaded, by what I have already seen in passing, with pleasure and with profit. It is a present which is very acceptable to me.

I am busy preparing a third edition of my *history of electricity*; but rather than inserting any new discoveries there, I am reserving them for a *Continuation of the history,* which I have intended to write for several years. In this continuation your work will be described.

I have done nothing in electricity for some time, and I am applying myself to unravelling the properties of different kinds of *air*. Part of my work you will find in the last volume of the Philosophical Transactions, and I continue my researches with much success.

Among other things I have recently discovered an *alkaline air*, which I obtain from volatile Alkali, by the same process which I used to procure the acid air.

It is very annoying that our *published* communications are so slow and so full of uncertainty. . . .

Calne Wiltshire, 10 Nov. 1773.

No. 60.

<small>FROM PRIESTLEY TO CALEB ROTHERAM</small>

Calne, May 31, 1774.

Dear Sir,

On Saturday the 22nd I sent from hence my *achromatic telescope*. You will find two eye-pieces; a short one, which inverts objects, and magnifies eighty times; and a longer, which magnifies fifty times. The former, therefore, is more proper for celestial objects, and the latter for terrestrial.

If you be viewing a small and very luminous object, as Venus, or a fixed star, it will be necessary to have a much smaller *aperture* than the diameter of the object glass. An opening of the diameter of an inch is quite sufficient. For this purpose I made a paste-board cap, to slip on to the end of the telescope, over which I had pasted another paper, with such a hole in it. If I had not lost it, I would have sent it you, but you will easily make one for yourself, or perhaps contrive something better. The use of it is only to exclude all the rays, except those that fall very near the centre of the object glass.

I believe you will find the telescope a very good one. Mr. Walker, the Lecturer in Experimental Philosophy, and myself, compared it with a reflector of his own of the same length, and which cost more, and he acknowledged mine was much better, and he had boasted of his very much, as a very good one of its kind; and this has the advantage of being much lighter, and more manageable. The screw near the eye-glass serves to adjust the instrument to the eye, and the distance of objects. It is now a good deal out of its place, in order to make the telescope go into the box.

I do not think of any thing else that I can say about it, to be of any use to you. Indeed, no telescope whatever can be more easy to manage. You will find the *Nautical Almanack,* which is published annually, price 1s. 6d., very useful.

I thank you, in Mr. Lindsey's name, for your subscription. I heard from him lately, and have the pleasure to inform you that his affairs are in a very good train. The sum I mentioned is raised; but I believe he will be obliged to build a place before the next winter, for which purpose a larger sum will be wanted; but that is not absolutely determined yet.

Almost all my friends are as much dissatisfied as you are with the reasons alleged by the Committee for postponing the application to Parliament. The plain fact was certainly no other or better than you say. Dr. Price and Dr. Kippis are exceedingly displeased at it; but this good may come of it, that having now done with this particular bill, they can begin again, if ever they do begin, without any *declaration,* which has divided and embarrassed us so much. I do not know the author of the pamphlet you mention. I think of it exactly as you do.

I do not expect that the account of my experiments on air will give you so much satisfaction as you expect, owing to the great difference between *seeing* and *reading.* I have not yet found any person, though ever so good a philosopher, and who has read my papers ever so carefully, but is surprised to see me actually make the experiments. But the directions I have given are sufficient to enable any person to do every thing after me.

In the preface to the third volume of my Institutes I have given some strictures on Dr. Oswald, Beattie and Reid; and I propose to consider the scheme of those writers more fully. But previous to that, I shall republish *Hartley's Theory of the Human Mind,* as far as it depends upon association of ideas only, with some dissertations of my own. This I am now about.

I believe I shall accompany Lord Shelburne in a tour through Holland, Flanders, and to Paris, towards the end of summer, but shall be glad to hear from you in the mean time. . . .

No. 61.

From Priestley to Jeremy Bentham

Sir

I think myself exceedingly obliged to you for the communication of your method of generating different kinds of air, and have no objection to it but that it appears to me that it must be rather troublesome in practice ——— As to procuring nitrous air very pure, it is not worth attending to; as its purity is continually changing if it be kept in water, and it is easy, in comparing different parcels of air, always to take the nitrous air from the same jar. Besides by losing a little of the first produce of nitrous, or any other kind of air, you may be certain of having it very pure.

It is certainly proper to distinguishing the *acid air* which I have described by the additional epithet of *muriatic,* or *marine,* and you will find that in one place I have done it, p. 236. But I did not chuse to make the term so complex, till the actual discovery of the other acid airs should make it necessary. Now, however, I have produced the other acid airs, with great variation; and accordingly, in the new edition of my treatise on air, I have, in the titles of that section, called the other acid air *marine.*

I have made very considerable additions to my observations on air, and am not determined whether to send an account of them to the Royal Society, or to make a *Supplement* to my book; but I rather think I shall do the latter. I have added nothing to the second edition.

I beg you would present my compliments to the author of the paper on Electricity. I think myself honoured by the communication, and am pleased with the ingenuity which it discovers; but he will excuse me if I observe, that I find no sufficient *friction* to produce electricity in the manner that he supposes. The motion that is perceived in small clouds during a thunder storm seems to me to be the *effect* of preceding electricity.

I should have answered your obliging letter sooner; but I have been confined by illness ever since I received it, but tomorrow, or the next day, I hope to venture out of doors.

I expect to be in London soon after christmas, and then shall hope to have the pleasure of an interview with you, when I shall deliver to you Mr Symond's tract; having no convenient opportunity of sending it in the mean time. . . .

Calne 16 Decbr. 1774.

No. 62.

FROM PRIESTLEY TO ANDREW OLIVER

Sir:

I think myself exceedingly obliged to you, for the communication of your excellent observations on the cause of the electricity of the atmosphere. As far as I can judge of them from the general ideas you throw out, they promise to unfold that great secret of nature which has hitherto been one of the great desiderata in philosophy. I shall be very glad to see your thoughts on this subject more at large.

I have read your *Essay on Comets* with attention and pleasure. My objection, however, to your theory is, that the atmosphere of the comets being of the same nature with those of the sun and other heavenly bodies, the particles of which they consist will not be repelled by them more than by each other; so that upon their approach, they will only surround the two bodies to an equal distance. How could the atmosphere of the sun, for instance, drive that of a comet to such a distance, when no part of that of the sun itself is driven by the same power to a tenth part of the distance? But I think your hypothesis will stand clear of this objection, if you suppose, what I believe to be true, that the sun and the comets, as well as the earth, have *proper electric atmospheres,* by means of which they will be enabled to act upon their ordinary atmospheres at a considerable distance.

I rejoice much that philosophical knowledge is so much cultivated on your side of the Atlantic and sorry I am that our attention to it will probably be called off to a struggle for power, the most unnatural and I fear the most fatal that men were ever engaged in.

I have of late been very much engaged in the prosecution of my experiments on different kinds of *air* and have had considerable success. I intend soon to publish a *Supplement* to the treatise which you very probably have heard that I have lately published on that subject. If there be any intercourse between the two countries at that time, I shall send you a copy, and shall be exceedingly glad to hear from you. . . .

Hon. Andrew Oliver, Jr., Salem, Massachusetts.
London, 12 Feb. 1775

P.S. L'd Shelburne desires me to present his most respectful compliments to you.

No. 63.

FROM PRIESTLEY TO GEORGE WALKER

[No date but probably
before 6 April 1775]

On Thursday next your papers will be presented to the Royal Society, but it may be several weeks before they can be read. . . .

A friend of mine, to whom I communicated your query about the doctrine of fluxions, writes to me from Paris, that the mathematicians there know of no treatise containing such a demonstration as you mention: but they tell him there is a sketch of something of the kind in the Encyclopedia. If you have no opportunity of consulting it, I will do it for you when I am in London. I wish however you would send your papers to Dr. Price, who will present them to the Society. I do not return to Paris. . . .

As you have not studied Hartley, it would do to no purpose to write to you about metaphysics. I believe nothing of any *original determination of the mind to objects of morality,* or to any other objects: and though you and Mr. Hutchinson say *there must be* such things, I do not see a shadow of proof for it. I do not expect however, that the reading of Hartley will convince you, any more than another reading of Hutchinson would convince me. We are both too old, to adopt a new general system of metaphysics. . . .

I have lately been very successful in the prosecution of my experiments on air, and intend soon to draw up a supplement to my Treatise on that subject. I have two more acid airs, the vitriolic and the vegetable, and also a species of air got from red lead, and other substances, that is near six times as good as common air. This very remarkable fact I hope will lead me much farther. . . .

I am also about to publish a Harmony of the Evangelists in Greek and English, upon the plan of that in the Repository. If you have any thoughts on the subject, I shall thank you for the communication of them.

No. 64.

FROM PRIESTLEY TO NEWCOME CAPPE

Calne, Aug. 28, 1775

Dear Sir,

I am glad to find that you approve of my Essays prefixed to the edition of Hartley. I think I shall compose some other essays on metaphysical subjects, and publish them separately, but not very soon. If it will amuse you, I will very gladly put them into your hands as they are composed. One is nearly finished. I shall be glad to hear your opinion of them.

I have made many observations on human nature, with a view to the illustration of Hartley's theory. They relate very much to the conduct of the mind and happiness, and they are so necessarily intermixed with observations on education, that I almost think it will be best to publish them altogether as one work, and consequently not very soon. I have not yet transcribed any of them. When I do, you shall see them, if you please.

I am satisfied that my argument for Peter not being one of the two disciples going to Emmaus was not well founded. I think to print the Greek Harmony this winter, and the English some time after. Mr Turner has engaged to add to the English, illustrations of all the difficult passages for the use of common readers. The dissertations will be common to both; but those who choose to have both, may have the latter without the dissertations. With these I have taken a good deal of pains, and I hope they will give you some pleasure. Among other things, I have a new interpretation of Daniel's prophecy of seventy weeks.

The sparry acid is an acid contained in what the chymists call *fluor*. In Derbyshire it is called *spar*, and they make vases and ornaments for chimney-pieces of it. The acid air is procured by pouring upon it oil of vitriol, and receiving the produce in quicksilver, as with the marine acid air. The first section in my new volume is on the vitriolic acid air, which is procured by heating in it any thing containing phlogiston. Phosphorus is too expensive for me to have much to do with. I should think myself happy if I had an opportunity of shewing your son some of my late experiments. I do not wonder at your anxiety about him, and shall rejoice when a suitable employment is provided for him.

I thank you for your anecdotes of Mr. Burgh. Have you any more? . . .

No. 65.

From Priestley to Matthew Boulton

Calne 22 Oct 1775

Dear Sir

As you are a friend of *science* as well as a great promoter of the *arts*, I make no apology for troubling you with a commission which I do not know to get executed any other way.

When I had the pleasure of seeing you at Birmingham, you gave me a few pieces of refuse *Derbyshire spar*. It lay, I remember, in an open Court, and I think you said was not fit for any use to which you applied such materials. I find it to be the same thing with the *fluor spatosus*, from which the *new mineral acid* is extracted, and by means of the pieces with which you furnished me I have completely investigated the nature of it, and prove, what no chymist who has treated of it has suspected, that the acid is no other than the *vitriolic* employed in the salutus of the spar, volatilized by the phlogiston it contains.

My stock of Spar is now almost exhausted, and I am at a loss to procure more. My friends and correspondents are also frequently applying to me for this spar. I beg, therefore, you would, as soon as you conveniently can, send me a few pounds of it *by the Coach,* directed to me at *Shelburne house Berkeley Square,* where I expect to arrive tomorrow. It is of little consequence what *colour* the spar is of, but the more white or yellow the better. However, send the pieces at Random.

If you should have as much by you as you had when I was at Birmingham, I wish that, after the parcel by the *Coach,* which I shall want immediately, you would send me ten or twenty pounds by the *Waggon.*

If you should have none of this spar by you, I shall take it as a favour, if you will write to your correspondent in Derbyshire, and desire him to send as above, and such pieces as are of no use to him. It is generally pounded before it is used, as I want it.

Depending upon your friendship in this emergency. . . .

P.S. Had Ld Shelburne been in the country I would not have put you to any expence for this letter.

I have in the press a *Second volume of Experiments on Air,* containing matter which I flatter myself will give you some pleasure.

No. 66.

FROM PRIESTLEY TO MATTHEW BOULTON

Dear Sir

On Saturday last, late in the evening I received the *box of Spar* you were so obliging as to send me; a day or two after your letter. But not hearing from you, or receiving the parcel, very soon, I had desired Mr Whitehurst, late of Derby, to order me a quantity, which I take for granted he has done; so that if the *larger quantity* be not sent off, you may save yourself the trouble. If it be sent off, I shall only have the more to spare for my friends. This is a very seasonable supply. I have promised to show Count Orloff and some other foreigners, some of my experiments &c on Wednesday next and should not have been able to show them those on this acid.

You need not *watch* for my book. It will be a pleasure to me to send you a copy as soon as any are printed, which will be, I expect, in a fortnight or three weeks. You can then judge whether this spar contain a really *new acid* or not.

It will be a great pleasure to me to see your improvements on *fire engines* and all your other valuable improvements in *mechanics,* and the *arts,* whenever I may have an opportunity of seeing Birmingham. In the mean I hope you will have many opportunities of giving me a call in London, if not at Calne. ———— I shall not quarrel with you on account of our different sentiments in Politiks ———— When I tell you what is fact, that the Americans have constructed a canon on a new principle, by which they can hit a mark at the distance of a mile, you will say their *ingenuity* has come in aid of their *cowardice.* I would tell you the principle of it, but that I am afraid you would set your superior ingenuity at work to improve upon it, for the use of their enemies. . . .

London. 6 Novb. 1775

No. 67.

From Priestley to Thomas Henry (extract).

Calne, December 31, 1775

[Dear Sir]

. . . He [Lavoisier] is an Intendant of the Finances, and has much public business, but finds leisure for various philosophical pursuits, for which he is exceedingly well qualified. He ought to have acknowledged that my giving him an account of the air I had got from *Mercurius Calcinatus,* and buying a quantity of M. Cadet while I was in Paris, led him to try what air it yielded, which he did presently after I left. I have, however, barely hinted at this in my second volume.

[This is the end of the extract, as quoted by William Henry.]

No. 68.

F<small>ROM</small> P<small>RIESTLEY</small> <small>TO</small> C<small>ALEB</small> R<small>OTHERAM</small>

London, Feb. 9, 1776

Dear Sir,

I blame myself much for not answering your former letter, but I was just then setting out on a tour upon the continent, and after that I had nothing very particular to write about.

I have been very variously employed ever since, and am now intent upon several courses of experiments which are very promising. Among other things, I have lately sent to the Royal Society an account of a set of experiments to ascertain the use of the *blood* in respiration, which I find is to discharge phlogiston from the system; and it affects air in the very same manner when congealed, and out of the body, as it does when fluid, and in the body. It is also acted upon by the air through a bladder, and a large body of *serum,* as well as in immediate contact. I have likewise proved decisively that *fixed air* is a modification of the nitrous acid. But the experiments, though very remarkable, are too particular for a letter.

We have just got a little news from America. A ship which left Virginia the 12th of January, brings an account that Lord Dunmore had landed, and in attacking some intrenchments of the Provincials, had been repulsed with the loss of seventy or eighty men, and with difficulty regained his ship. By their last accounts from Canada, General Montgomery was preparing to attack Quebec in a few days. The ministry say he had made an attempt, and had been repulsed with loss. Nothing new at Boston —— provisions very scarce, but it is thought the troops in it may hold out.

To-morrow will come out an excellent pamphlet of Dr. Price's. He sent me a copy last night, and I sat up till after one o'clock to read it. Very soon, Israel Manduit is to come out with something on the other side of the question. There is nothing that looks like a disposition to relent on the side of the court, but, on the other hand, the most determined rancour, and infatuated confidence of success.

I sent your very proper and sensible paper to the *Evening Post*. They promised to insert it.

I shall be very glad to hear from you. . . .

No. 69.

FROM PRIESTLEY TO BENJAMIN FRANKLIN

London 13 Feby. 1776

Dear Sir

I lament this unhappy war, as on more serious accounts, so not a little, that it renders my correspondence with you so precarious. I have had three letters from you, and have written as often; but the last, by Mr Temple, I have been informed he could not take. What is become of it I cannot tell.

This accompanies a copy of my second volume of *Observations on air,* and of a *pamphlet,* which may perhaps make you smile. Major Carleton, brother to the Governor of Quebec, has undertaken to convey the parcel to you.

By the same hand you will receive a most excellent pamphlet by Dr Price, which, if anything can, will, I hope, make some impression upon this infatuated nation. An edition of a thousand has been nearly sold in two days. But when Ld G. Germaine is at the head of affairs, it cannot be expected that anything like *reason* or *moderation* should be attended to. Every thing breathes *rancour* and *desperation,* and nothing but absolute impotence will stop their proceedings. We therefore look upon a final separation from you as a certain and speedy event. If any thing can unite us, it must be the immediate adopting of the measures proposed by Ld Shelburne, and mentioned in Dr Prices pamphlet.

As, however, it is most probable that you will be driven to the necessity of governing yourselves, I hope you have wisdom to guard against the rocks that we have fatally split upon; and made some better provision for securing your natural rights against the incroachment of power, in whomsoever placed.

Amidst the alarms and distresses of war, it may perhaps give you some pleasure to be informed that I have been very successful in the prosecution of my *experiments* since the publication of my second volume. I have lately sent to the Royal Society some *observations on blood* (which I believe have given great satisfaction to my medical friends) proving that the use of it in respiration is to discharge phlogiston from the system, that it has the same power of affecting air when congealed and out of the body, that it has when fluid and in the body, and acts thro a bladder and a large quantity of serum, as well as in immediate contact with the air. In pure air it becomes of a florid red, and in phlogisticated air black; and the air to which it has been exposed is affected in the same manner as it is by respiration, the calcination of metals, or any other phlogistic process.

I am now in a very promising course of experiments on *metals,* from all of which, dissolved in spirit of nitre, I get first nitrous air as before, and then distilling to dryness from the same materials *fixed air,* and dephlogisticated air. This proves that fixed air is certainly a modification of the nitrous acid. I have, however, got no fixed air from gold or silver. You will smile when I tell you, that I do not absolutely despair of the transmutation of metals.

In one of your letters you mention your having made a valuable discovery on your passage to America, and promise to write me a particular account of it. If you ever did this, the letter has miscarried, for which I shall be sorry and the more so as I now almost despair of hearing from you any more till these troubles be settled.

The club of *honest whigs,* as you justly call them, think themselves much honoured by your having been one of them, and also by your kind remembrance of them. Our zeal in the good cause is not abated. You are often the subject of our conversation.

Not to burden my friend too much, I give him only one copy of my book; but I hope you will communicate it to Professor Winthrop, with my most respectful compliments. . . .

P.S. Lord Shelburne and Col. Barré were pleased with your

remembrance of them, and desire their best respects and good wishes in return. The best thing I can wish the friendly bearer of this letter is that he may fall into your hands, as I am sure he will meet with good treatment, and perhaps have the happiness of conversing with you, a happiness which I now regret. Your old servant, Fevre, often mentions you with affection and respect. He is, in all respects, an excellent servant. I value him much both on his own account, and yours. He seems to be very happy. Mrs Stephenson is much as usual. She can talk about nothing but you.

No. 70.

FROM PRIESTLEY TO ALESSANDRO VOLTA

London, 25 April 1776.

Dear Sir,

I have very lately received the printed sequel of your letter to me, and also another letter containing a concise account of your discovery. It is, indeed, a very curious one, and the study and application of it will, I doubt not, contribute greatly to improve the science of Electricity, and must do you the greatest honour with all who know the real value of it. We have begun to make the instrument in England, and succeed very well with small ones. We shall soon attempt some of a larger size. It must give you great pleasure to make so fine an experiment of your own discovery.

I have just been favoured with Sig.^{r} MOSCATI's letter, and little tract, which gives me great pleasure, as it coincides with my own ideas; but he has proceeded farther, than I have done. I beg my most respectful compliments to him, and I congratulate the world on the acquisition of so valuable a member of the philosophical body.

I shall take the first opportunity of sending him a copy of my *Observations on respiration and the use of the blood,* which is printed for the Philosophical Transactions.

I have been disappointed of an opportunity of sending you my *second volume* on air. It has been some time in the hands of a gentleman who was going abroad, but who has been prevented.

It is much to be regretted that the correspondence of philosophers is so precarious and expensive.

I am, at present, much engaged with my experiments relating to *air,* and similar subjects, and hope to have a third volume again the next winter. I should have thought myself so happy in having you for my translator as any other person whatever. You do me honour by the proposal. . . .

No. 71.

FROM PRIESTLEY TO MATTHEW BOULTON

Dear Sir

As I know you will take pleasure in every thing in which the advancement of science is concerned, I take the liberty to recommend to you Mr Warltire, who [has] been some time in this part of the [co]untry, and who is going to read Lectures on the subject of *air* at Birmingham. I think him an excellent philosopher, as well as a modest and agreeable man. He is perfectly acquainted with his subject, and has prepared a set of experiments which have given the greatest satisfaction wherever he has been. He has been so obliging as to spend some time with me, and has given me much assistance in my late experiments, of which he can give you some account.

I have been fortunate in the prosecution of my experiments, and am preparing a *third volume,* which I hope to publish before the next spring. I hope you re[ceived] the *second volume,* which I desired my [book] seller to send you. . . .

Calne 28 Sepbr. 1776

No. 72.

FROM PRIESTLEY TO ALESSANDRO VOLTA

Dear Sir,

I have received your elegant treatise on the *Native inflammable air of marshes,* and have received very great satisfaction from the perusal of a great part of it. I rejoice in having so able an associate in the investigation of the properties of different kinds of air. I was much struck with your letter to me on that subject, and take the liberty to publish a translation of it in the Appendix to my third volume on air, which I hope you have received. I lament exceedingly that the correspondence of philosophical persons, living at a distance from each other, is so difficult and expensive; but there seems to be no remedy for it. I have desired Sig.^{r} LANDRIANI to endeavour to get letters, and small parcels, conveyed to one from you by means of the *Imperial ambassador.* If that could be done, it will save me a good deal of expence.

As you are in so happy a train, I hope you will persevere in it, and I doubt not that, in so fruitful a field, and with so happy a genius, you will continue to make valuable discoveries. I shall always rejoice to hear of your success. Since I have got your books, I have several times amused myself in verifying your curious observations, and have never failed to collect inflammable air whenever I have sought for it. I often think I should have very happy to accompany you in the excursions you so well describe.

Since the publication of my third volume I have made several new observations, but none of much consequence. One is, that if a quantity of lead or tin be mixed with mercury, and the mixture be agitated in contact with *common,* or *dephlogisticated air,* it throws out all the lead action, mixed with a black powder. The air is phlogisticated and the black mass yields fixed air. By this means the mercury may be as effectually cleansed from lead or tin if it had been distilled, and in much less time. Agitating the mixture in contact with any other kind of air has no effect. Yesterday we ate a pigeon which I had kept in nitrous air near six weeks. It was perfectly sweet and good. But the water in which it had stood was very putrid, and had been changed several times. This use of nitrous air may be very useful in a family. I shall flatter myself with the hope of hearing of your progress in these inquiries. . . .

Calne, 6 June 1777

No. 73.

FROM ANTOINE LAVOISIER TO BENJAMIN FRANKLIN

Sir

We have set aside next Thursday, the 12th of the month, to repeat a few of the principal experiments of M. Priestley on different kinds of air. If you are interested in these experiments, we would think ourselves very honored to do them in your presence. We propose to begin at about one o'clock and take them up again immediately after dinner. I sincerely hope that you can accept this invitation; we will have only M. le veillard M. Brisson and M. Beront —— too large a number of people not being, in general, favorable to the success of experiments. I hope that you will be so good as to bring your grandson. . . .

At the Arsenal 8 June 1777

No. 74.

FROM PRIESTLEY TO NEWCOME CAPPE

Dear Sir

I have desired Mr Johnson to send you a Copy of my *Disquisitions on Matter and Spirit* which I shall be obliged to you if you will be so good as to read with some care, that, if it be necessary, I may yet make alterations in it before it be published. A second volume on *Necessity* is nearly printed off, and that will also be sent to you for the same purpose.

It is very probable that in the Disquisitions you may find many things that you will disapprove, and I may not see reason to alter; but I hope by the help of such friends as you to send it out free from any *gross mistakes,* or passages *needlessly offensive.* I hope you will make as much dispatch as you conveniently can.

I am now busy in writing notes and occasional paraphrases for my *English Harmony* and I have made so many new *experiments,* that I must make another publication on the subject; but I shall change my title, and begin a new work. My experiments are more in the way of chemistry than before —— I shall probably go deeper in this business than ever, in consequence of having undertaken to teach Philosophy to Ld Shelburne's children, and having a noble apparatus for that purpose. I often wish I had your son with us. . . .

Calne 14 Septr 1777.

P. S.   I must beg you would not shew the Disquisitions to any body or speak of them till they be published.

No. 75.

FROM PRIESTLEY TO MATTHEW BOULTON

[n.d., but before November 1777]

Dear Sir

Having experienced your readiness to assist me in my philosophical inquiries, I am encouraged to apply to you again. I wish to procure air as it is actually breathed by the different manufacturers in this kingdom and hope you will be so obliging as to procure me the proper samples from Birmingham.

The method of doing it is simply this. Fill a clean phial (about eight ounces) with clear water, and emptying it in the place the air of which you would take; immediately cork it well, and open it no more —— I only wish you would do this in those places where you expect the air to be the worst, on account of bad fumes or a number of people working together &, and not at your place in the country, but in the middle of the town. I should be glad also to have the air of some of your closest streets, and likewise the best in your neighbourhood, noting the state of the weather at the time.

I hope this will not be very troublesome to you; and I shall be glad to pay any expence that may attend it. Send the box of phials to Shelburne house Berkley Square London.

I am told you are acquainted with Mr Keir the translator of Macquer's Dictionary. I have just got the new edition of that work, and his treatise on different kinds of air. I have not yet read the whole of it, but have cast my eye on one of his own experiments, by which he controverts any idea of the constitution of atmospherical air, and think it would be right to inform him that it is quite fallacious, as the minium will yield just as much air, and of the same quality, without the oil of vitriol, as with it, and that in the experiment of mine which he criticizes he has overlooked the principal circumstance belonging to it —— Whether it be owing to the persons being unaccustomed to these experiments, or some other cause, I find very few who make them with due circumspection. I consider Mr. Keir as a very able chymist, and useful writer, but I cannot help smiling at his new phraseology, and his puffing of Van Helmont. . . .

P.S. Please to direct to me under a cover directed to Ld Shelburne, Calne, Wilts.

No. 76.

FROM PRIESTLEY TO MATTHEW BOULTON

Dear Sir

I took the liberty, some time ago, to beg the favour of you to send me some phials of air from Birmingham. I have not had the pleasure to hear from you in answer to my request; but three weeks ago I received a box of 13 GREEN PHIALS, which had been filled with quicksilver, and carefully numbered. As there was no letter accompanying them, I presume you wrote one, and that it has miscarried. If you did send the phials, and the letter has miscarried, I must beg the favour of you to write again, explaining the Nos. of the phials.

I am very sensible of my obligations to you. . . .

Calne 25 Nov. 1777

No. 77.

FROM PRIESTLEY TO JAMES KEIR

Dear Sir

Ever since I had the favour of your last I have been in expectation of receiving your *Treatise on gases,* and on that account deferred writing to you. At present I have not your letter before me, it being packed up together with other papers, and sent to London, where I expect to be in a day or two.

You wished to be satisfied about the effect of *heat* on the *precipitate per se.* For my part, I had no doubt about what Mr. Lavoisier &c asserts. What Mr. Warltire had from me was what remained, after I had made my experiment, and it could not be *altered,* because that part had not been affected. However, for your satisfaction, I lately took a Dwt of the precipitate, and exposed it to the heat of a common fire in a glass tube, when I revivified the whole except 2½ grains, and nothing like a *calx* remained, the loss of weight being certainly the D^d [i.e., dephlogisticated] air it had yielded. In fact, I take it to be the same thing with the *red precipitate,* tho prepared in a different manner.

Among other things, which I do not mention to you because I hope you will soon see them in print, I think I have fully proved, by the firing of inflammable in common air, that this and nitrous air contain, in equal bulks, equal quantities of phlogiston.

I must also mention another thing because I only discovered it yesterday, and it is realy curious. I find that the *black matter,* into which I had imagined that *Vitriolic acid air* was changed by the electric spark is *mercury Superphlogisticated;* which proves that a mercurial vapour is diffused thro the whole mass of air even when cold. This is the more extraordinary, as the black matter is produced, tho I take the spark between wires several inches above the surface of the mercury. If I take the spark in the same air, over water supersaturated with it, I get no black powder. This is the case also with common air over water, tho the blackness is produced when taken in the same air over mercury.

My observations on the *purification of air in water* I hope will give you pleasure, tho I want *sun-shine* to complete them —— *Sea water,* I find, yields air much better than common air. I have got this from Dr. Dobson of Liverpool, and I hope that other friends in sea ports will likewise send me accounts of their observations on the same subject.

My work is so large, that I believe I must make *two volumes* of it, but my printer does not go on to my mind —— When I get to London, I hope to do better. As soon as ever a volume is finished, I shall send you the sheets, and shall hope for the favour of your remarks, for I am afraid of tripping on chemical ground. My walk is between what is called *chemistry,* and other branches of *Natural Philosophy.* On this side I am pretty well received, but on the other there are some that show a willingness to peck at me, and therefore it behoves me to be on my guard, and secure as able seconds as I can. . . .

Calne 4 Feby. 1778

P.S. I shall be in London two or three months from this time, and while I am there you may direct to me as usual, under cover to Ld Shelburne.

No. 78.

From Priestley to Marsilio Landriani

[Dear Sir]

I was much pleased with the news you kindly sent in your last letter, especially the report on volcanoes. I am also pleased with the accuracy of your new barometer, and will consider myself greatly honoured if you keep me informed about it, as you have so graciously promised. I sent your letter to Mr Bewly, whose admiration for you is great; Mr Bewly appreciates your mention of his name.

After your latest letter, I was informed of the strange discovery of the Abbé Fontana, concerning the absorption by hot charcoal of air confined over mercury. I have repeated the experiment successfully and am now anxious to see his report of the experiment and his subsequent observations on it.

I have also repeated my experiments on the vegetation of plants in enclosed airs and find one plant especially that appears to absorb completely any kind of air. It is the *Epilobium hirsutum* of Linnaeus. As it grows well in water, I put the plant in a glass jar whose mouth is immersed in the same water in which the plant is growing. In one experiment the plant absorbed more than $9/10$ths of a jar of common air; another time almost half a jar of inflammable air and when $1/3$d of the air was gone, I found the remainder as inflammable as before. Many other plants probably have the same characteristics.

I can now explain the different results of experiments on plants growing in vitiated air. In several experiments the air was vitiated by the plants themselves, but in general this happened when the plants were not healthy. Some times the vitiated air was not only restored, as I reported in my first experiments, but common air was changed to dephlogisticated air. I have many conclusive examples of this and by using different plants. My method is to introduce shoots, from strawberry plants growing in my garden, into jars of air with their mouths immersed in water.

But what I believe you will find the most unusual is the spontaneous production of dephlogisticated air from the green matter which grows in jars in which water has been kept a long time. This green matter looks like a vegetable; but I cannot yet say that it really is so. Observing a phial covered with that substance, I inverted over it a large jar filled with water and partially coated on the inside with the same green matter, and in about two days I collected approximately a half pint of very pure dephlogisticated air, without heat and without any other chemical process whatever. This is another way that nature restores the vitiated atmosphere. I will try to diversify this experiment.

I am writing another volume of experiments, but have many more to do before I can complete it and am now in a place where I cannot experiment for several months.

Please inform M. Volta, to whom I shall write shortly, about these experiments so that I will not need to repeat these observations to him. . . .

Milford, 24 July 1778.

No. 79.

From Priestley to the Abbé Roger Joseph Boscovich

A monsieur l'abbé Boscovich

Sir

I am very sorry to have any cause of complaint against a person for whom I have always had so great an esteem as I have had for the Abbé Boscovich —— You have been informed, it seems, that I have represented you as "a favourer of the most extravagant" materialism; which you consider as "abominable, detestable, and impious." You call my conduct "an atrocious calumny, which attacks your religion, probity, and honour". You say, I "must retract what I have advanced, that I shall find in you a zealous opponent, that you shall be obliged to give public notice, in the Journals, of this insult of mine upon you, and that what I have advanced has been without even reading your book."

All this, and more to the same purpose, you express in a letter to Lord Shelburne, which his Lordship has just put into my hands. Now I cannot help observing that, had you had something better than mere *hearsay* for all this, it would have become a man of honour to have remonstrated to *myself* on the subject, and not to have immediately written to my *patron* about it; when you must have been sensible, that it could only tend to do me an injury; and for any thing that you knew, it might have been an irreparable and fatal one.

But, Sir, it would have become a man of your years and character, to have seen what I had actually said before you had used such language as this on the occasion. Had you done this, you would have found that, whatever guilt I have contracted by my late publication, I have not made *you* an accomplice with me in it; for that I have only adopted your theory of *the nature of matter*, without supposing that you had the most distant idea of the *use* that I have made of it.

As to my doctrine itself, it is the object of my work to prove it to be the only one that is consonant to the genuine system of revelation, and that the vulgar hypothesis, which I combat, has been the foundation of the grossest corruptions of true christianity; and especially [those] of the church of Rome, of which you are a member; but which I consider as properly *antichristian,* and a system of abominations little better than heathenism.

If, as you seem to hint, you chuse to write against me, I hope that, for your own credit, you will first see what I have written; and if anything you advance shall appear to me to be *worth my notice,* I shall certainly reply to you: but I must take the liberty to say that, from the specimen you have given of the imprudent violence with which you express yourself in the outset of the business, I have not, at present, any expectation that this will be the case.

If, as you have thought proper to threaten, you should proceed, in the mean time, to animadvert upon my conduct in this business in any of the *literary journals,* you will, if you have any pretensions to the character of a man of honour, give me proper notice of it, that I may have an opportunity of replying to you in the same.

You must allow me to say that, after the many very agreeable conversations that I had with you at Paris, in which I frequently expressed a high approbation of your work, I am particularly surprized that you could suppose I had quoted it without having read it myself. I shall be glad to see a translation of so valuable a work into a language so generally known as the French.

It is a great mortification to me that anything should contribute to lessen the good opinion I have hitherto entertained, and which I have always expressed of you. As a man of genius, and one who has rendered important services to the interests of science, I shall still honour you; but the very inconsiderate and violent step which, without any provocation, you have taken with respect to me, will make me more sparing of my encomiums with regard to other things, which, however, are by much the most valuable ingredients in the human character. If you be capable of feeling any impropriety of conduct, and of making reparation for the injury you have done me, I shall expect to see another of [your letters] to Lord Shelburne, written in a strain somewhat different from that [of] your last.

I am, not without respect, but with much less than formerly. . . .

19 Aug. 1778

No. 80.

FROM BOSCOVICH TO PRIESTLEY

Monsieur,

I received the letter which you did me the honor of writing to me on the 19th of August as I was about to leave Paris on an extended trip. As it was written in English, which I do not understand, I was unable to reply until I found, by chance a few days ago, someone who knew your language. You complain, Monsieur, at the application I made to your patron, Lord Shelbourn, and say that I have done you a cruel injustice without provocation, that I did this with the sole purpose of doing you ill; that my complaints against you, conveyed in that letter, are unfair, because, you say, your work does not contain what I have been led to believe it does; and you demand reparation in a letter of correction to be written to his Lordship.

I can say nothing of the contents of your work from personal examination, and I will be unable to do so in Paris, as it is written in a language which I do not understand. I have had the account of one of the principal members of the Royal Academy of Sciences, who understands it well, and who had read the work. He assured me, and reiterated in many conversations we have had on this subject, that to his great astonishment you teach in your work pure and unconcealed materialism, without the least circumspection: that you claim to deduce this from my theory of matter, in this way making me party to a doctrine that I detest and abhor as impiety in religion and senseless to sound philosophy. He added that you spoke of my theory as if someone had told you about it.

You can well imagine how this account affected me, especially as I had declared in my work, with all the clarity and precision possible, my contrary beliefs in speaking of the great difference which exists between matter and spirit, and in writing all that I have in my appendix on The Soul and God. I cannot suspect my friend either of ignorance or inaccuracy: therefore I could see no usefulness in any application that I could have made in writing to you yourself, not expecting from you a formal retraction of that which I regard as an atrocious published slander of an appearance of complicity in a doctrine of this nature. I never had the honor of writing to you nor of having letters from you. His Lordship has always shown kindness for me: I have had the honor of writing to him before, I had an occasion to write at that time: I took it to ask that he induce from you a retraction, for I was well aware of the influence he has on your understanding. This was not in the least for any desire to do you ill, nor in any spirit of vengeance, but to discover the most effective manner to indemnify me, since an imputation of that nature, besides the horror it inspires in me, must do me infinite injury among the large numbers of persons who do not examine things thoroughly and who know your great reputation in natural philosophy [*Phisique*].

I cannot, as I have said, judge your statements for myself: when I am in Paris, I will endeavor to find someone who can give me a translation of that which concerns me. But meanwhile, I see even in your letter that I have ample reason to complain exceedingly of you, and that you have challenged me, in doing me a great injury that I shall be obliged to redeem in the journals. You say there that you have adopted my theory of matter, and that you have drawn from it consequences, although without saying that these consequences were mine, by which you accuse of error all the different branches of Christianity accepted today, and particularly the Roman Church, of which even by your own account, I am a member, reviving the ancient injurious names, ascribing to its head that of Antichrist. Can you believe that it is not a serious injury you have done me in publishing that what I must regard and do regard as impieties and follies, are the necessary consequences of my theory, from which they are as distant as heaven from earth? What, in all my theory, can have the least appearance of agreement with materialism, and above all with the scurrilous injuries of an Antichrist Pope, which among gentlemen of good sense are so long since outmoded that the custom of burning the Pope in effigy has even been abolished among the populace. The simplicity of the elements of matter, and their lack of extension which is common to me and the monads of Leibniz, the points of Zeno, the elements of a number of the Parapatetics, which have only a kind of so-called virtual extension, the mutual attractions and repulsions which are common with me and the Newtonians, the method of proving their law, with the infinity of the repulsion with increasingly small distances, with as much of the passage from one to the other, and the manner of deducing from this the general properties, and particularly the different types of bodies, which is properly my own, certainly have nothing to do with the views that I abhor: I hope that I can make everyone see this, and I cannot even imagine by what means you could yourself endeavor to make of it even the slightest connection involving me.

I esteem your great merit in Natural Philosophy [*la Phisique*] in which you have made important discoveries, but without doubt, you would have done well not to pass those limits, and you should not have attempted to make of me an accomplice in publishing in a printed work that these propositions which you well know must be regarded by me as (I repeat the description) impieties and absurdities, were a necessary consequence of my theory.

You will see, Monsieur, that I am not in a position to retract to his Lordship; but rather of renewing my complaints on the material stated in your letter, if not indeed on all the rest, when I will have had a translation of the part of your work relating to me. I do not seek argument on the rest, liking to use my time in cultivating the sciences as usual, and leaving to others the care of defending or even of avenging religion improperly attacked; I confine myself only to pointing out the injustice that you have done me, in declaring my theory an accomplice to your excesses. I ask that you excuse the expressions that I have used in this letter, and in the earlier one to his Lordship: there are none too strong, when it is a question of protecting my religion and my honor. Amicus usque ad aras [a friend up to the altar]. . . .

At Bigno near Sens
17 October 1778

No. 81.

FROM PRIESTLEY TO GIOVANNI FABRONI

Dear Sir

I should have answered your obliging letter sooner, but that I have been engaged in a multiplicity of business not of a philosophical nature. I have however made some observations, which I flatter myself will give you some pleasure. The *facts* appear to me to be rather extraordinary. You must help me to explain them, for I am a very bad theorist.

Your observations on the firing of gunpowder I think very just; but I must reflect on the subject a little more, before I can pretend to enter into particulars with you. Since, however, the acid of nitre is capable of forming such an union with its own base as constitutes d^d [dephlogisticated] air, I think Dr Ingenhousz well founded in supposing that part, if not the whole, of the d^d air is produced in this manner. All the p^n of the charcoal must be exhausted in nitrous air before any d^d air can be formed.

My experiments with the *willow plant* this year have hitherto been, in some respects, different from those of the last. None of these plants have yet absorbed more than one fourth of common air, and have not much ph^d [phlogisticated] it. They have considerably improved ph^d air, absorbing very little of it; but they devour inflammable air at a great rate indeed. One of these plants has sometimes absorbed near a pint of this air in a few days; and when it is reduced to about one fifth, it ceases to be inflammable, and is even tolerably pure

The vigour which these plants enjoy when growing in this air is, indeed, astonishing. Even the leaves under water are of a vivid green, and both the leaves and the stalk emit abundance of air bubbles. Having turned the roots of some of these plants into a jar of water, I have frequently collected of this air, and always find it much better than common air, and sometimes with a mixture of inflammable air, the whole together making a very loud explosion.

When the leaves are in common air the air collected from the roots is very pure. But, what you will think extraordinary, the air yielded by the root when the leaves were in *fixed air* was the best of all. Equal measures of this and of common air occupied the space of 0.9

In d^d air one of these plants would not live long, and even when the plant was dead, the air was but little injured.

The marsh in which these willow plants grew contains so much inflammable air, in its muddy bottom, that, without changing my place, I can sometimes fill a receiver containing three pints with it. These plants may, therefore, be very useful in such a situation. Two other plants growing in the same place, which have likewise very *hairy leaves,* live equally well in inflammable air, but do not seem to absorb much of it. The willow plant thrives better in the strongest inflammable air from iron and oil of vitriol than in that which comes from the marsh. I shall make trial of other plants, but I am not a botanist, and cannot describe them. I must therefore send the plants themselves to some of my botanical friends in London, in order to get the names of them

I am making farther observations on the *green matter* deposited by water before its emission of d^d air, and I find that more depends upon it than I had imagined. When a glass vessel is once coated with it, and then filled with water which never would yield any air, even by exposure to the sun, it presently begins to emit air very copiously. The water then poured out of the vessel contains a great quantity of air, sparkling like champaign wine, and will even continue to yield more air of itself. It appears, therefore, that the air exists in a concentrated state in this green matter, and is disengaged from it gradually, impregnating the water contiguous to it. In time, however, its power of giving air is exhausted. I have many more experiments to make upon it.

I have made several observations in taking the electric spark in vitriolic acid air, and also in common air, which prove that this metal is easily converted into vapour, which invisibly pervades a large mass of incumbent air. For the black powder, which is made by the electric spark at a considerable distance above the surface of the mercury, is *mercury superphlogisticated,* and with the vitriolic acid air, I think, approaches to the nature of *athiops mineral.* When I take the spark in vitriolic acid air over water superimpregnated with it no black powder is formed. I shall pursue this subject still farther. The conducting power of the Torricellian vacuum, I doubt not, is made by a mercurial vapour gradually, but not immediately, diffused thro it, and therefore at first it will not conduct.

When I went to London I left some mixtures of the strongest vitriolic and nitrous acids. At my return I found the stoppers of the bottles out, and all that remains in the phials is a pure, but very weak vitriolic acid. In dissolving iron no part of the air is nitrous, but all inflammable.

When I write to you I consider myself as writing to Mr Kirwan. You are also at liberty to communicate the observations to any other of our common friends. I shall be glad to be assisted by your common observations in return; but you must remember that I am an Englishman, and must forbear the too complimentary style of your last. . . .

Calne 20 June 1779

PS. Since I composed the above, I observed that a quantity of common air in which some *duckweed* was growing was considerably increased; and, examining it, I found it to be much purer than before. The measure of my test was 1.04. I see there is also a proportionable addition to a quantity of inflammable air, in which some of the same duckweed is growing: but I have not examined it. I must diversify this experiment many ways.

I shall be much obliged to you if, when you favour me with another letter, you will write down what you take to be ascertained concerning the constitution of *spirit of wine, sugar, oil,* and other things into which the same acid enters; I do not perfectly recollect what you told me on that subject.

I shall take the liberty to keep your *tract on Arsenic* a little longer.

No. 82.

FROM PRIESTLEY TO ALESSANDRO VOLTA

Dear Sir

I never think of you without lamenting the distance at which we are placed from each other, the tediousness of writing letters, and the expence and uncertainty of their conveyance; which the present war much increases. I have not yet seen your letter to me in ROZIER's *Journal,* and I wish much to see that, as well as that you speak of to Mr MAGELLAN, and others. I am much pleased with the idea of your lamp with inflammable air, but more with your being able to discover so small a portion of inflammable air when mixed with respirable. Mr MAGELLAN says, he has no letter containing an account of the method of doing this. I suppose it will be in your printed letter.

I hope that by this time you have received the copy of my late philosophical work which I desired Mr MAGELLAN to convey to you.

I am still pursuing my experiments, and with some success, especially on the growth of certain plants in different kinds of air. I find that the *epilobium hirsutum* of [Linnaeus] flourishes most of all in inflammable air, of which it absorbs an astonishing quantity; but I have had the most pleasing results from my experiments on the exposure of various substances to the *sun beams in water*.

Flesh, and most vegetables, turn green in those circumstances, and, notwithstanding their becoming putrid, emit great quantities of the purest air. But there are great varieties in the results, too many to be described in a letter.

Some vegetables, expecially onions, given great quantities of inflammable air, but nothing turns *green*, or consequently yield dephlogisticated air, but in the light. I am still busily engaged in the prosecution of this subject.

I have also been making experiments on the propagation of sound in different kinds of air and find that it is nearly in proportion to their density. In inflammable air a bell is hardly heard at all; but it is very loud in fixed air. It is also louder in dephlogisticated than in common air.

I am also examining the nature of that kind of nitrous air in which a candle burns with a hight and enlarged flame, and find that, in many respects, it is hardly to be distinguished from dephlogisticated air.

There are other things that I have done, and am about, but one [our?] principal communication must be by means of the press. . . .

Calne 5 Aug. 1779

P.S.   We have an excellent work published now on *Animal heat* by Mr Crawford. I shall desire Mr Magellan to send it to you.

No. 83.

FROM PRIESTLEY TO GIOVANNI FABRONI

Calne 5th Sepbr 1779.

Dear Sir

Presently after I had written my last letter to you, I fully satisfied myself that the *green matter,* which I had discovered to produce dephlogisticated air, is *a vegetable;* chiefly by finding that when I used *fresh distilled water,* and exposed it to the sun, (together with such substances as with other water produced the green matter and the air) and also nearly cut off all communication with the atmosphere, neither *green matter* nor *pure air* were produced.

Having found this *air producing substance* to be a *vegetable,* growing wholly in water, I immediately tried other plants growing in water, and was pleased beyond what I can express, by finding that, without any exception that I have yet found, they *all* yield pure air, and in great abundance. From about a handful of one of the kinds (I am not botanist enough to know the names) I get, in a few hours, an ounce measure of the air. This air issues visibly from all parts of the plant, and from both sides of the leaves. Nothing can be more beautiful than the experiment. I have now eight or ten jars in which this process is going on; for I have many things to determine relating to it. It is rather too late in the year. I shall seize with eagerness the return of spring.

I have no doubt, therefore, but that *all* plants imbibe air in one state (separating it from water &c) and emit it, as you very properly say, as *excrementitious* in another, and that the reason why my experiments did not always succeed with *mint* &c confined in small jars was, that they will not always enjoy perfect *health* in that confined state; whereas the plants that grow in water are in as perfect health in my jars, (at least for a time) as in the open pond, and therefore perform all their natural functions in perfection.

I find that old *urine* imbibes both D^d and nitrous air in the same proportion, and in both cases from being *pale* becomes of a *dark* colour. It imbibes inflammable air, but more slowly, and without changing colour. It has no effect on phlogisticated air. Can you explain this? I shall diversify the experiment.

Have you any theory to explain the phenomena of nitrous air reduced to a state in which a candle burns in it? In this respect it is sometimes hardly to be distinguished from D^d air; and even when inflammable air is mixed with it, the explosion is little inferior to that made by a mixture of inflammable and D^d air. Yet this air is perfectly noxious. I am continuing my experiments upon it. This air evidently contains a *vapour,* absorbable by water, capable of taking P^n from bodies in a state of ignition, but not from the lungs of animals.

I believe there was that fallacy in the experiments I mentioned in my last, in which I supposed that fixed air was changed into D^d air. This, I suspect, came from unperceived green matter in the water.

I hope you have received your MS. —— I sent your *former letter* to Mr Bewly. When he returns it, I shall write to you again on the subject. . . .

P.S. I greatly admire Mr Crawford's work.

No. 84.

FROM PRIESTLEY TO RADCLIFFE SCHOLEFIELD

Calne, Sept. 14, 1779.

Dear Friend,

Having brought the experiments, the beginning of which I had the pleasure of shewing you, to a pretty satisfactory conclusion, I fancy it will be agreeable to you to be acquainted with the result.

The green matter that you saw producing the pure air, I found to be a vegetable substance, the seeds of which must be invisible in the atmosphere: for when the communication with the air was cut off, it was never produced. On this I tried other plants that grew wholly in water, and I find that they all, without exception, yield the same pure air, and some of them much more copiously; so that I conclude that all plants do, in fact, the same; imbibing air in an impure state, and emitting it, as excrementitious to them, in a dephlogisticated state; and the reasons why my mint, &c., did not always answer, was, that they were not always healthy, in a confined state; whereas these water-plants are as much at their ease in my jars as in the open pond.

That it is the air they extract from the water that is their immediate pabulum, I found by this experiment. In all cases I observed that the quantity of air bore a certain proportion to the contents of the jar, in general about a tenth. A quantity of water plants having yielded this proportion of air, which then began to be diminished, and continued to be so, three days, I put fresh

[177]

water, of the same kind, to the plants, and they were almost instantly covered with bubbles of air, and in a few hours I collected near an ounce measure.

I have many experiments to make in the prosecution of this business, but I think they fully establish, extend, and explain, what I first discovered, of the purification of the atmosphere by vegetation.

If you could do it conveniently, I wish you would acquaint Mr. Keir, with these particulars, some of which he knows already; but not all. I have done a good deal more since you were here, but they would not interest you, and therefore I do not recite them.

If you should see Mr. Keir, tell him I shall be much obliged to him, if, when he writes to me next, he will inform me what is the best and easiest test of the presence of nitrous acid in vitriolic.

I am now a widower, my wife being gone to London with my daughter, who will go from thence to Leeds, in her return from whence she will, I hope, have the pleasure to give you a call at Birmingham. This will be some time the next summer, for we hardly expect her home again in less than a year.

The tools you were so obliging as to send me I find exceedingly convenient. I shall get Dr. Withering's book and then, with this microscope, I shall be furnished for a botanist. But oral instruction would do much for me. However, another summer I do propose to take some pains with this business. I am at this time exceedingly at a loss for the names of my water plants.

I hope you have received the sermon I sent you by the post. . . .

No. 85.

FROM PRIESTLEY TO BENJAMIN FRANKLIN

Calne Sepr. 27. 1779

Dear Sir

Though you are so much engaged in affairs of more consequence, I know it will give you some pleasure to be informed that I have been exceedingly successful in the prosecution of my experiments since the publication of my last volume.

I have confirmed, explained, and extended my former observations on the purification of the atmosphere by means of vegetation; having first discovered that the *green matter* I treat of in my last volume is a vegetable substance, and then that other plants that grow wholly in water have the same property, all of them without exception imbibing impure air, and emitting it, as *excrementitious* to them, in a dephlogisticated state. That the source of this pure air is the impure air in the water is evident from all the plants giving only a certain quantity of air, in proportion to the water in which they are confined, and then giving more air in fresh water. I also find that the water before the plants have been confined in it yields impure air, and afterwards pure air.

From these observations I conclude, that the reason why my sprigs of mint sometimes failed to purify air, was their not being always *healthy* in a confined state, whereas these water plants are as much at their ease in my jars as in the open pond.

I have made many other new observations, but they are chiefly of a chymical nature, and not worth making the subject of a letter; tho, when you see an account of them in my next publication, I flatter myself you will think some of them curious and important

As the expence of my experiments is necessarily considerable, Dr Fothergill (who, in a very obliging manner, interests himself much in them) has, of his own motion, engaged a few of his friends to contribute about forty £ per ann to assist me in defraying the expence. Indeed, without this assistance I must have desisted altogether. While I had but a small family I suffered myself to be drawn by my success into expences, that now appear to have been rather imprudent.

I have been made very happy by the communication of your very ingenious paper on the *Aurora Borealis,* and by several accounts of the good state of your health and spirits. May this long continue. . . .

No. 86.

FROM PRIESTLEY TO GIOVANNI FABRONI

Dear Sir

I cannot let you go out of this country without acknowledging the receipt of your last favour, which I value very much, tho' I am much straitened for time, as you go so soon. As far as I can judge in a short time, all your remarks on my last volume are very just, and they will be of great use to me in the prosecution of my experiments. I cannot look over your letters without regretting that I cannot have the benefit of your company and conversation, both as a companion and a master. My knowledge in chymistry is very imperfect, and I want just such a guide as you would be.

I have done nothing of consequence since my last communication by Mr Vaughan, but I am still doing something with nitrous air brought into a state in which a candle burns in it, tho' I have not yet come to any conclusion about it.

I have just read and am much pleased with Dr Ingenhousz's work. The things of most value that he has hit upon, and that I had missed, are that *leaves,* without the rest of the plant, will produce pure air, and that the difference between day and night is so considerable.

I shall be very glad to see your publications, and hope you will find some method of conveying them to me, as I shall not fail to send you any thing that I may publish in the philosophical way. But you must not expect to hear from me often when you are so far off as Florence; distant correspondence being so tedious and uncertain — as well as expensive.

I shall rejoice exceedingly if any occasion should bring us together again, and in the mean time, I shall expect great things from your attention to experimental inquiries. . . .

Calne 17 Oct. 1779

No. 87.

FROM PRIESTLEY TO BENJAMIN VAUGHAN

Dear Sir,

I send you among a few others a copy of my *letters* &c for the sake of collecting such remarks as I may avail myself of in the page or two that remain vacant at the end of the Preface —— I wish to see what you have written on the subject of *cause and effect,* but I dare say it will not clash with what I have written, at least materially ——

I thank you for your repeated accounts of Ld Shelburne, and am glad he is in so good a way —— Last night I wrote him a short letter of congratulations on his recovery; but, in the present state of his mind with respect to me, I do not think that either that, or any thing else I can do, will please ——

I have been busy with some *experiments,* and among other things have satisfied myself that it is altogether without reason that the Abbé Fontana (in Dr Ingenhousz) pretends that the measure of *good* and *bad* nitrous air comes to the same thing in his method of applying the test. I am astonished, and provoked, at the little care with which some persons make experiments, and the confidence with which they report them.

I thank you for procuring me the *thermometers,* which came safe. They seem very well adapted to the purpose, provided they be sufficiently sensible.

Mr Arden has observed, and I saw the experiment very fairly tried, that *air* parts with its heat in *condensation.* I intend to repeat the experiment, with different kinds of air ——

I wish you could get done with the *Letters* before the end of the Week, as I may possibly want the copy when I come to town. But I wait a letter from you before I determine about my journey. . . .

Calne 26 March 1780.

No. 88.

FROM PRIESTLEY TO RICHARD KIRWAN

Dear Sir:

I think myself much obliged to you for the Notes which, at my request, you have been so obliging as to write on this work of Mr. Scheele. I was very desirous that a treatise of one of the first chemists in Europe, on a subject in which he has been a fellow-labourer with myself, should be easily understood in this country; and as I was sensible that many things in it would want illustration, and probably some correction, a mere translation, however well executed, would not be sufficient. I am far from pretending to a complete knowledge of chemistry, but Dr. Forster's translation, and your Notes together, seem to have answered all my wishes; and all that I have to add, are a few observations on some points of difference between Mr. Scheele and myself, with illustrations from some of my late unpublished Experiments.

Mr. Scheele always found that when he exposed fixed Air to iron filings and brimstone, it was almost wholly absorbed by that mixture; whereas, I had found, (Vol. I. p. 41.) that after this process, a considerable proportion of the fixed Air was immiscible with water, though not rendered fit for respiration, as he, by a mistake of my meaning, says.

On this I would observe, that the *fact* was exactly as I represented it; but I now think that I was mistaken with respect to the *cause*. In the trials which I then made with this mixture, whether in water, or in vacuo, no Air of any kind was produced; but I have since found, that by allowing it more time, inflammable Air is yielded by it; though when a considerable quantity of common Air is exposed to it, it is simply phlogisticated by the process, and nothing inflammable is found in it.

In other processes also, in which respirable Air is simply phlogisticated, I have found that when it is made in quicksilver, or water, without any Air, a small quantity of inflammable Air has been produced; so that when inflammable Air is generated very slowly, and has immediate access to a sufficient quantity of respirable Air, it is decomposed as it is formed, the phlogiston incorporating with respirable Air; whereas, if a large quantity of inflammable Air be mixed with common Air, they will continue together a very long time, without much affecting each other.

I was led to these observations, by inquiring into the cause of the seeming conversion of nitrous Air into inflammable Air, mentioned in the last volume of my Experiments. For using less and less nitrous Air, and at last none at all, I found that inflammable Air was continually, though slowly, produced from the iron filings and brimstone; and this Air being in time more in quantity than the nitrous Air, (which itself becomes mere phlogisticated Air by long standing in water) the result of the whole process was a pretty strong inflammable Air.

You have yourself very well observed the difference between the methods in which Mr. Scheele and myself agitated both phlogisticated and inflammable Air in water, in consequence of which we had different results.

The fact of the *purification of respirable Air by vegetation,* which Mr. Scheele denies, has been so fully proved, that I shall only inform you and our readers of what I had observed before the publication of Dr. Ingenhouz's book on that subject. At the time of the publication of my last volume, I had observed that a *green matter,* which I then supposed to have been deposited by the water, yielded a great quantity of very pure Air when exposed to *light,* but that mere *warmth* had no such effect upon it. I at first suspected this green matter to be a plant, but not being able to discover anything like the *form* of a plant by a microscope, I continued to call it simply green matter. Several of my friends, however, who were better skilled in botany, never entertained any doubt of its being a plant; and presently after the publication of that volume, I had myself the clearest proof, that though I could not discover the lineaments of a plant, it *must* necessarily be a vegetable substance. Immediately upon this, I tried other plants that grow wholly in water, and found that all of them, without exception, produced the same effect, yielding, when placed in the light, and especially in that of the sun, a certain quantity of the purest Air. This process, however, as in that of the green matter, always had its *limits,* never exceeding one tenth, or at the most one eighth of the capacity of the vessel in which it was made.

The quantity of Air thus produced, bearing a certain proportion to the quantity of water, I was satisfied it must be the water, or something contained in the water, that furnished the materials for this pure Air; and this I ascertained by changing the water after the production of Air had ceased. For the moment that the same plants, which now yielded no Air at all, even in the sun, were put into a quantity of *fresh water* of the same kind, they immediately yielded Air as briskly and in as great a quantity as before; but after this, the production of Air stopped 'till the water was changed again.

That it was the Air contained in the water, and not the *water itself* that furnished the materials for this pure Air, I found by examining the Air contained in the water before and after this process. For expelling Air by heat from the water which had not been used in this manner, I found it to be either of the standard of common Air, or something below it; but when this water had been used in this manner, that is, when it had been exposed to the action of the plants and of the sun, it yielded the purest Air; this being still retained in the water after a considerable quantity more than could be contained in it had been disengaged from it, and lodged on its surface. This pure Air also contained in the water was in much greater *quantity* than the impure Air contained in it before. For as pure Air is diminished whenever it is phlogisticated, so, on the contrary, the quantity is encreased when it is dephlogisticated.

The action of these plants therefore being to dephlogisticate the Air contained in water in which they grow, I immediately concluded, that *all plants,* growing in water, or out of water, must purify the Air to which they have access, whenever they are placed in a sufficiently strong light, and therefore that there could be no room to entertain any doubt with respect to my first observations on this subject, though at that time I was ignorant how much *light* had to do in the business.

I also found that some plants growing in Air, produced this

effect in a small degree when they were put into water, though this not being their natural element, they could not bear it long; but I did not suspect that *leaves alone* would retain so much life as to produce this effect, when separated from the plants, until I saw Dr. Ingenhouz's book, which abundantly proves it, and which I had a great pleasure in perusing, notwithstanding some mistakes he has been led into, and which I know I shall give him pleasure in rectifying in my next publication on this subject. Some of them I mentioned to him in person afterwards.

You have, I perceive, adopted the opinion, that phlogiston converts atmospherical Air into fixed Air, in which I cannot say that I am at present disposed to agree with you. I have, indeed, been inclined to think that fixed Air may be a factitious substance, and have described some processes in which I thought I procured it in considerable quantities from materials which had not been supposed to contain it; and thence I was led to suspect that the appearance of it, even in the phlogistication of common Air *might* be occasioned by a real production of it, though I had no conjecture concerning the immediate cause of that production. But, upon the whole, I am inclined to think that all the fixed Air that is discovered in this case, is nothing more than that which is naturally contained in, and incorporated with, the atmospherical Air; and therefore that it is merely *precipitated* by the phlogistication of that Air.

I think that if phlogiston be capable of converting any *part* of a mass of Air into fixed Air, it might make the same change in the *whole* of it, which is never the case; and no more fixed Air is produced in phlogistic processes than the common Air may be supposed to contain. That it does contain *some* seems to be evident from the precipitation of lime in lime-water, simply exposed to the common Air. I was engaged in a course of Experiments, which I think calculated to decide this question, when my late tedious illness, and the change of my situation, with the consequent interruption of all my Experiments for almost the whole of this summer, prevented the completion of them.

Mr. Scheele explains the phenomenon of *fulminating gold,* by supposing a generation of Air, to which he gives the properties of phlogisticated Air. Now, whenever I have thought upon the subject, since the discovery of *alkaline Air,* I have had no doubt but that the explosion of that substance must be occasioned by the suddenly setting loose a quantity of that kind of Air; and because a much greater quantity of this Air may be contained in many substances than of fixed Air; and also because the whole of it may perhaps be restored to its elastic state more nearly at the same time, this explosion is greater than that which is made by the *pulvis fulminans,* or any other composition into which merely fixed Air enters. The same solution has likewise occurred to other persons since the discovery of alkaline Air; and I even fully intended to have mentioned this solution in two of my last publications on the subject of Air, but it escaped my memory at the time.

Your partiality to me is too apparent in the course of your Notes; however, I am truly sensible of the value of that *friendship* from which the partiality proceeds. . . .

London, Aug. 1780.

No. 89.

FROM PRIESTLEY TO WILLIAM HERSCHEL

August 12, 1780

Dear Sir,

I do not keep up a regular correspondence with Mr Michell, but if you will be so good as to send me an account of the *construction* and *effects* of the telescopes you have made, and what farther views you have in the same way, I will not fail to take an early opportunity of writing to him to procure an account of what *he* is doing, and when I have his answer, shall lose no time in transmitting it to you. . . .

[This is the end of the letter, as it appears in the extract published by J. L. E. Dreyer. Dreyer further comments that "there are no other letters from him [Priestley] to Herschel in existence." Constance A. Lubbock in *The Herschel Chronicle* (Cambridge, The University Press, 1933), p. 91, publishes an extract of a letter from John Michell, dated 21 January 1781, which she identifies as his reply to the information transmitted to him by Priestley. Dreyer instead identifies it as a letter from Michell to Sir William Watson.]

This set of correspondence provides a fairly complete catalogue of Priestley's scientific researches of the period. The work on nitrous acid air (nitrogen dioxide) is not mentioned, and that on dephlogisticated nitrous air (nitrous oxide) only as it supports combustion, but the remainder of the major chemical investigations — on alkaline air (ammonia), vitriolic acid air (sulphur dioxide), dephlogisticated air (oxygen), fluor acid air (silicon fluoride), the uses of blood in respiration, and the late studies in photosynthesis — all make their appearance in the course of events. Unfortunately, the letters are, for the most part, neither timely nor substantively informative.

For example, Priestley's most notable discovery of this period, and of his career, was of that air "near six times as good as common air" (No. 63) which he was to call dephlogisticated air and Lavoisier was to transform into oxygen. But the letter here presented dates from two weeks after those to Pringle and Price, which were published in the *Philosophical Transactions* paper which publicly announced the discovery, and it fails to reveal nearly as much about the discovery as that paper or the later account in volume two of his *Experiments and Observations*.[3] Indeed, though he had actually obtained the new air by heating nitre sometime in 1771 (see Nos. 53, 54) and again, still without realizing it, by heating *mercurius calcinatus per se* in August 1774, the correspondence so far uncovered, including the extract of that letter to Thomas Henry (No. 67), merely confirms that he failed to

---

[3] Priestley, "An Account of further Observations on Air," *Philosophical Transactions*, 65 (1775), 384–394; *Experiments and Observations on Different Kinds of Air* (London, 1775), vol. 2, sections III-V.

recognize that he had found anything new in this connection prior to the spring of 1775.

The extended series on photosynthesis is somewhat more informative. From the time he first noticed the phenomenon in the summer of 1771, Priestley had chipped away at the problem of reconciling apparent anomalies in the production of air by plants. Here we see some of the experiments, beginning with the summer of 1778, by which Priestley reached the limits of his understanding of the process. Even here, however, the new material is primarily significant for its support of Priestley's claim that he had recognized the vital agency of light prior to reading IngenHousz's *Experiments on Vegetables* (Nos. 82, 83).

These two examples illustrate the form and essential substance of the letters, so far as the scholarly record is concerned. They comprise an independent calendar of experiments against which the published accounts may be verified and, in some few instances, made more precise, and they suggest how widely one must assume Priestley's experiments were known prior to their publication. Not only was he unwilling to postpone publishing until he could provide a final rationalization of his experiments, he also deliberately set about to circumvent the inevitable delays in publication of the undigested parts (see, for example, Nos. 78, 81). This correspondence shows Priestley as a member of an international community of scientists who visited or wrote to one another, communicating news of their researches even during wartime. Anyone in contact with, or part of, this community, may reasonably be expected to know something of Priestley's work before the volumes in which it was described could be published and distributed.

The historian, however, must analyze experiments as well as calendar them and trace their line of descent. Priestley's caution to his friend Rotheram (No. 60) on the difference between reading and seeing, and still more Keir's evident inability to reproduce the experiments on mercuric oxide (Nos. 75, 77) and Scheele's failure to find that plants "purify" air (No. 88) do more than emphasize Priestley's skill as an experimenter and observer: they also illustrate again that experiments are harder to perform and interpret for the first time than they are after being assimilated into the canon of accepted science. It is mock historical humility to repeat this, however, and yet to continue to accept or reject Priestley's experiments depending upon whether they can be "reproduced" under modern controlled laboratory conditions, while it evades the real problems of analysis and merely conceals the anachronisms to justify rejections on such simplistic grounds as Priestley's failure to do quantitative work or his acceptance of the "theory" of phlogiston. Indeed, Priestley's reference (No. 77) to his having proved that inflammable air and nitrous air contain "in equal bulks, equal quantities of phlogiston" at once invalidates both these explanations.

There is no doubt that Priestley seldom took quantitative results seriously. This has been mentioned earlier in connection with the electrical researches and goes hand-in-hand with his innocence of mathematics again revealed in this correspondence (No. 63). But Priestley's volumetric observations are uniformly good, and this one, like those praised by William Henry on the amounts of alkaline air "saturated" by different acid airs, could have led a differently thinking man to Gay-Lussac's law of combining volumes.[4] The reference also shows some of the quantitative possibilities of phlogiston and, along with the work on the use of the blood (Nos. 68, 69), reveals something of the flexibility and explanatory powers of that derided concept. The phlogistic interpretation of respiration is, in many ways, the logical and

---

[4] William Henry, "An Estimate of . . . Dr. Priestley" (p. 66), cited by Partington in *A History of Chemistry*, vol. 3, pp. 267–268. One must note, however, that these results as published by Priestley did not lead his contemporary "quantitative–thinkers" to this law.

"mathematical" equivalent of Lavoisier's oxidation interpretation and, in any event, was a necessary preliminary to it.

When a scientist of Priestley's character and ability reports
his observations, one must accept them and, when these
"could not have been so," by tracing the prior circumstances
of laboratory or hypothesis, find explanation for anomaly.
Frequently, the first stages of this kind of historical analysis
are fairly easy. After reading Priestley's comment to Bentham
(No. 61) that procuring nitrous air "very pure . . . is not
worth attending to," his observation of "a different kind of
salt" generated by the mixing of alkaline and nitrous airs
(No. 57) can be explained, for ammonium nitrate will be
formed in these circumstances, in the presence of the common
air that one must assume was mixed with either (or both) of
his presumed constituents. The statement to Bentham, however, was justified on the grounds that most of the tests made
with nitrous air were comparative ones. Though reagent impurity may explain the continually varying results of Priestley's eudiometry, it is not sufficient to justify our ignoring all
these results. The air obtained by heating sea water (No. 77),
for example, *is* better than common air.

Now it is not particularly surprising that Priestley's reagents
should be impure nor, being unaware of what his results
"should be," that he frequently failed to recognize that they
were so. It is, however, very revealing of Priestley's attitude
toward chemistry that he seems never to have concerned
himself with the transference of impurities from one of his
processes to another. No suspicion appears to dampen Priestley's confidence (Nos. 68, 69) that metals dissolved in nitric
acid could produce fixed air (CO_2), "proving" the latter to
be a "modification of the nitrous acid," though the more extended discussion of these experiments show the many avenues
by which carbon impurities had entered his samples.[5] A

[5] Priestley, *Experiments and Observations on . . . Air* (London, 1777),
vol. 3, pp. 10–16.

similar explanation may serve for the experiments which supported his conviction (No. 65) that fluor acid air was a modification of the vitriolic acid "volatilized by the phlogiston it contains." It is hard indeed to determine what he can have been doing, but it seems possible that the vitriolic acid air (SO_2) found in his experiments was obtained in some way from the residual calcium sulphate which was produced along with the fluor acid air from calcium fluoride and sulphuric acid, or from an excess of the sulphuric acid itself.[6] A more extreme example, and indeed one whose influences are practically impossible to trace, is that revealed in his paper, "On the noxious Quality of the Effluvia of putrid Marshes":

Happening to use at Calne, a much larger trough of water . . . than I had done at Leeds, and not having fresh water so near at hand . . . I neglected to change it, till it turned black and became offensive, but by no means to such a degree as to deter me from making use of it.[7]

From the pneumatic trough in this condition, Priestley collected bubbles of noxious gases which spontaneously rose to its surface and found that common air agitated in the water or even in contact with it was rendered unfit for combustion. One would like to know which of his experiments previously performed at Calne were also rendered unfit by the use of the trough in this state and, still more, one would like to hope that later experiments were never performed under similar circumstances.

It is an easy conclusion, and one that many persons have reached from instances such as these, that Priestley was simply not a good chemist. This view, moreover, has the strong support of Priestley himself, as is seen in this correspondence,

---

[6] Priestley, *Experiments and Observations on . . . Air* (London, 1775), vol. 2, p. 207.

[7] *Philosophical Transactions*, 64 (1774), 91–92.

from his disdainful remark, "I have made many other new observations, but they are chiefly of a chymical nature, and not worth making the subject of a letter" (No. 85), from the ambiguity of his comment, "The *facts* appear to me to be rather extraordinary. You must help me to explain them, for I am a very bad theorist," (No. 81) and from his flat disclaimer, "My knowledge of chymistry is very imperfect" (No. 86).

The difficulty is that no one really knows what a good chemist was, in the eighteenth-century sense, apart from the chemical discoveries he might make, and on this scale Priestley would receive a high rating. On 30 November 1773, he received the Copley Medal of the Royal Society for his experimental researches on airs, and, if the address of Sir John Pringle upon making the presentation dwells rather more than we can appreciate on the invention of artificially carbonated water, still there is no doubt that all Priestley's work was recognized and that the award was richly deserved.[8] This event was followed by seven more years of fruitful research, and, though he was already being replaced as the leader of pneumatic chemistry, it is only in retrospect of the revolution won by Lavoisier's new-model chemistry that it becomes clear that Priestley was not only not a *good* chemist, but may not have been a chemist at all.

Even then it is not sufficient to say that Priestley was ignorant of the chemistry of his day. His acquaintance with chemical literature was surely as extensive as might be expected of him, his personal acquaintance and correspondence with contemporary chemists was wide, and his failure to apply the information and discoveries of others is no more remarkable than his failure to transfer his own discoveries from one set of experiments to another.[9] Two comments by Priestley

[8] Pringle, *A Discourse on the Different Kinds of Air, op. cit.*

[9] Regarding Priestley's acquaintance with chemical literature, see Schofield, "The Scientific Background of Joseph Priestley," *op. cit.*, pp. 148–163.

are revealing in this connection. In a letter of 13 April 1777 to Newcome Cappe, he writes:

My manner has always been to give my whole attention to a subject till I have satisfied myself with respect to it, and then think no more about the matter. I hardly ever look into anything that I have published, and when I do, it sometimes appears quite new to me.

And in his *Memoirs,* he writes:

As I have not failed to attend to the phenomena of my own mind, as well as to those of other parts of nature, I have not been insensible of some great defects, as well as some advantages, attending its constitution; having from an early period been subject to a most humbling failure of recollection, so that I have sometimes lost all ideas of both persons and things, that I have been conversant with. I have so completely forgotten what I have myself published, that in reading my own writings, what I find in them often appears perfectly new to me, and I have more than once made experiments, the results of which had been published by me.[10]

If to this failure to retain knowledge of his previous studies is added his practice of using all books merely as references for the specific materials of immediate use to him, it is easy to see how Priestley can have known of the literature and remained unaware of its relevance to his own work. Nonetheless, however extensive his acquaintance with contemporary chemistry, the failure to recognize that this was continually relevant to his work does suggest that he did not think of that work as chemistry.

More important still, though as yet less clearly defined in the context of the time, is Priestley's apparent failure to under-

[10] From Priestley to Newcome Cappe, 13 April 1777; Burndy Library, Norwalk, Connecticut. Priestley, *Memoirs,* pp. 105–106.

stand the basic nature of chemical operations. The great eighteenth-century Swedish chemist, Carl W. Scheele, was to say, "The object and chief business of chemistry [is] skilfully to separate substances into their constituents, to discover their properties, and to compound them in different ways."[11] Now this was easier to state than to practice before the precise definition of a chemical element distinguished the processes of separation and composition. It was the chief accomplishment of Lavoisier's "Chemical Revolution," as ratified by John Dalton, that mass became the parameter by which ultimate chemical simplicity could be determined. One of Priestley's most persistent errors was his failure to think in terms of composition and decomposition, for his fundamental problem was one of attitude. Never does he seem to have appreciated the long-range significance of gravimetric determinations in his work.[12] Rarely in discussing his experiments does he use the verbs "compound," "combine," "decompose," "break down." In these letters, as in his books and published papers, he extracts air from substances (No. 65), his operations do not form gases, they "release" them from materials in which they are "contained" (No. 64). Even his plants in photosynthesis do not transform one gas into another; air exists in the green matter in a concentrated state from which light acts to disengage it (No. 81). Materials are modified and restored rather than created and destroyed. It is in this, rather than in a presumed ignorance of contemporary chemical literature, failure to do quantitative experiments, or acceptance of phlogiston, that the real criticism of Priestley as a chemist must lie.

[11] Quoted by Abraham Wolf, *A History of Science, Technology and Philosophy in the 18th Century* (London, [1952]), revised ed., ed. Douglas McKie, p. 358.

[12] For a discussion of this problem and some possible reasons for it, see Schofield, "Joseph Priestley, The Theory of Oxidation and the Nature of Matter," pp. 291–294.

But if Priestley was not a chemist, what was he? Though a complete identification would require more information on eighteenth-century theories of matter than we now possess, it is sufficient to describe him as a natural philosopher in that English mechanistic tradition, including the work of Boyle, Newton, John Keill, John Freind, and Stephen Hales, for which all natural phenomena must ultimately be explained by the primitive particles, their motions, and the forces between them. Priestley's fondness for Boscovichian atomism is consistent with that tradition, and so also are his predilection for physical process and his conviction mentioned in an earlier chapter and derived, he tells us, from Newton, that electricity, optics, and chemistry were related means for exploring the nature of matter.[13]

Throughout this period he continued to correspond on electricity, and his books describe chemico-electrical experiments, though he early implied to Volta that he had given up original electrical investigation (No. 59). The selling, in 1774, of the telescope he had purchased seven years earlier when he began the study of optics (No. 14) suggests that that subject at least was being abandoned. By 1777, however, he was collaborating with John Warltire in an attempt to measure the refractive indices of gases; in 1780 he agreed to get some optical information for William Herschel; and the inventory of his laboratory equipment destroyed in the Birmingham Riots lists five telescopes, including a refractor with a fourteen-foot focus.[14] Rather than dropping subjects to concentrate on chemistry, Priestley appears to have added them and, consistent with the mechanistic tradition in which we have placed him, his experiments on sound (No. 82) and his interest

[13] See chapter 2, *supra,* footnote 6.
[14] Priestley, *Experiments and Observations on Air* (London, 1777), vol. 3, pp. 365–368; Douglas McKie, "Priestley's Laboratory and Library and other of his Effects," *Notes and Records of the Royal Society of London,* 12 (1956), 119.

in heating by compression (No. 87) constitute further examples of his physical approach to the chemistry of gases.

Still more obviously in line with that tradition (which also includes John Locke) is Priestley's work in psychology and metaphysics. Disagreeing with the "Scottish common-sense philosophers," Reid, Beattie, and Oswald, he wrote a treatise criticizing their views and then prepared an edition of David Hartley's mechanistic, associationist *Theory of the Human Mind* (Nos. 60, 63). Unfortunately, those "many observations on human nature, with a view to the illustration of Hartley's theory," which he began to collect at this time (No. 64) and which in the course of time extended to several volumes, were destroyed in the riots of 1791.[15] From psychology he went on to develop the extreme mechanistic metaphysics, extending from matter to the soul, described in his *Disquisitions relating to Matter and Spirit* (London, 1777; No. 74). The physical arguments in that work were based on the *Theoria Philosophiae* of the Abbé Roger Joseph Boscovich, much to the Abbé's dismay (Nos. 79, 80).

Boscovich was not the only person to raise strong objection. So violent was the reaction to this work, particularly toward what were regarded as its atheistical tendencies, that its publication has been regarded as the cause of Shelburne's dismissal of Priestley from his service.[16] Whatever the reasons, the period which had begun so well for Priestley threatened to end in illness and uncertainty. Nevertheless, a solution was found, one which, in many ways, was superior to what he had lost. The position of this provincial, dissenting minister in

---

[15] Priestley: *An Examination of Dr. Reid's Inquiry . . . Dr. Beattie's Essay . . . and Dr. Oswald's Appeal . . .* (London, 1774); *Hartley's Theory of the Human Mind* (London, 1775); *An Appeal to the Public on the Subject of the Riots in Birmingham* (Birmingham, 1791), p. 38.

[16] Since this occurred some three years later, the interpretation is open to some question. Shelburne remarried the year before Priestley was dismissed, and it has also been conjectured that the second Lady Shelburne brought about the separation of the two men.

a noble household had always had its incongruities. Priestley later wrote: "I used to make no scruple of maintaining, that there is not only most virtue, and most happiness, but even most true politeness in the middle classes of life."[17] Such sentiments, if expressed to his patron's family and guests, must have made him seem alien. Now, with the help of his friends, he was to find a home again in those middle classes. Throughout this period his associations with Birmingham had steadily increased. By 1780 he was acquainted, either directly or through correspondence, with Matthew Boulton (Nos. 65, 66, 75, 76), James Keir (No. 77), William Withering, and the Rev. Radcliffe Scholefield (No. 84), the minister of one of the prominent dissenting meetinghouses of that city. Given any freedom of choice, it is not surprising that he should have settled there, and the opportunity of resuming his calling as a minister sealed his happiness with the decision. By the end of 1780, he could view the future with confidence and look to a resumption of his science, "on a larger field of experiments than ever," in a "situation . . . in all respects, a very agreeable one."[18]

[17] Priestley, *Memoirs*, pp. 82–83.
[18] From Priestley to Benjamin Franklin, 21 December 1780; American Philosophical Society, Philadelphia.

CHAPTER FIVE

On the Defensive
Birmingham and London
1781-1794

THE FIRST NINE YEARS of this period were probably the most personally satisfying of Priestley's career. Living again in the Midlands, in which he had his roots, he was part of the most brilliant of provincial intellectual gatherings, the Lunar Society of Birmingham, from which he could draw advice and assistance as well as admiration. Secured a comfortable living by the generosity of individual patrons and the pension paid him by Lord Shelburne, he could have had ample leisure for scientific study. Instead, he chose to devote a major part of his time to other activities. He had scarcely moved to Birmingham before he was invited to become one of the two ministers to the dissenting congregation at the New Meeting-house. This was one of the most theologically liberal congregations of England, and the terms of their invitation allowed Priestley to do virtually as much or as little as he chose. Naturally, he accepted the invitation, and once again he happily occupied himself in what he regarded as the most worthy position a man could hold.

Not surprisingly, this is also the period of his most extensive theological writing and controversy. Within two years of his settling in Birmingham Priestley published a two-volume *History of the Corruptions of Christianity* (Birmingham, 1782), which promptly involved him in an interminable paper war with theological orthodoxy leading to an annual volume of *Defences of Unitarianism*. Out of the same controversy came his four-volume *History of Early Opinions Concerning Jesus Christ* (Birmingham, 1786) and the first two volumes of his *General History of the Christian Church* (Birmingham, 1790). And, to the time and labor needed for the more than twelve volumes for these studies and for their attendant controversies, must be added that spent on writing numerous pamphlets and published sermons and on the editorial labors associated with the revival of his controversial periodical, *The Theological Repository* (Birmingham, 1784, 1786, and 1788).

The apparent security of these years in Birmingham was ended abruptly in 1791, when Priestley's militant dissent and his support of the French after their revolution combined the forces of orthodoxy and reaction against him. Three pamphlets — *A Letter to the Right Honourable William Pitt* (Birmingham, 1787), *Familiar Letters, Addressed to the Inhabitants of Birmingham* (Birmingham, 1790), and *Letters to the Right Honourable Edmund Burke* (Birmingham, 1791) — attest to the increasing acerbation of relations between establishment and dissent brought on by attempted repeal of the Test and Corporation Acts and by the French Revolution. The ultimate result was the Birmingham Church-and-King Riots of July 1791, which ended Priestley's residence in Birmingham and finally led to his self-imposed exile to the United States in 1794.

It is against this background of theological activity and controversy, of political struggle and ultimate violence, that Priestley's scientific work of this period, described briefly in

[199]

the *Memoirs* and more completely in the correspondence, must be viewed.

. . . I consider my settlement at Birmingham as the happiest event in my life being highly favorable to every object I had in view, philosophical or theological. In the former respect I had the convenience of good workmen of every kind, and the society of persons eminent for their knowledge of chemistry, particularly Mr. Watt, Mr. Keir, and Dr. Withering. These with Mr. Boulton, and Dr. Darwin, who soon left us by removing from Litchfield to Derby, Mr. Galton, and afterwards Mr. Johnson of Kenelworth and myself dined together every month, calling ourselves the *lunar society,* because the time of our meeting was near the full moon. . . . Here I have never long intermitted my philosophical pursuits, and I have published two volumes of experiments, besides communications to the Royal Society.

[The above part of the *Memoirs* was written *c.* 1787 and ends in that year. The *Memoirs* were continued down to 1795 by Priestley, and then until his death by Joseph Priestley, Jr.]

To resume the account of my pursuits where the former part of the Memoirs left it, I must observe that, in the prosecution of my *experiments,* I was led to maintain the doctrine of phlogiston against Mr. Lavoisier and other chemists in France, whose opinions were adopted not only by almost all the philosophers of that country, but by those in England and Scotland also. My friends, however, of the lunar society were never satisfied with the Antiphlogistic doctrine. My experiments and observations on this subject were published in various papers in the Philosophical Transactions. At Birmingham I also published a new edition of my publications on the subject of *air,* and others connected with it, reducing the six volumes to three, which, with his consent, I dedicated to the prince of Wales. . . .

On occasion of the celebration of the anniversary of the French revolution on July 14th, 1791, by several of my friends, but with which I had little to do, a mob encouraged by some persons in power, first burned the meeting house in which I preached, then another meeting house in the town, and then my dwelling house, demolishing my library, apparatus, and, as far as they could, every thing belonging to me. . . . Being in some personal danger on this occasion I went to London . . . it shewed . . . [courage] in Dr. Price's congregation, at Hackney, to invite me to succeed him, which they did . . . some time after my arrival in London. . . .

On the whole, I spent my time even more happily at Hackney than ever I had done before; having every advantage for my philosophical and theological studies, in some respect superior to what I had enjoyed at Birmingham. . . . I found, however, my society much restricted with respect to my philosophical acquaintance; most of the members of the Royal Society shunning me on account of my religious or political opinions, so that I at length withdrew myself from them, and gave my reasons for so doing in the Preface to my *Observations and Experiments on the generation of air from Water,* which I published at Hackney. For, with the assistance of my friends, I had in a great measure replaced my Apparatus, and had resumed my experiments, though after the loss of near two years.

Living in the neighbourhood of the New College, I voluntarily undertook to deliver the lectures to the pupils on the subject of *History and General policy,* which I had composed at Warrington, and also on *Experimental Philosophy and Chemistry,* the *Heads* of which I drew up for this purpose, and afterwards published. . . .

The bigotry of the country in general made it impossible for me to place my sons in it to any advantage. . . . My own situation, if not hazardous, was become unpleasant, so that I thought my removal would be of more service to the cause of truth than my longer stay in England. At length, therefore, with the approbation of all my friends, without exception, but with great reluctance, I came to that resolution [to leave England and settle in the United States][1]. . . .

Priestley was mistaken. His situation at Hackney was not superior in any respect to what he had known at Birmingham so far as "philosophical" studies were concerned, nor, in spite

[1] Priestley, *Memoirs,* pp. 97–98, 115, 118–122, 127.

of appearances, was the settlement in Birmingham as favorable to scientific work as he thought. Now, it is not surprising that his science should suffer by the forced removal from Birmingham. The suspension of his research, his need for reestablishing his laboratory, and the lack of sympathetic associates could not but combine to reduce the amount and significance of his work between July 1791 and 1794. During this period he published only the thirty-nine-page pamphlet, *Experiments on the Generation of Air from Water* (London, J. Johnson, 1793), of which twenty-two pages were a reprint of an earlier paper in the *Philosophical Transactions* of 1791, and the *Heads of Lectures on a Course of Experimental Philosophy, particularly including Chemistry* (London, 1794), which gives some over-all view of his attitudes toward science but contains no original research.

Yet even during the Birmingham years his science had fallen, both in quantity and quality, from its previous level. Of the two volumes of experiments Priestley mentions publishing during the Birmingham period, the first was essentially completed during his stay with Lord Shelburne, while more than a quarter of the second volume consists of republications of the *Philosophical Transactions* papers he delivered in 1783 and 1785. Moreover, the papers read to the Society in 1788, 1789, 1790, and 1791 are merely variations on the same themes, repeated with increasing stridency to deafening ears. In light of his multitudinous interests in earlier years, his preoccupation now with other activities provides only a partial explanation for this decline.

It is, of course, unreasonable to expect that Priestley should long have continued creative research at his age. Though his scientific career had been late in blooming, he was forty-eight by the time he was established in Birmingham, and important original research in the physical sciences by a man in his forties is a rare event. More important than his age, however, was the change in the tenor of his scientific activities. Very early in this period Priestley was put on the defensive by Lavoisier's new interpretation of the entire field of chemistry. The following letters, even more than his published writings, show how little Priestley was aware of the fundamental changes which had taken place, as he continues to defend old concepts with the irrelevancies of new experiments.

No. 90.

FROM PRIESTLEY TO JOSIAH WEDGWOOD

Birm. 26 May, 1781.

Dear Sir

I must take the liberty to give you this trouble about the *earthen retorts* you were so good as to promise me, and of which I am in great want. I am analyzing various earthy substances, especially to ascertain the pabulum of subterraneous fires, and have already made several experiments which throw great light upon the subject.

The common *blue slate* yields an amazing quantity of air, and is then a black glassy substance. A *sandstone* also that I find here yields air in considerable plenty, but it is just now in a white heat, and I cannot tell what the residuum will be.

I have also made some other experiments of considerable consequence since my return from London, especially some that I think are decisively in favor of my theory of respiration, against a series of papers by Mr Lavoisier in the last volume of Parisian Memoires; but having hurt my hand, I write with difficulty. You will therefore [excuse] my adding nothing more at present. . . .

P.S.   If there be any earthy substance that you wish me to examine in my way, especially such as you may suspect to be found in places where volcanoes abound, and that have not been exposed to heat already, I shall be much obliged to you if you will send specimens of them, along with the retorts.

The retort in which I heated the blue slate cracked before the experiment was over.

No. 91.

FROM PRIESTLEY TO JOSIAH WEDGWOOD

Birm. August 8th, 1781.

Dear Sir

I have been favoured with your obliging letter and also *two boxes* of retorts, &c., which came to hand only on Saturday last. The cover of the larger box was quite off, and ten of the retorts broke, most of them so as to be of no use at all. They were sent late at night, and I had paid the carriage (4 sh.) before I was aware of the accident. I suppose there is no remedy in the case. Mr Boulton says *you* will be more likely to get it than *I*. I shall, however, speak to the book-keeper here.

I do not know how to desire a reparation of the loss, but indeed I shall soon want them much. I have used two that were whole and find them very good, and yet those of the porcelain kind are more compact and better for some purposes.

Your specimens were very acceptable. The *basalte* is precisely the same thing with our *Rowley rag*. I had some from London as well as yours. The *lava* from Vesuvius gave a good deal of air, but before the process was over, the retort cracked. The remainder of the specimen I put into a retort I particularly valued, it having sustained the greatest heat I can give it three times before; but it cracked presently this time, an accident I lament much. It was peculiar to both these experiments with the lava, that I found the retort when cold broke into many pieces, as if by the expansion of the matter in cooling. It is a perfectly black glass.

The *toadstone* yields much air and becomes a black glass also. Mr Keir however thinks that even the basaltes may have been in fusion, and that, tho' a perfect glass at first, it might become the substance it now is by *length of time*. What think you of this? I mean to try what a heat of a week or two will do. Are your fires at all convenient for an experiment of this kind?

If you could favour me with another piece of the same kind of *lava,* I should value it much. It resembles a *stone,* and not a *cinder.* The latter do not so well answer my purpose.

The *granate* gives a good deal of air, and at the last pretty pure; as also was the last from the lava; for the retort, by some means or other, closing before the process was over, I got both the first and the last produced. I think a great deal would have been given. . . .

P.S. — Please to direct the next parcel to Wm. Russel, Esq., with (P) under the name. It will come readier and cheaper. I do so with all my parcels from London. I hope you have used the *furnace*.

No. 92.

FROM PRIESTLEY TO JOSIAH WEDGWOOD

Birm. 6th March, 1782.

Dear Sir

Having made an experiment which I think will give you pleasure, I take the first opportunity of acquainting you with it.

I throw the focus of a burning lens on some *calx of lead* (out of which all air has been expelled) when confined in *inflammable air*. The air is rapidly absorbed, lead is formed, and what remains of the air is as inflammable as before. This simple experiment seems to prove, that what we have called *phlogiston* is the same thing with *inflammable air in a state of combination with other bodies,* just as fixed air is contained in chalk. From 40–ounce measures of air I received about 5 dwts. of lead. The inflammable air was got from iron by oil of vitriol.

I have made a similar experiment with charcoal, proving that common air becomes phlogisticated by a combination of inflammable air with it. And I have also succeeded in making *nitrous air* from *nitrous acid and inflammable air*. I am pursuing the experiment farther, as I have opportunity; but I want sunshine, and for that I must wait.

I am ashamed to be so troublesome, but another cargo of the *smallest sized retorts* No. 5 would be very acceptable and useful to me, as also the vessels you make of the same materials with your *mortars* that you supplied Mr Boulton with. I should like mine to be 12 inches high and about 1½ inches or 2 inches in the inside. They are to stand in a sand heat. Pray would they bear a red heat? If they would, they would be excellent for many purposes. I want much something that will hold alkalis in fusion; but am afraid no such thing can be got.

I expect to be in London in about a month, and should be happy to meet you then.

No. 93.

FROM PRIESTLEY TO JOSIAH WEDGWOOD

Birm. 21 March, 1782

Dear Sir

I have received your obliging letter containing your generous contribution, and that of Dr Darwin, to the expences of my experiments. Whatever be my *success,* with such assistance I should be much to blame if my *zeal* and *assiduity* should be wanting.

Since my last I have found that *alkaline air* [reduces] the calx of lead with as much ease as *inflammable air,* and I think in greater quantity. This you will think a very extraordinary fact; but it agrees with several of my former experiments, and throws great light upon them, and other things in the theory of chemistry; especially my converting alkaline air into inflammable air by the electric spark, the production of volatile alkali from iron superphlogisticated, and the affinity of all acids both with alkalis and phlogiston, which appear to be modifications of each other. However, when the calx has absorbed all the alkaline air that it can, there is a large residuum of phlogisticated air, whereas what remains of the inflammable air is unchanged; which seems to prove that the inflammable air is the more simple principle of the two.

Other remarkable facts have occurred in the course of these experiments; but as I want *sunshine* to ascertain them, I shall not trouble you with the mention of them at present.

I thank you for the communication of Dr Darwin's note, and shall write him on the subject.

Before my late experiments phlogiston was indeed almost given up by the Lunar Society, but now it seems to be reestablished. Mr Kirwan, in a letter I have received from him this day, says that he has given in a paper to the R. Society, to prove, from my former experiments, that phlogiston must be the same thing with inflammable air, and also that dephlogisticated air and phlogiston make fixed air. This last I much doubt. . . .

P.S. I thank you for the retorts, which I hear are arrived. Mr Boulton had mentioned to me your curious and valuable thermometer. It will be very useful to me, and many other persons.

No. 94.

From Priestley to Samuel Vaughan, Jr.

London 17 Apl. 1782

Dear Sir

Yesterday I received both your letters, of the 11 & 13 Inst, and am glad to find that your little excursion was so agreeable and instructive to you. I shall think myself obliged to my friends for the civilities they shewed you, and I thank you for your attention in procuring me the *Specimens* you mention.

As your father does not think to send you abroad till he has some more certain prospect, we thought you had better remain at Birmingham till my return (which, if all be well, will be friday sennight) than come hither for the very little advantage you can derive from my being with you here, especially as care will be taken that you shall have the same advantage whenever you come.

When you have finished your excursions you cannot do better than keep on in the way you were before, composing something now and then, reading the *Lectures on History* and proceeding with the *Introduction to Chemistry* &c at the same doing any process that you fancy —— As to *Phosphorus,* you certainly did very right to make Mr Reynolds &c a present of some; and if you like the process, I would have you repeat it; but I think it will be as well to leave it till my return, as I have got a couple of genuine *Hessian retorts* of Mr Godfrey, who imports them for the purpose. He sells his phosphorus for *five pounds an ounce,* and says he has 80 Ounces now by him. He never makes more than 8 or 9 ounces at a time and uses many retorts in the same fire.

I wish you would endeavour to get some *phosphoric acid,* by lay a piece or two of the phosphorus on a glass funnel inserted into a phial, and placed on one of the shelves within the large chimney. It will there burn away slowly, and the acid will descend into the phial. It must be kept very cool, and the sticks will be some weeks in dissolving. I would have you begin in the morning, and look at it now and then, lest it be too warm and take fire.

I have sent a box of [blankets and] [illegible], and have many more things to send down. I wish you would inform Mr Benton, that I have borrowed for him the *books* he wanted but the *Introduction to Chymistry* which you are reading is not to be got at present. Please to get from him a fresh stock of *charcoal* against I come —— I am pretty well tired of this place, and begin to wish I were with you. . . .

No. 95.

FROM PRIESTLEY TO BENJAMIN FRANKLIN

Dear Sir

You have made me very happy by your letter, as I find by it that notwithstanding the unpleasant state of Politicks, your usual humour and pleasantry has not forsaken you. I am only concerned that you have not mentioned the case of my friend Mr Russell, about which I wrote you so particularly. But I have taken the liberty to assure him, that, notwithstanding this omission, I am as confident that you have not neglected the business as if you had given me the most express assurance of it. One line, however, informing me what you think of the case will give me great satisfaction.

Having at length got *sunshine,* I am busy in prosecuting the experiments about which I wrote to you, and shall soon draw up an account of them for the Royal Society.

Please to inform the Duc De Rochefocault, whose civilities to me I remember with pleasure, that my experiments are certainly inconsistent with Mr Lavoisier's supposition, of there being no such thing as *phlogiston,* and that it is the addition of *air,* and not the loss of any thing that converts a metal into a calx. In their usual state calces of metals do contain air, but that may be expelled by heat; and after this I reduce them to a perfect metallic state by nothing but inflammable air, which they imbibe *in toto,* without any decomposition. I lately reduced 101 Ounce measures of this air to *two* by calx of lead, and that small remainder was still inflammable.

I explain Mr Lavoisier's experiments by supposing that *precipitate per se* contains all the phlogiston of the metal mercury, but in a different state; but I can shew other calces which also contain more phlogiston than the metals themselves. That mercury in its metallic state, does contain phlogiston, or inflammable air, is evident from the production of nitrous air by the solution of it in spirits of nitre, and I make *nitrous air* from nothing but *nitrous vapor* and *inflammable air,* so that it indisputably consists of those two ingredients.

I have already ascertained the proportion of inflammable air that enters into the composition of *lead, tin, copper,* and *silver,* and am proceeding to the other metals as fast as I can. When the whole is completed, I shall give you a farther account of it.

I am exceedingly concerned to find that it is so difficult a thing to make *peace;* but I hope that before the campaign be over all parties will have had enough of *war,* and be sensible that they will gain nothing by continuing it. If I had any voice in the business, the prospect of seeing you once more in this country would be a strong additional motive to accelerate the negotiations. . . .

Birmingham 24 June 1782.

P.S. If you should think it proper, I have no objection to your sending a Copy of my former letter to *Rosier's Journal,* as a general outline of what I am doing. I wish to have every new fact to be as speedily, and as generally known as possible.

No. 96.

FROM PRIESTLEY TO ARTHUR YOUNG

Dear Sir

I am much concerned that, by one accident or other, your obliging letter has lain so long neglected. In return, I can only express
my wishes that any observations of mine may favour your most
valuable pursuits; but I do not see how they can be applied to
practice.

For tho' I have no doubt but that phlogiston is the *essence,* as
we may say, of the food both of plants and animals, they are not
capable of extracting it, except from certain substances, and in
certain circumstances; and phlogiston administered in any other
way infallibly kills both.

If any hint that may hereafter occur to me on this subject shall
appear to me to be likely to turn to any account in your hands,
I shall not fail to communicate them. In the mean time, I shall
be happy to hear the result of the experiments you have begun,
and on any other subject. . . .

Birmingham 1 July 1782

P.S. If you should ever travel this way, I shall be very happy to
see you, and favour your inquiries as much as maybe in my power.

No. 97.

FROM SAMUEL VAUGHAN, JR. TO PRIESTLEY

Wanstead 9 Sepbr. 82

Revd Dr Priestley, Birmingham

We had the pleasure of a letter from John last Saturday, dated
in June, when he was well —— The account he gives is very dis-
couraging both to my Father & self —— 9/ a day Boarding &
£ 25 p.Cent discount for Bills on Europe, will lengthen my stay

in these parts. —— The time however will not be lost, while I have such an object as chemistry; & to make this more than a speculative pursuit, my Father thinks I should procure one of Dr Blacks furnaces. —— I recollect your considering this as useless, to carry to America; however, as there is very little probability of my going before a Peace, than which nothing seems more uncertain; this should imagine is no longer an objection, unless you can point out a better compendium of instruments for the operations by fire than this furnace & its apendajes. —— Mr. Kirwan wishes also to have one —— both which, you would oblige me in requesting Dr Withering to order with particulars as mentioned at the end of this letter.

The Derbyshire papers were finished a forthnight last Wednesday, but as I wished to have Mr Kirwans opinion, I lent them to him. I hope however to forward them in all next week.

I have seen Mr Parkers lens, which I believe was not up when you left London, —— its effects are really astonishing. —— Platina was perfectly melted in 17 Secds; & the clay of Mr Wedgewoods Pyrometer was fluid in I believe a shorter time. —— I saw Asbestus turned to a Glass & different Irons melted in a few seconds. —— A Diamond however, in 18 minutes, was not dissipated as in the Paris experiment. The surface only becoming rough, a crack widening & a few fumes arising. —— Tomorrow I carry many derbyshire substances, particularly Toadstones & clays to try its effects on them. . . .

One furnace for Mr Kirwan, having the opening longer at Top than Dr Priestley's, to put in Retorts with greater ease. —— but if this cannot be, the dimensions must be larger. ——

One furnace for S V —— of the dimension of Dr P's at least, —— with any new improvement, & every necessary utensile. The Expense of Mr K's is presumed about 3 Gs.

No. 98.

FROM PRIESTLEY TO JOSIAH WEDGWOOD

Birm., 16 Sept., 1782

Dear Sir

As you are pleased to interest yourself so much in my philosophical pursuits, I flatter myself it will be agreeable to you to be informed that I have of late been very busy, and very successful.

The late sunshine, of which I hardly lost a single hour, has given me an opportunity of ascertaining beyond all doubt the identity of phlogiston and inflammable air; but I have not succeeded so well as I expected in ascertaining the *quantity* of inflammable air that enters into the composition of all the metals, because the heat of the lens is capable of decomposing iron, and some other metals. Also, though I made *bismuth,* and regulus of *Cobalt* I cannot make *zinc,* or regulus of *arsenic,* or of *antimony,* except in alkaline air. I made *sulphur* readily, by evaporating oil of vitriol to dryness in inflammable air. It incrusts all the sides of the glass vessel in which the experiment is made.

It will perhaps surprise you to be informed, that the heat produced by this lens reduces the whole of charcoal (perfectly made) to inflammable air, without the least particle of fixed air in it. The ashes are so little as not to be discerned.

I have also completely proved that the *electric matter,* is, or *contains,* phlogiston, by taking the electric spark in common air confined in a glass syphon by spirit of salt: for in these circumstances the air is diminished and phlogisticated, though no metal, as before, was contiguous to it. When I use oil of vitriol or spirit of nitre, in this manner, I get an additional quantity of air, and this is all dephlogisticated air, being produced from the pure acids faster than the electric matter can injure it. I never could procure this air, except when the acids were previously combined with some earthy base. It seems therefore to prove that *pure air* is *pure acid* in another form, perhaps with the addition of latent heat. When I use the phosphoric acid, the common air is first phlogisticated, and then is increased by an addition of inflammable air. I shall pursue these experiments much farther.

I have been measuring heats in this town by your excellent method. My usual white heats, I find have been 136, that of the heat when cast iron nails are made is 139, and the greatest we can ever raise on purpose [being] 142. Twice the clay and case were both melted and reduced to one shapeless mass; but we could not do it again, and therefore imputed it to something it came in contact with in the fire. I have yet to try the heat used in casting steel. I wish much to know how you ever reached 160. I am told that your clay melts in the focus of Mr Parker's lens; and that for such heats as that *magnesia* will probably do better. I cannot melt the smallest bit of your clay with my lens.

I have much enlarged my apparatus, and should be particularly happy to show you my laboratory in its present state. . . .

P.S. —— I have made a pretty remarkable experiment in the melting of malleable iron in pure air. Many circumstances are curious. I can only say here, that the iron is afterwards a perfect *glass,* not affected by acids.

No. 99.

FROM PRIESTLEY TO JOSIAH WEDGWOOD

Birm. 10th Oct., 1782

Dear Sir

When I received your favor I was just about to try the *dephlogisticated marine acid,* and I find that the electric matter transmitted through it affects the air in the very same manner as when metal wires are employed, diminishing and phlogisticating it; so that there hardly remains any doubt but that the electric matter *itself* must contain the phlogiston with which the air becomes saturated.

Your observations on zinc, arsenic and antimony, are certainly very just, and account very well for the failure of my experiments with those semi-metals. I want sunshine for the prosecution of my experiments on *charcoal*. Pitcoal, I perceive, will leave more ashes than wood, and calcined bones a much greater proportion still.

I am exceedingly pleased with Mr Playfair's method of reducing the scale of your thermometer to that of Fahrenheit. I think it cannot fail to answer, provided due precautions be taken in conducting the experiments, and those you mention are certainly very important ones. As the light acts upon one surface only, the pieces should be turned, and exposed on all sides. I suspect, however, that it will be impossible to be very accurate if you go very near the focus, and therefore it should be tried with Mr Parker's lens. I have also sometimes thought that the heat increases in a greater proportion than the increase of the square of the diameter of the pencil. But that should be ascertained by common thermometers in the first place, and then it would be as easy to compute on one proportion of increase as another.

I have heard that *magnesia,* pressed into a cubic form, was diminished in bulk by Mr Parker's lens more than any substance whatever, and it retained its form without fusion.

You have heard of a pretended transmutation of quicksilver into gold by Dr Price. Yesterday I had a letter from Mr Kirwan, who, after some account of it, adds: "But I have lately seen him and he has owned, that he believes that he was deceived, and that his mercury previously contained gold: that he bought it from one that had it from the makers of *Or moulu,* &c I said so much to him, that he is now satisfied to pass only for a mere able extractor of gold and says he uses a preparation of *arsenic,* of which I persuaded him to promise he would give a paper to the Royal Society."

If you have not heard this before you will like to have the information. . . .

I have just seen an American gentleman, who left Dr Franklin three weeks ago. He says he breaks very fast, and thinks he will not survive many months. He says he only wishes to see a peace concluded before he dies. Mr Lawrence told this gentleman that he hoped there would be a peace in the course of this winter.

No. 100.

From Priestley to Josiah Wedgwood

Birm. Dec. 8, 1782.

Dear Sir:

I have had considerable success in my experiments since I had the pleasure to write to you last; but I was unwilling to trouble you with an account of *details,* or things of small consequence. I think, however, it will give pleasure to be informed that I have succeeded in converting pure *water* into *permanent* air by previously combining it with quicklime, and then subjecting it to a strong heat. This air has a small proportion of fixed air in it, but the bulk of [it] is air a little worse than that of the atmosphere.

I had no certain expectation of this event; but was led from various considerations to try the result of exposing to a strong heat such *volatile substances* as are held in firm combination with others, so as, *in that state,* to bear the heat.

I had also a general idea that if the parts of any bodies be rarefied beyond the sphere of *attraction* they will be in a sphere of repulsion to each other.

Knowing your readiness to promote all philosophical investigations, I make no scruple to inform you that a fresh supply of such small retorts as the last you favored me with will be very acceptable. I must inform you, however, that they often crack after they have been exposed to a strong heat (about 140) about an hour, but some of them are perfect; the mass will seldom serve twice. . . .

P.S. I wish the retorts may be directed to myself and not to Mr Russell.

No. 101.

FROM PRIESTLEY TO JAMES WATT

Fairhill, Birmingham,
8th Dec. 1782.

Dear Sir

I have the pleasure to inform you that I readily convert water into a permanent air by first combining it with quicklime and then exposing it to a red heat. This, I believe, agrees with your idea on the subject. I have not though, much merit, as I had only random expectations from exposing volatile substances in general to a red heat, when combined with other substances, in imitation of the method of converting the acids into air, when combined with the calces of metals or with alkaline bodies. When I have the pleasure of seeing you, I will inform you what kind of air I get, and what quantity, &c. . . .

No. 102.

FROM PRIESTLEY TO EDMUND BURKE

Dear Sir

I take the liberty you were so good as to give me, to trouble you with a few *covers*; and as you seemed to give some attention to the object of my experiments, I presume it will not be disagreeable to you to be informed of a pretty remarkable one that I have made since I had the pleasure of seeing you.

I readily convert *pure water* into *permanent air,* by previously combining it with quicklime, and then exposing it to a strong heat, the air being the full weight of the water.

The air thus produced from water is in part fixed air, but the bulk of it is such as a candle would barely burn in, and which would probably be the very best for the growth of plants; which would purify it, and prepare it for respiration. Such air would be supplied in abundance by volcano's and might perhaps be the original atmosphere of this earth. . . .

Birmingham 11 December 1782.

No. 103.

From Priestley to Jean André DeLuc

Dear Sir

Flattering myself that it will give you some pleasure, I write to inform you of a pretty remarkable experiment that I have made since I had the pleasure of seeing you. I also think it may receive some illustration from your general theory of the powers of nature

I readily convert *pure water* into *permanent air,* weight for weight, by previously combining it with quick-lime, and then exposing it to a strong heat. When I have used an Ounce of Water, no part of it has come over in the form of *steam,* and a glass balloon, placed between the retort and the recipient for the air, has continued perfectly *cool* and *dry.*

The air is in part fixed but the bulk of it is of a kind in which a candle will hardly burn, but probably the best possible for vegetables. Such air as this would be furnished in abundance by volcano's, from calcareous matter in the earth. This, then, might perhaps be the original atmosphere of this earth, before it was purified by the growth of plants; which according to Moses, or explained by your excellent Theory, were created a long time before any land animals.

I have made several other new experiments, especially on *charcoal* and *soot,* the latter of which I find often yields pretty pure air; and, like charcoal, is almost wholly convertible into air.

I give you, and all other *christians* and *philosophers,* joy on the prospect of *peace.* It will remove many obstructions to the progress of science. For my part, I shall think almost any terms good ones. But, perhaps, I am too little of a politician.

Mr Johnson will, I hope, have sent you the second edition of my *Disquisitions,* in which you will find some strictures on your reply to me. There will be nothing in the *manner* of it that you can dislike. . . .

Birm. 11 Decbr 1782

No. 104.

FROM PRIESTLEY TO ARTHUR YOUNG

Dear Sir

If I had had any remarks, or hints, respecting the subject of your experiments, I should certainly with much pleasure have communicated them long ago. I meant, indeed, to have made a few more experiments on the growth of plants in the course of the last summer; but the weather was so bad, and the sun shine so little, that I dropped the scheme — All I can do, therefore, in return for your *facts,* is to mention one that I have lately observed.

I readily convert *pure water* into *permanent air* by first combining it with quicklime, and then exposing it to a strong heat. The weight of the air is equal to the weight of water: and no part of the water is turned into *steam* in the process. [For] the whole of it, a glass balloon interposed between the retort and the recipient for the air, remains quite *cool* and *dry.*

The air I procure in this manner is in part *fixed air;* but the bulk of it is such as a candle would hardly burn it, but is such as I should imagine would be the best for plants, which would purify it, and render it fit for respiration. And as this kind of air would be yielded in great abundance by volcano's, from calcareous matter in the earth, such was perhaps the original atmosphere of this earth, which, according to the Mosaic account (which you must allow me to respect) had plants before there were any land animals.

I think you inclosed a *Cover* for yourself in your last; but, if so, I have unfortunately mislaid it, which gives me some concern, as you can hardly think this letter worth paying for; your objects and mine are so very different, tho now and then coinciding. But mine have seldom any practical uses, at best no immediate ones. Whereas yours are highly and immediately beneficial.

Wishing you the greatest success, and wishing you, and all philosophers, joy of the near prospect of *peace.* . . .

Birm. 12 Decbr. 1782.

P.S.   I had never heard that I *could* be quoted as favouring *any* system of agriculture. It must be very little to the purpose.

Charcoal, by means of a burning lens, in vacuo, is *resolved* into its weight of inflammable air. The *ashes* made in this manner are barely visible, as they float in the air, and now and then cross the sun beam.

No. 105.

From Priestley to Sir Joseph Banks

Dear Sir

I think myself much honoured by your sending me the *Derbyshire mineral,* and shall endeavour, in due time, to give you the best account that I can of it. At present I have made only one experiment upon it; but this seems to afford sufficient data for explaining the phenomenon you mention.

It yields, I find, a considerable quantity of very pure or dephlogisticated air by heat. Supposing, therefore, that the oil incorporates with it, and thereby loses its fluidity, heat will be generated, as when water incorporates with lime &c and the pure air, which that heat expels from it, will contribute to promote the escape of its phlogiston, and so produce a proper *accension,* as is the case with substances that contain nitre, or any thing else that yields pure air with heat.

I should think it very possible to make artificial mixtures of this kind, that should have the same property in any required degree, and it is very easy to conceive that a most dangerous use might be made of them. But whatever is capable of doing mischief, is likewise capable of doing good.

I should have answered your obliging letter sooner, but that I have been much intent on the prosecution of a singular kind of experiment, which seems to shew that *water* is convertible into *permanent air,* even without combination, with any other substance, and with a very moderate heat.

Endeavouring to distill water in an earthen retort, very little of it comes over in the form of *steam,* but a most astonishing quantity of *air* is always produced. An ounce of water has just given me *ninety five Ounce* measures of air, and this the second time that I have used the same retort for the purpose. The air has no mixture of fixed air in it, and is such that a candle will barely burn in it.

When I incorporate the water with quicklime, and expel it again by heat, I get no water at all, but sometimes the whole weight of permanent air of the quality abovementioned, but with a mixture of fixed air. The most difficult circumstance attending these experiments is that they do not succeed with *glass* retorts. Some other curious facts have occurred in the investigation of this business, which I am far from having completed. You are at liberty, however, to mention what I have observed to whom you please, and I shall be particularly obliged to you, if you will mention these things to our common friend Mr Kirwan, as it will save me the trouble of writing to him till I have don[e so]mething farther.

I rejoice that we have so zealous and so able a promoter of philosophical researches at the head of the Royal Society. . . .

Birmingham 28 Decbr 1782

No. 106.

FROM PRIESTLEY TO JEAN ANDRÉ DELUC

[*Jan. 1783*]

[Dear Sir]

I write to you on the day of receiving your letter, addressing mine to Paris, as you requested. The objections which you tell me have been made in London to my late experiments are so little founded, that I will not dwell on them, but there are some new circumstances to examine, before thinking of their publication. When I employ an earthenware retort, although perfectly impermeable to Air, both before and after the Experiment, I can repeat it as often as I wish, putting new water on the same lime, having newly calcined it; & I always find the same results: that is to say, I always obtain *air* for the *water,* weight for weight. But if I use a glass retort, all the *water* issues as *vapour,* and I obtain no *air* at all. When I employ a gun-barrel, I obtain much *air,* but it is *inflammable air,* which burns with a *lambent* flame. I think that this consists of the *inflammable air* usually emitted by a gun-barrel alone, mixed with *fixed air.*

If I put only a small quantity of water in an earthen retort, and attempt only to distill that water, very little is changed to vapour, and often none at all, but much air is produced from it. One ounce of water, treated in this manner, has produced nearly 100 times its volume of air, nearly as pure as atmospheric air. This I have often repeated with the same retort. But although these retorts are impermeable to air, they imbibe water, thus this fact is properly of the same nature as the first. Water united to chalk or gypsum also gives much air in an earthen retort.

I have not yet discovered the cause of the difference of these results. The facts are as I relate them to you, and I tell you of them for what ever use you think proper to make of them. But I think proper to defer all formal publication, and to make no mention of them as *philosophical news,* until I have pursued these researches farther. I have already made a great many experiments to this end, of which several are very curious, but the account would be too long for a letter.

It is all the more probable that *water* can be converted to Air, since when I decompose, by electric spark, *dephlogisticated air* with *inflammable air,* I always get much *water,* even when the two *airs* were generated over mercury and have never been in contact with *water.* Your facts and your arguments are very curious and they merit particular attention; but I hope to understand you better still, when I have discussed them with Mr Watt. . . .

No. 107.

FROM PRIESTLEY TO JOSIAH WEDGWOOD

Birm. 23 Jan., 1783.

Dear Sir

I am much obliged to you for all your queries, and shall be happy to give you all the satisfaction in my power. I have a tolerably good habit of circumspection with respect to *facts*; but as to conclusions from them, I am not apt to be very confident. [Qu. What becomes of 7–8 of the water not converted into air?]

1. Part of the water always gets through the retorts, and is seen rising from it in vapour, though they are absolutely impervious to air.

[Qu. If water passes through the retort outwards, may not air pass inwards?]

2. As there is a considerable resistance to the escape of the air before it can be collected in my recipients, it would certainly make its escape through the pores of the retort, if it could, and could never *enter* that way. Besides, why does the process stop, if air could enter by the retort, and get into the recipient? —— I have frequently tested the *empty retorts,* and the air they give is a mere trifle.

3. Some have said that the air I get is that which is attracted by the inside of the retort, as it cools, and is condensed in its pores. But after a process I have put the mouth of the retort into a basin of water, while it was all red hot, on the fire, and letting it cool in that situation have plunged it in water, and filled it, without even giving its pores an opportunity of getting any air, and yet it has always, after that, given air as usual.

4. The retorts certainly gain nothing in the fire.

5. I find great differences in the retorts with respect to their property of giving air from the water put into them. The *three* last give very little, owing perhaps to the texture being too compact. I could wish to have one, if possible, of a more porous texture than No. 5, and thicker, to prevent the air, in so spongy a substance, getting through. —— I could also wish to have one or

two of a texture the most nearly approaching to *porcelaine,* but rough in the inside, that there then may be no pores for the water to get into.

As so much depends upon the *materials* of which the retorts are made, would you be so good as favour me with an account of the composition of No. 5?

I shall thank you for a few more *thermometer pieces,* along with these retorts. I have had ample experience of your goodness, and therefore make no apology for so many wants.

I have heard nothing of late from Paris, and am much rejoiced at the intelligence you send me; a few days must ascertain the truth. . . .

No. 108.

From Priestley to Arthur Young

Birmingham 27 Jan. 1783

Dear Sir

There is no person I should serve with more pleasure than *you,* because there is no person whose pursuits are more eminently useful to the world. You alone have certainly done more to promote agriculture, and especially to render it reputable in this country, than all that have gone before you. But the little I might do to aid your investigations will be reduced to a small matter indeed, by my distance from you. All that I should be able to do with *water* would be to expel by heat all the air it contains, and then examine by nitrous air, how much phlogiston that air contains; but it is very possible that the fitness of water for meadows may depend upon something besides the phlogiston it contains. Experiment alone can determine these things.

I never heard before of the inference you say has been drawn from my doctrine with respect to the use of *light in vegetation.* I know of no use that light is of to the *soil.* The whole effect is on the *living plant,* enabling it to convert the impure air it meets with in water or in the atmosphere into pure air. When that end is effected, that water is of no farther use to it. Plants will not thrive unless both their leaves and roots be exposed to air in some degree impure. This I have fully ascertained, but I am afraid that the doctrine is not capable of much practical application.

I know no method of conveying phlogiston to the roots of plants but as combined with water; and this seems to be done in the best way by a mixture of putrid matter. Water will not imbibe much inflammable air.

I find volatile alkali to contain much phlogiston. It is indeed almost another modification of the same thing. Metals are revived in alkaline air as well as in inflammable air, and the electric spark taken in alkaline air converts it into three times its bulk of inflammable air.

Since my last I have hit upon various methods of converting *water* into *permanent air*. It is sufficient to give it something more than a boiling heat, & If I only put an ounce of water into a porous earthen retort, I get a hundred ounce measures of air from it, and when I have, in this manner, got near an ounce weight of air from the same retort, it has not weighed one grain less than it did. . . .

P.S.   I shall be glad to hear the result of your experiments.

No. 109.

FROM PRIESTLEY TO JOSIAH WEDGWOOD

Birm. 7 Mar., 1783.

Dear Sir

Your retorts will be very acceptable; and I shall trouble you also for a few more of the *porcelain texture,* as I find a very remarkable difference in the results of some experiments made with them. In these retorts I have never failed to convert *whiting,* which is a pure calcareous earth, into a *flinty substance,* that will neither imbibe water, nor be affected by any acid; or at least very little. When I apply the same heat to the same whiting in the other retorts, I only calcine it, after which it will imbibe water, and become whiting again, and this as often as I please.

I have just ascertained by direct experiment what Mr Kirwan inferred from former ones, viz., that *fixed air* is a compound of dephlogisticated air and phlogiston or inflammable air. I mix *red precipitate,* which gives only the purest dephlogisticated air, and *iron filings,* which gives only inflammable air, and the residue is a great quantity of the purest fixed air, almost wholly absorbed by water; whereas neither of the kinds of air of which it is composed are absorbed by water at all, except in the smallest quantity.

I have nearly finished my present experiments on *water,* and shall soon draw up an account of them for the Royal Society. . . .

P.S. ——— I beg my respects to Mr Chelsam [Chisholm], and wish you would mention to him the facts above recited.

No. 110.

From Priestley to Arthur Young

Dear Sir

I received from Mr More two bottles of Water, one marked X, which Mr Boswell informed him was from the spring mentioned p 11 in his Treatise on Water meadows, and another without any mark, from a spring rising from a bed of Sand, and I examined them immediately, which was the 14 Inst. when I found the former to contain air much purer than that of the atmosphere; but the latter air that was much worse, ie more phlogisticated. A candle would hardly have burned in it. This last I should think to be the better spring for the watering of meadows. Or perhaps it might have been better corked; for on the 19th, tho I put the corks in again immediately, but without any cement &c I found the air in both very pure, more so than the purest before, and hardly to be distinguished, and they were so this day when I examined them again. They should be examined on the spot. The air in the spring from the sand was much worse than that in my pump water, or than that of Water in general. But water exposed to the open air soon loses the phlogiston it contains.

Perhaps much of the effect of water on Meadows is that, at this time of the year, it comes out of the earth considerably *warmer* than the roots of the grass. What think you of this?

I expect to set out for London this day three Weeks, and shall stay there about a fortnight. I should be glad to meet you there, when we shall find an hours conversation better than all our correspondence.

Wishing you success in your truly laudable pursuits. . . .

Birm. 31 March 1783.

No. 111.

FROM PRIESTLEY TO JOSIAH WEDGWOOD

London 6 May 1783

Dear Sir

Having just finished some experiments of a pretty extraordinary nature, I make haste to give you some account of them.

By means of Mr Parker's lens, I heat an earthen retort, filled with moistened clay. When the neck of it is well luted to the upper orifice of a glass receiver, which is placed in a bason of water, and a glass tube communicates with the inside of the retort. In consequence of this, the water from the clay comes into the receiver, while the air in the receiver passes through the retort, and is delivered at *a*; the water in the bason rising within the receiver, and covering the retort. If it be inflammable air, it comes through inflammable, if nitrous, nitrous. This must be by the air losing its *aerial form* while it combines with the earth of the retort, and recovers its aerial form in the inside of it. If the retort was not perfectly air tight, the water could not rise within the receiver. Spirit of wine comes thro the retort into the receiver, just as the water does.

This renders *one* of my processes of the conversion of water into air fallacious, after I had fully satisfied even Mr Kirwan of the reality of that conversion. Another experiment is not so easily explained.

Making water to boil in a glass retort, I make the steam go thro a red hot tobacco pipe; When I always get much air mixed with the steam. In the same manner spirit of wine makes inflammable air, and spirit of nitre the purest dephlogisticated air. But if the tobacco pipe be not hot, I get only *vapour,* and no *air* from any of the liquors.

I cannot in a letter enlarge on all the particulars of these experiments, which excite a good deal of attention here. I shall lay them before the Royal Society, and pursue them at my leisure as soon as I get home.

I thank you for your excellent *Address to your neighbours,* and am much disappointed in not meeting with you here. . . .

[Another letter on the same subject was earlier addressed to James Watt: see Priestley to Watt, 29 April 1783, in H. C. Bolton, *Scientific Correspondence of Joseph Priestley,* No. 25.]

No. 112.

FROM PRIESTLEY TO SIR JOSEPH BANKS

Dear Sir

I certainly meant to submit my paper to the Royal Society, as it contains a series of remarkably new facts, completely ascertained, whatever *deductions* (about which I am not solicitous) be drawn from them. As I have opportunity, I shall prosecute the experiments farther; and if any thing materially new should occur to me, I shall send you a supplemental paper on the subject.

Mr Watt wishes to withdraw his paper; but he is now engaged in a course of experiments, in which he thinks he shall prove the actual conversion of water into air, tho mine certainly prove no such thing.

When I see the young man who made the air gun, I shall mention to him your desire of having it. It is very generous in you, and worthy of a President of the Royal Society, to interest yourself, as you do, in all scientifical pursuits, however foreign to your own. It is a wide and noble field that we are employed in; and the truly liberal will rejoice in, and promote, each others success — I thank you for your intelligence from Paris. For my own part, I wish to see either Dr Crawford's or Mr Lavoisier's *facts* unexceptionably ascertained, by competent witnesses.

I have just heard from Mr Kirwan, and shall write to him as soon as I have anything worth communicating. In the mean time, I wish you would inform him, that I have, in a glazed earthen retort, got 787 Ounce measures of dephlogisticated air from *two ounces of purified nitre*. . . .

Birmingham 23 June 1783.

No. 113.

FROM PRIESTLEY TO JEAN ANDRÉ DELUC

Dear Sir

I have taken the liberty to beg your acceptance of a copy of my *Letters to Dr Horsley*. It is an historical research of a curious nature, and whatever you may think of my *opinion,* I hope you will perceive marks of fairness in my manner of conducting the controversy.

Mr Watt, I understand, has written to you on the subject of some advices which we have both received from Paris about M Lavoisier having advanced the idea of water consisting of pure air and phlogiston, which had occurred to him a long time ago, and of which the paper which you will receive from Sr Joseph Banks is sufficient evidence. You will please to deliver the inclosed to him, and I doubt not he will give order for its being delivered to you.

I have been making a little excursion and am now setting about various experiments. If anything worth notice should occur to me you may depend upon hearing from me. . . .

Birm. 13 Decbr. 1782

[The above date should be 1783, however, as the letter is endorsed by DeLuc as of 1783, and the contents require the later date.]

No. 114.

From Priestley to Sir Joseph Banks

Birmingham, 14th December, 1783

Dear Sir:

Thank you for your obliging attention to me in sending me the account of Mr. Lavoisier's paper and I beg you would deliver my compliments and thanks to Mr. Hobson, for making the transcript for my use.

Mr. Watt is the person who is properly concerned in this business. For the idea of water consisting of *pure air and phlogiston* was his, I believe, before I knew him; and you will find it in the *letter* which he addressed to me, and which was delivered along with the last paper that I sent to the Royal Society, but which he afterwards withdrew.

This letter he now wishes to put into the hands of Mr. De Luc who will make some use of it. You will oblige us both therefore, if you will give orders to have this letter delivered to Mr. De Luc, who will wait upon you for the purpose.

I thank you also for your account of the air balloons which though at present they only amuse the idle, may in time answer some important purposes in philosophy, enabling us to explore the upper regions of the atmosphere. . . .

No. 115.

FROM PRIESTLEY TO JEAN ANDRÉ DELUC

Birm. 27 Decbr. 1783

Dear Sir

I am sorry to perceive that you are intirely mistaken with respect to the concern that I have in the discovery concerning the constitution of water. I really have no merit at all with respect to it. No *fact* of my discovery proves that water consists of pure air and phlogiston. My experiment only shows the transmission of air thro an earthen retort, while water passes in a contrary direction; and it was Mr Cavendish who first found water on decomposing dephlogisticated and inflammable air. In my opinion, Mr Watt first entertained the idea you mention, and the experiment of Mr Cavendish proved the justness of it, tho Mr Cavendish had not that idea himself.

That red precipitate (which gives only pure air with heat) and iron filings (which give only inflammable air) do, when mixed together, give pure *fixed air,* I discovered in March 1783; when, in my first trial, from half an ounce of each I got 26 Ounce measures of fixed air, nearly as pure as can be got from chalk by oil of vitriol. A still purer fixed air is got by using charcoal instead of iron filings, when the charcoal is reduced to such a state, as to give only inflammable air by heat.

Your intention with respect to me is very obliging, but all I wish for is *justice*; and you have certainly formed much too high an idea of my merit in this business. If any thing should occur in the course of my experiments that I can think will give you pleasure, I shall not fail to take the first opportunity of communicating it to you. . . .

No. 116.

FROM PRIESTLEY TO HENRY CAVENDISH

Dear Sir

According to my promise, I have repeated the experiment with the *lead and mercury* with all the precautions I could think of, and with a result sufficiently agreeable to what I observed before.

Having dissolved two Ounces of lead in mercury, I expelled as much of it in the form of black powder as weighed six Ounces, without even blowing into the phial, either with a pair of bellows, or my mouth. From this I expelled, in a coated glass retort, $4\frac{1}{2}$ Oz measures of air, 2 of which was wholly absorbed by water, leaving a small residuum almost wholly phlogisticated, as also was the common air contained in the neck of the phial that came over first; my test (with equal quantities of nitrous air) being 1.8. I did not urge this process very far, and there remained $1\frac{1}{2}$ Ounces of blackish powder.

Being satisfied that the fixed air did not come from the bellows, or my breath, I expedited the remainder of the process by blowing with the bellows, which were very clean, and in contant use; and by this means got 18 Ounces more of the black powder, from which, together with what remained of the former process, I expelled $23\frac{1}{2}$ Oz measures of air in six portions, the quantities of which, with what remained after washing in lime water, and the purity of residuum, are expressed in the following table

Air received	Residuum	Quality	
5	4	1.6	
5	.75	1.44	Equal quantities
5	.5	0.8	of nitrous air
5	.75	0.8	
2.5	1.1	0.6	Two equal quantities
1.	.5	0.63	of nitrous air
$23\frac{1}{2}$	7.6	16	

Both the quantity and the quality of the air seems to depend, in a great measure, on the manner of applying the heat. In all the cases the first phlogiston that is expelled affects the common air contained in the retort, the next seems to contribute to the formation of *fixed air,* and when it is almost wholly expelled, the remaining air comes over pure.

After agitating this mixture some time (viz after about 300 strokes) it grows hot, the *liquid* mass then becoming in part *solid.* This is also the case when I squeeze the mercury out of the coagulated mass in a cloth. It is sometimes as hot as I can well bear to handle.

To give you some idea of the *expedition* of this process, I observed that, towards the end of it, with 400 shakes of the phial (which would take about two minutes, blowing into it after every hundred shakes) I got six Ounces of the black powder, so that the whole took up no great time.

Nothing I well know is so acceptable [to] yo[u as] truth; and therefore, if it be agreeable to [you] I [will] send you an account of the result of so[me] other experiments which I am about to make relating to this subject. In the mean time it will give me great satisfaction if you, or Dr Blagden, will inform me what you think of this experiment, and whether you have succeeded in making it. . . .

Birmingham 31 May 1784

No. 117.

FROM HENRY CAVENDISH TO PRIESTLEY, DRAFT

[After 13 May and probably before 16 June 1784]

D.P.

I am much obliged to you for the account of your exper & shall be very glad to be informed of any other experiments that you may make As soon as I make any more experiments about it myself I will be sure to send you an account of them but I am so far from possessing any of your activity that I am afraid I shall not make any very soon

I cannot at all conceive what should be the reason of the difference in our experiments the air in mine being not only almost free from fixed air but also about 8 times as great in proportion to the black powder or to the lead employed as in yours If one could suppose that your powder was mixed with a sufficient quantity of the particles of the cloth in which it was squeezed it would account for both these circumstances but it seems very improbable that that should be the case If it should appear on trial as you seem to suspect that the quality of the air expelled $\frac{33}{3} \times \frac{18}{23\frac{1}{2}} = \frac{11 \times 18}{24} = \frac{11 \times 3}{4} = 8$ from the same black powder would be different according as the heat was applied slow or quick the heat in both cases being at last raised high enough to expel all the air it would seem a decisive proof that the fixed air was generated in the experiment You do not say with what heat the powder was urged in your exper. In mine it was sufficient to vitrify the lead

The heat produced by the shaking & by the squeezing out the ☿ [mercury] is very curious . . . .

No. 118.

FROM PRIESTLEY TO HENRY CAVENDISH

Dear Sir

As you wish to be informed of the progress of my experiments, I shall briefly mention what I have done since my last; stating the *facts* only, as you will be better able than I am to draw the proper *inferences* from them.

Resuming my experiments on the seeming conversion of water into air; I find that a vessel of *chalk* answers as well as one of *clay. Mercury* comes thro in the form of a black powder, tho, in the same degree of heat, I cannot with an air pump force a particle of the mercury thro the retort, which in this case was made of pipe clay. Alkaline air is transmitted as well as air of other kinds.

Throwing the focus of a burning lens upon shavings of iron, in d^d [dephlogisticated] air confined by mercury, both very warm and dry, the air disappeared, no water was found, but some fixed air; and the slag to which the iron was reduced had gained as much weight as that of the air that had vanished In the open air 24 grains of iron imbibed 5 grains of air, and 24 grains of steel imbibed 7½ grains. After this my lens could not melt it, nor will any acid, except the marine, dissolve it. It is the same thing as the *scales of iron* from a smiths forge.

Throwing the focus of the lens on irons thus saturated with pure air, in inflammable air, confined by mercury, all very dry, the air disappeared, and the iron lost so much weight that the d^d air expelled from it would have saturated the inflammable air that disappeared; and in this case as much water was produced as I imagined would have been equal to the weight of the air.

Having mixed a quantity of d^d air, and of inflammable air from *iron* in the usual proportion of 1 to 2, I exploded 3½ Ounce measures of it, and found neither water nor fixed air; but using inflammable air from *charcoal,* (which shewed no sign of containing any fixed air) I got 4/5 of an Ounce measure of fixed air, and an evident quantity of *water.*

To prosecute these experiments to advantage I much want a burning lens of greater power than mine. However, I shall d[o] as well as I can, and shall not fail to acquaint you with the results, hoping [to] be favoured with your observations on them, and you are at liberty to mention the facts to any of your acquaintances. . . .

Birmingham 16 June 1784

No. 119.

From Priestley to William Wilkinson

Dear Sir

Though I do not know that such experiments as mine are very interesting to you; yet, as I am desirous of giving you any satisfaction that may be in my power, I wish to communicate the result of some that I have lately made, and that my friends think to be of importance. You may get Joseph to transcribe the account for M. Senebier, or any philosophical persons that he may meet with.

A very interesting problem with us of late has been to determine what becomes of dephlogisticated and inflammable air, when they are made to unite, as by exploding them with the electric spark &c.; some saying that they make *water,* others *fixed air* &c. The following experiments shew that, in different circumstances, they make *both*; and also that dephlogisticated air incorporates with *iron* in a great proportion.

Throwing the focus of a burning lens upon some small pieces of malleable iron in dephlogisticated air, confined by mercury (both very warm and dry) the air disappeared, no water was formed, but some fixed air; and the *slag,* to which the iron was reduced, had gained as much weight, as that of the air that had been absorbed. Melting the iron in the open air, 24 grains gained five grains, and the same quantity of *steel* gained $7\frac{1}{2}$ grains of pure air. After this my lens could not melt it, nor could any acid, except the marine, dissolve it. It appeared to be the same thing as the *scales of iron* from a smith forge.

Throwing the focus of the lens upon iron thus saturated with dephlogisticated air, in inflammable air, confined by mercury (all very dry) the air disappeared, and the iron lost as much weight as if reduced to dephlogisticated air, would have saturated the inflammable air that had disappeared; and, in this case, as much *water* was produced, as, I imagined, would have been equal to the weight of the air.

Another experiment that I have made shews a remarkable difference between inflammable air from *metals,* and that from *charcoal.* Having mixed a quantity of each of them with half as much dephlogisticated air, I exploded that from *iron,* by means of the electric spark, and found neither water nor fixed air; but firing the mixture that contained the inflammable air from *charcoal* (which shewed no sign of its containing any fixed air) $3\frac{1}{2}$ Ounce measures of the mixture yielded an evident quantity of *water,* and likewise almost an Ounce measure of pure *fixed air.*

Resuming my experiments on *the seeming conversion of water into air,* I find that a vessel of *chalk* answers as well as one of *clay,* and *mercury* as well as *water,* passing thro the retort one way in the form of a *black powder,* while the air passes the contrary way; and when, in the same degree of heat, an airpump cannot force a particle of mercury thro it. Also Alkaline air is transmitted as well as air of any other kind.

As it will save some expence of postage, I also wish that Joseph would transcribe this account and send it, with my compliments, to *Sig.ʳ Marsiglio Landriani at Milan.*

We are all well except Sally, who has been confined to her room and bed by a rheumatic fever, and is indeed very far from being recovered. She joins with your sister and all of us, in best wishes to you both. Mr & Mrs Barbauld are now with us, and are to take William with them; and Harry is expected from school tomorrow or the next day — I shall be glad to hear of your labours, and hope that Joseph will behave to your satisfaction. . . .

Birm. 16 June 1784

[H. C. Bolton in his printing of this letter (No. 31 in his *Scientific Correspondence of Joseph Priestley*) implies that the addressee is John Wilkinson.]

No. 120.

FROM PRIESTLEY TO JEAN ANDRÉ DELUC

Birmingham 9 Sepbr. 1784

Dear Sir

I am sorry that I neglected to make the experiment you wished me to make till Mr Watt reminded me of it. I then, however, immediately set about it, and when I had filled a vessel with *fixed air,* very dry, I found that a pair of cork balls, when electrified in it, repelled one another just as they would have done if the vessel had been filled with common air; so that fixed air is certainly no conductor of electricity.

Having had good sunshine since we had the pleasure of seeing you here, I have abundantly confirmed the facts that I then acquainted you with; viz that iron saturated with dephlogisticated air, heated in inflammable air, loses weight, and that water is produced equal to that weight. Moreover, that the weight lost by the iron, if reduced to dephlogisticated air, would be about twice the bulk of the inflammable air that disappears in the experiment; which is just the proportion in which they saturate each other when decomposed by electricity.

I have lately found that *inflammable air* most readily unites with a certain quantity of *water*, and has its specific gravity increased by it. I suspect also, but have not yet ascertained it by experiments made on purpose, that it likewise unites with a certain quantity of *fixed air*, so that it is not discoverable by lime water, but only when decomposed by electricity together with dephlogisticated air.

I am completely analized *alkaline air*. It revives more lead than inflammable air, and always leaves a residuum of about one fourth *phlogisticated air*. But if any thing be heated red hot in it, the quantity is nearly doubled, and is then all, or nearly all, *inflammable* air; tho still it is possible, that one fourth of it may be phlogisticated air. This I shall particularly examine.

I thank you for the very valuable present of your *Recherches* &c. . . .

P.S. Water is absolutely necessary to the formation of inflammable air. In a dry receiver I could decompose only two grains of charcoal, and this must have been owing to some concealed moisture. When air is produced by steam passing thro hot charcoal, the air weighs much more than the charcoal. But you will hear more from me, or Mr Watt, on this subject.

No. 121.

FROM PRIESTLEY TO JOSIAH WEDGWOOD

Birm. 8th Nov'br, 1784.

Dear Sir

I know you will not be displeased with my telling you, that I was never more impatient for anything, than I now am to receive the *earthen tubes* you have been so obliging as to promise me, especially when I give you the reasons for it.

Hitherto I have used a *copper tube,* because water did not act upon it. But sending thro' it *spirit of wine* in vapour, it was totally dissolved, and actually fell in pieces in a very short time. I was astonished at the production of inflammable air in the process, which resembled the blowing with a pair of bellows. Four ounces of spirit of wine did the business for this tube which was about $\frac{1}{4}$ of an inch thick. What was condensed by the warm tub was mere *water.* The inflammable air which had no fixed air in it had come from the copper. The inside was reduced to a black powder.

Iron, I find, gained one-third in weight in this process, and gives one-half more inflammable air than it does when dissolved in acids, the reason of which I believe to be that much of the phlogiston is always retained in the solution of metals in acids. On comparing the experiments, I *now* think that the inflammable air is furnished by the iron, and that there is no decomposition of the water. Mr. Watt thinks so too.

Iron that is thus increased in weight, and has yielded so much air (which, by the way, has not the least *offensive smell* which has been so much complained of in filling balloons) is reduced to its former state by heating in charcoal. In this process, instead of yielding *water,* as we all imagined it would, it yielded a prodigious quantity of *inflammable air,* but of a peculiar kind, for it is about as heavy as common air, owing, as I found, to its containing a great quantity of *fixed air* combined with it, so as not to be separated by lime water, but only by decomposition with pure air, by the electric spark.

[238]

Mr More of the Adelphi was with me when he observed, by his stop watch, that, heating about one foot of my copper tube (not quite ¾ of an inch in diameter) filled with iron shavings I always filled a vessel containing 30 ounce measures of air in 50 seconds. There can be no doubt, therefore, but that this process must be abundantly the best for filling balloons. . . .

No. 122.

FROM CAVENDISH TO PRIESTLEY, DRAFT LETTER

20 Dec. 1784

D. P.

I am very much obliged to you for your letter last June & would have acknowledged the favour before had I not delayd it in hopes of sending you an account of some exper. in return but by the trouble of removing my house & one thing or another I was prevented from making any exper. all the summer I have lately however gone on with the exper I told you I was making about the Electric spark I believe I mentioned to you when in town that on taking the electric spark through impure dephl. air confined by lime water & ☿ [mercury] no cloud was formed in the lime water & that none was formed also on letting up some fixed air but that on adding to that a little caustic vol. alk a brown sediment was immediately formed The 2 last circumstances seemed to show that an acid was formed in the operation which dissolved the lime & the first circumstance shewd that no fixed air was generated by it What was the reason of the brown colour of the sediment I do not know unless a little of the ☿ was dissolved. As this [illegible] some of the phlog. air with which the deph. air was debased was turned into N. acid I lately took the spark through a mixture of deph. & common air confined between sope leys & ♀ adding fresh air as required till no more would be absorbed The quantity of sope leys employed was such as with nitr. acid would have yielded about ¼ gra. of nitre & the air absorbed containd about 69 of pure deph. air & 32 of phlogist. air.

[239]

I believe I told you when you was in town that I had just tried an exper of the same kind as this but that by accident & a bad method of trying the sope leys I could not tell whether any nitre was produced or not

The sope leys after the operation was found to be intirely neutralized & on evap it yielded a small quantity of saline matter which proved to be true nitre

Though the exp. & the burning of nitre shews that part of the phlogist air of the atmosphere consist of the Nr. acid united to phlogist. yet it might be doubted whether the whole is so & whether there are not rather various different substances confounded together by us under the name of phlogist. air but from the following exper. it should seem as if the whole was of the same kind as on taking the spark through some of the same air confined as before till about 75 parts of phlogist air were absorbed & after that adding some pure deph. air & continuing the spark till the diminution was nearly ceased & then adding liver of sulphur to absorb the dephlog. air it was reduced to less than one measure so that out of the 76 parts of phlog. air employed there was only one which was not absorbed or as we may conclude from the former exper turned into nitr acid

I shall at any time be very glad to hear how you go on in your exper. & will with pleasure send you an account of any thing I do my self but as I make not a tenth part of the exper that you do & as my facility in writing falls short of yours in a still greater proportion I am afraid you will think me a bad correspondent & that the advantage lies intirely on my side. . . .

No. 123.

FROM PRIESTLEY TO HENRY CAVENDISH

Dear Sir

I am glad that my experiments give you any pleasure; but you greatly overrate both my readiness in making them, and my facility in writing; and may not perhaps consider that my time is likewise much engaged in things of a very different nature.

I am much obliged to you for the account of your experiments on *phlogisticated air,* which I consider as one of the greatest, perhaps the very greatest, and most important, relating to the doctrine of air. You seem, indeed, fully to have proved the existence of the nitrous acid in that kind of air, and consequently to have discovered the true source of *nitre* in all the processes for making it.

Presently after my last to you, I discovered the fallacy of the conclusion from my former experiments, and the truth of your hypothesis, that *water* is a necessary ingredient in *inflammable air.* Iron filings, in their ordinary state, gave air a whole day in a gun barrel, and a common fire, but at length ceased, but the process was renewed by putting water to them —— I likewise found that when I had no *wet leather* for my receiver to stand upon, but made every thing as *dry* and as *hot* as possible, I could not disperse more than two grains of charcoal by heat in vacuo.

On this I repeated the *Parisian experiments* only sending steam from a separate boiler, thro a hot *copper cylinder,* containing *iron filings,* or *charcoal,* with the results which they describe, but I see no reason to conclude that the inflammable air, in either of these cases, comes from the *water.* Iron, in this process, yields one half more inflammable air than it does when dissolved in acids, and exactly of the same kind, except that it is free from all offensive smell. In this manner there can be no doubt, but that balloons may be filled with the purest air, in the cheapest manner.

It is remarkable that iron, treated in this manner, is one third heavier than it was before, and is, in all other respects, the very same thing with iron saturated with d^d air. When heated in *inflammable air,* it loses that weight, which is found in *water,* but when heated with *charcoal* it yields no water at all, but an immense quantity of *air* part of which ($\frac{1}{5}$ at the beginning) is fixed air, and the remainder, tho inflammable, is quite as heavy as common air. The reason of this appears when it is decomposed with d^d air, for then the fixed air it contains is separated from it. After either of the two processes, the iron is restored to its own final properties.

Steam of water has no effect on *Copper* but sending thro my copper tube, only 4 Ounces of *Spirit of wine in vapour,* it was dissolved, and came in [pieces], being converted into a *black powder.* On this I took *earthen tubes,* and putting copper into it, formed a curious combination of copper and spirit of wine. I have done the same with *lead,* and *silver,* and shall try all the metals.

Putting into the earthen tube pieces of other earthen tubes (in order to expose more red hot surface) I convert the whole of *spirit of wine, ether,* and *oil of turpentine* into inflammable air, remarkably different from each other That from *ether* will not fire with d^d air. It burns with a white lambent flame. The pieces of earthen retorts &c with which I fill the earthen tubes, in some of these experiments, are fastened together with a remarkable kind of *charcoal,* the same, I suspect, with that describe in my paper on charcoal. I have great quantities of it, and shall try its electrical properties soon.

With respect to *the seeming conversion of water* [*into*] *air,* I find that the transmission of vapour and air depends upon actual *pores,* tho th[e process] succeeds with the closest *white marble.* It [must] therefore be owing to some kind of *attraction of co-hes*[*ion*] tho I cannot explain it.

I think I told you before, that I convert *alkaline air* into *inflammable,* by heating anything in it red hot.

I shall be obliged to you if you will shew this letter to Dr Heberden, who is pleased to interest himself in my experiments, and to whom I have not written [very] lately, tho he is already acquainted with many particulars in this letter. . . .

Birm. 30 Decbr 1784

No. 124.

FROM PRIESTLEY TO THE PHILOSOPHICAL SOCIETY AT ORLÉANS, FRANCE

No. 225.

Birmingham 12 May 1785

Sir

I think myself much honoured by being elected a member of the Philosophical Society at Orleans, and I beg you would Signify to that body, in the most respectful manner how sensible I am of it. From the labours of so many persons Engaged in the same pursuit we cannot doubt but that the Knowledge of nature will be rapidly advanced; and the pleasing Emulation of philosophers of different countries must accelerate the improvement which will be Equally beneficial to all.

An account of some of my late experiments is just printed for a philosophical transactions and I shall beg your acceptance of a copy which I shall transmit to M. Lavoisier at Paris.

I am, Sir, your most obedient humble Servant. . . .

Lu à le Societé 27 mai 1785

[The above letter is manifestly a copy which has been transcribed, with the number "225" at the top, from what appears to be an English translation of an original in French.]

No. 125.

THE AMERICAN PHILOSOPHICAL SOCIETY CERTIFICATE

To all PERSONS to whom these PRESENTS shall come,

GREETING.

THE AMERICAN PHILOSOPHICAL SOCIETY, held at *Philadelphia,* for promoting useful Knowledge, desirous of advancing the Interests of the Society, by associating to themselves

Men of distinguished Eminence, and of confering Marks of their Esteem upon Persons of literary Merit, have elected,

The Rev. Joseph Priestley Ll. D. F.R.S Birminghm. a Member of the said PHILOSOPHICAL SOCIETY, hereby granting unto him all the Rights of Fellowship, with all the Liberties and Privileges thereunto belonging.

In Testimony whereof the said Society have caused the Seal of their Corporation to be annexed to this Certificate, and the same to be attested by the Names of the proper Officers, this Twenty Second Day of Jany. in the Year of our LORD One Thousand Seven Hundred and Eighty Five. 1785.

ATTESTED,

James Hutchinson
R. Patterson
Sam. Magan D. D.
(Secretaries)

John Ewing D. D.
(Vice Presidents)

[Another certificate with the same wording as above but engrossed on parchment is in the collection of the Historical Society of Pennsylvania at Philadelphia. The date is given as the "seventeenth Day of June in the Year of our Lord 1785." The attesting officers are: R. Patterson, James Hutchinson, Sam. Magan, Secretaries; and John Ewing, William White, D.D., and Sam Vaughan, Vice-Presidents.]

No. 126.

FROM PRIESTLEY TO THE SECRETARY, AMERICAN ACADEMY
OF ARTS AND SCIENCES

Revd Sir

I am truly sensible of the honour that has been done me by being elected a member of the American Academy of Arts and Sciences, and should have acknowledged it sooner, but that, living a a distance from London, I have not known of proper opportunities of conveying my letter: My friend Mr Vaughan going to America very soon makes it easy for me to do now what ought to have been done a long time ago.

I rejoice that, after so noble and successful a struggle for your *liberties,* you are now, in time of peace, attending to matters of *science.* I hope you will have the same success in your exertions in this way.

As you are so obliging as to inquire after my *Observations on Air &* I shall beg to have the honour of presenting my *five volumes* on that subject to the Academy, and hope that Mr Vaughan will take care of their conveyance.

I am still engaged in the same pursuits, and two papers of mine on that subject are published in the Philosophical Transactions. . . .

Birmingham 23 June 1785

No. 127.

FROM PRIESTLEY TO MARTIN VON MARUM

Birmingham 14 Sepbr 1785

Sir

I have received much pleasure both from your book, and your obliging letter, and I promise myself and the Public great advantage from the excellent institution in which you preside. I rejoice that it has fallen under the direction of so scientifical a person. The experiments you have already made are of a very capital nature, and being on so large a scale, are perfectly decisive with respect to several objects of great consequence

I have nothing particular to propose as from myself, with respect to the future application of your noble machine and battery, except that I think you may probably repeat my experiments on the circles made by explosions on the surfaces of metals, those on the colours of metallic plates, on the lateral explosion, the lateral force of explosions, and those in imitation of earthquakes and hurricanes, with particular advantage, and with the prospect of ascertaining some new circumstances relating to them.

D Withering, an ingenious friend of mine in this town, desires me to send you the following hints.

1. Burn diamonds by electricity.
2. Try its effect upon lime water, and upon perfectly caustic fixed alkali.
3. Will the phlogiston of the electric matter blacken concentrated vitriolic acid?
4. Will it phlogisticate the acid of phosphorus?
5. Try its effects upon luna cornea.
6. Does it check the vibration of a musical string?
7. When a man is insulated, and filled with the electric fluid of this grand machine, do the pupils of his eyes become luminous?

It gives me particular satisfaction that a person of so philosophical a mind as yours gives attention to subjects of *theology*. I am particularly flattered with your approbation of any of my writings in that way, as I have those objects more at heart than anything relating to philosophy. I have now in the press a large *history of opinions concerning Christ*, which I hope to publish about April next, when I shall be happy to send you a copy of it.

Be assured it will give me great pleasure to see you, whenever you visit this country. . . .

No. 128.

FROM PRIESTLEY TO ARTHUR YOUNG

Birm. 11 Nov. 1785

Dear Sir

I should think myself very happy if it was at all in my power to give you any assistance in your most valuable pursuits; but I really do not see that I can. It has been only this consideration, and that of [avoiding] the expence of correspondence to us both, that has been the reason why I have not written to you oftener.

I have examined the two phials of air that you have sent me. They were perfectly well corked, and therefore I presume unchanged in the conveyance. The larger phial contained air of a very peculiar kind, and besides containing about $\frac{1}{20}$ of loose fixed air, separable by water, it contained more than half its bulk of *combined fixed air,* discoverable only when decomposed by electricity with dephlogisticated air. The smell is very peculiar, but what I cannot account for.

The smaller phial contained inflammable air, with hardly any loose fixed air, but about a fourth of its bulk of combined fixed air. It burned with a lambent blue flame, like the other, but with less violence.

Both the phials contained a small portion of common air, the larger less than the other.

I have several kinds of inflammable air that contain *combined fixed air,* and it occurs to me that it is very possible that it may be favourable to vegetation. I will try the first opportunity, and inform you of the result. . . .

No. 129.

FROM PRIESTLEY TO MARTIN VON MARUM

Birmingham 9 June 1786.

Dear Sir

I think myself honoured by being elected a member of the Society at Harlem, and by you signify my acceptance of it in the most respectful manner.

I shall be happy to receive the second part of your experiments, with the great electric machine, not doubting but they will give me as much pleasure as the first has done. I ordered my bookseller to send you my *6th volume of experiments* just published, and likewise my *History of early Opinions concerning Christ* 4 Vols I hope you will soon receive them, and I shall be glad to find that they give you any satisfaction. . . .

No. 130.

FROM PRIESTLEY TO JAN INGENHOUSZ

Dear Sir

I beg leave to recommend to your notice a young man, (Mr R. Pearson) a student in Medicine, travelling to improve himself. He is brother to an acquaintance of mine in this town; and not knowing him personally, I can only say that I hope you will not find him unworthy of your favour.

I thank you for the French edition of your work, which I received some time ago; but I am sorry to perceive, in the preface, something that looks as if you, or your friends, thought I wished to detract from your merit, which is very far from being my disposition. I do not indeed distinctly see what ground there is for any interference between us.

That plants restore vitiated air, I discovered at a very early period. Afterwards I found that the air in which they are confined was sometimes better than common air, and that the green matter, which I at first, and several of my friends always, thought to be a vegetable produced pure air by means of light. Immediately after the publication of these facts, and before I had seen your book, I had found that other whole plants did the same. All the time that I was making these experiments, I wrote to my friends about them, particularly to Mr Magellan, and desired him to communicate my observations to you, as well as to others; but I believe you had not heard of them; so that what you did with *leaves* was altogether independant of what I was doing with *whole plants*. The same summer, and the same sun, operated for us both, and you certainly published before me.

This appears to me to be a true state of the case; and surely it leaves no room for suspicion of anything unfair, or unfriendly. But whatever your friends may say, I have no thoughts of troubling the public with any vindication. I value you, and your friendship, too much to wish to have any altercation on the subject. Indeed, there is nothing to contend about. If, on any future occasion, you will do me the justice to give this state of the matter, I shall be happy. If not, I shall not complain.

I hope you have received my last volume of experiments, which I sent you. I am now busy with others. I have lately proved that a great proportion of the weight of fixed air is water, and what is perhaps of more consequence, I find that, in many cases, the decomposition of pure and inflammable air produces *little water,* but *some acid,* tho no acid was employed in procuring either of the two kinds of air that are so decomposed. What the acid is, I have not yet ascertained, but hope to do it soon. . . .

Birmingham 24 Novbr 1787

No. 131.

From Priestley to Josiah Wedgwood

Birmingham, 8 Jan. 1788.

Dear Sir

As the experiments in which I am now engaged promise to be of some consequence with respect to what has of late been the subject of philosophical discussion, I give you the earliest account of the probable issue of them.

They completely refute the hypothesis of d^d and inflammable air composing *only water.* The decomposition of them always produces *acid,* and Dr. Withering finds it to be as yet in all cases the nitrous. They give reason to think that the great quantity of *water* that has been found in this case is nothing more than was diffused through the airs or was necessary to their aerial form. I almost conclude that water is the basis of all kinds of air. One of my experiments (on terra ponderosa) proves that it is a considerable part of fixed air, not less than one-third of its weight; tho' it has been thought to consist of nothing but d^d and inflammable air.

My experiments seem to render doubtful the conclusion that Mr. Cavendish draws from his, as I get nitrous acid from d^d air without any that is phlogisticated. This is the case whether the d^d air be got from manganese, red precipitate or red lead.

I should be happy if you could find time to give me a call as you go thro' Birmingham to show you my apparatus for these experiments. They are not yet completed, and they are very laborious as well as expensive. I shall soon proceed to diversify my process by the use of the excellent tubes you sent me, and shall not fail to give you an account of the results. . . .

No. 132.

From Priestley to Josiah Wedgwood

Birm. 18th August, 1788

Dear Sir

Such is the interest you take in philosophical discoveries, and such are my numerous obligations to you with respect to those that I had in this business, that I cannot help giving you an early account of everything I do that I think will give you any pleasure.

Since my last, by Mr. Landriani, I have greatly diversified my process for the decomposition of the different kinds of air, and see clearly the cause of the fallacy in Mr. Lavoisier's experiments and my own, in which we found *pure water*, when I now always find some *acid*. This was the *small quantity*, and the extreme *volatility* of the acid, owing to its high phlogistication. I can procure either pure water or a dry and condensed vapour at pleasure.

Mr. Berthollet, suspecting the purity of my *precipitate per se*, desired I would send him a specimen of it. This I did, and he has sent me some in return, and with this I have a result much more favorable to my conclusion than I had imagined it would be. For, heating it in inflammable air, I find a considerable quantity of *fixed* air in the vessel. This I had overlooked before, and ascribed the acidity of the drop of water to nitrous acid. I have the same result from using *minium*, which is a substance quite as unexceptionable as the precipitate, since it yields only pure air with heat. This process is therefore similar to that in which iron is heated in pure air. In this case the inflammable air from the iron uniting with the pure air in the vessel forms fixed air, and the same is formed by the union of the pure air from the precipitate or minium, and the inflammable air of the vessel.

The objection that Mr. Cavendish and Dr. Blagden made to my experiments was that the acid I procured was from *phlogisticated air;* but this I have abundantly obviated, for in all the processes the more there is of this air (or of any other kind that cannot be decomposed by it) the less air [acid] I find.

On Monday I set out on a visit to Mr. Galton, at the seaside, near Exeter, having some little occasion for it on account of my health. . . .

P.S. I desired Mr. Johnson to send you a copy of my Additional Observations, with one for Mr. Darwin.

No. 133.

From Priestley to Martin von Marum

Dear Sir

It gives me the greatest concern to find that neither the letter I wrote to you, on the receipt of your kind present of a Copy of the Teylerian experiments, nor the copy of my *History of Early Opinions concerning Christ,* which I sent at the same time, have reached you. My bookseller had orders to send them to you immediately after I received your letter. This has happened to me so often, that I now despair of getting anything conveyed abroad with certainty.

I took the liberty to send you the theological work, because I was happy to find, by your letter, that you gave some attention to the subject. A philosophical and rational christian is a character on which I set the highest value

You have obliged me very much by the communication of your curious experiment, which appears to me to favour the opinion of the principle of inflammability being contained in charcoal, and not in water; tho some substances will not part with all their water even in a red heat; and on this principle I account for the water you got in procuring the air.

A second paper of mine, on the subject of the first, is now published in the P. Transactions, and a third is before the Royal Society. You may depend upon having copy of it transmitted to you as soon as it is printed. In it I prove that when the inflammable and dephlogisticated airs are already formed, the decomposition of them produces the *nitrous acid;* but that if either of them unite with the other in the act of its formation, as it is dislodged from the substance that yields it, the produce, in all the cases, which are very many, is uniformly *fixed air.* Water is clearly, in my opinion, an element in the composition of all kinds of air.

Along with my letter I sent you some hints for electrical experiments, with your great machine, from Dr Withering. I greatly admire all that you have done, and have never heard, I do assure you, that the truth of any of your experiments was ever called in question by any person. . . .

Birmingham Decbr 12. 1788.

No. 134.

FROM JAMES KEIR TO PRIESTLEY

[n.d., but probably 1789?]

Dear Sir,

I return you Doctor Blagden's letter, with thanks for the pleasure of reading it. When you write to him, be so kind as to give him my thanks for his obliging communication respecting the freezing of the vitriolic acid.

The more we discover of Nature, the further we are removed from the conceit of our being able to understand her operations.

I wish M. Berthollet and his associates would relate their facts in plain prose, that all men might understand them, and reserve their poetry of the new nomenclature for their theoretical commentaries on the facts.

I have wished much to call on you to hear of the progress of your experiments, but have been much indisposed with the rheumatism. I long to know what acids you get with the other inflammable airs. If you get different acids from the inflammable air made from sulphur and water, that made from marine acid and copper (for I would avoid iron on account of its plumbago and carbon), and that made from charcoal and water: —— I say, if these acids are different (suppose, according to my notions, vitriolic, marine, and fixed air), then, will you not be obliged to admit that there is not one inflammable but many inflammables, which opinion you now think as heterodox as the Athanasian system. However, there are wonderful resources in the dispute about phlogiston, by which either party can evade, so that I am less sanguine than you are in my hopes of seeing it terminated. One consolation remains, that in your experiments you cannot fail of discovering something, perhaps of as great or greater importance to us to know. . . .

No. 135.

FROM PRIESTLEY TO JOHN PARKER

Birmingham June 8 1789

Dear Sir

I desired Mr Lindsey to inform you that the lens arrived very safe, and how sensible I am of your kindness in making me so noble a present. We have not had much sun shine, but I have tried the full force of it, and find it to be considerably superior to the 12 inch lens, tho not in proportion to its greater size. I have made some important experiments with it already, of which I give an account in a Paper which I have drawn up for the Royal Society, and in it I have not failed to make what I thought a proper mention of your name.

As the power of the lens may be increased by another, to bring the rays to a nearer focus, I am very willing to be at the expense of one for the purpose, and shall think myself much obliged to you if you will provide me such an one as you know will suit it, and charge it to me along with the expense of the two glass plates for the Electrical Machine, which you were so good as to get for me some time ago. I can easily get it fixed in its proper place &c here. . . .

P.S. Please to inform your son that, if he dissolve the Ashes in water, and then put to it a weak solution of oil of vitriol, such as will not decompose common salt, he will easily find the proportional quantity of alkali in the ashes. It is only a [strong] concentrated o[il of] vitriol, or a weaker with heat, that [will deco]mpose common salt.

No. 136.

FROM PRIESTLEY TO MARTIN VON MARUM

Dear Sir

The direction you were pleased to give me to your private lodgings, being on the back of letter, I have mislaid; but I hope this, to *Mr Adams,* will find you. I wished to have been able to give you an account of my repetition of the experiment on the decomposition of water by Mr Bertholet; but I have not yet succeeded. I have, however, repeated my own former experiment with more precautions, especially using no air pump, but still, the purer the dephlogisticated air is, the more acid I find. I do not, however, question the result of Mr Bertholet's experiment. He is too cautious a man to be deceived, but I imagine more than we were aware of depends on the different methods of combining the two kinds of air; which is a circumstance that deserves close attention, and such I propose to give to it.

With this you will receive a copy of my *History of Early Opinions concerning Christ,* the third, I believe, that I have endeavoured to convey to you.

Please to shew Mr Johnson (No 72 St Paul's) this letter, and if he has not sent you a copy of the *new edition of my Philosophical work,* he will deliver one according to the order that you shall give him.

On monday next our little philosophical society meets, and

happy should all of us have been to have had you of the party.
The experiment of Mr Bertholet will be much the subject of our
conversation. . . .

Birmingham Aug 21. 1790

No. 137.

From Priestley to Josiah Wedgwood

Birm., Feb. 26, 1791.

Dear Sir

Knowing the interest you take in matters of philosophy, I
thought it would not be displeasing to you to know the late results
of my late experiments, especially what is really curious. I can at
pleasure make either *nitrous acid,* or *pure water,* with the same
materials, viz., dephlogisticated air and inflammable air. If there
be a surplus of the d^d air, the result is always acid, if of the inflammable air, it is mere water. Extraordinary as this is, it is uniform,
so that both Mr Lavoisier and myself have been right. The doctrine of *phlogiston,* however, stands firm; as it only appears that
it is one element in the composition of water.

I shall send a paper on this subject to the Royal Society in the
beginning of next week. It will decide this long contest. . . .

P.S. My eldest son is at length fixed at Manchester, and I hope
to advantage.

Have you seen Mr Paine's answer to Mr Burke? It is most excellent, and the boldest publication that I have ever seen.

No. 138.

From Priestley to the Duc de La Rochefoucauld
["Mr De Rochfocault"]

Dear Sir

Having an opportunity of writing to you by my friend, and a
friend to your glorious revolution, Mr T. Christie, I was unwill-

[255]

ing to neglect it, partly to congratulate you on that wonderful event, and in part to give you a short account of some experiments that I have lately made. For tho' the greatest part of your valuable time, I presume, is given to the greater interests of your country, I trust that science will never be wholly neglected by you. For that concerns not only France, but all the world.

Exploding inflammable and dephlogisticated air, I constantly find that, if there be a surplus of the latter, the produce is *nitrous acid,* but if of the former, *pure water;* but then there is always a production of *phlogisticated air,* which, according to my former experiments, contains both *phlogiston,* and the *principle of acidity* which is in dephlogisticated air. This air, as I make it, contains no sensible quantity of phlogisticated air, and I make no use of an *air pump,* but fill a copper vessel with water, and then displace it by the mixture of air; so that the objections that were made to my former experiments are intirely obviated. The dephlogisticated air I used before was quite pure, but it did not *appear* to be so, in consequence of my trying it with *nitrous air from copper,* whereas that from *mercury* diminishes respirable air much farther.

I sent you by Mr Vaughn a copy of my *answer to Mr Burke,* the Aristocrat of our country; but it related chiefly to ecclesiastical matters. Mr Paine's is a much more proper answer, as it relates to the revolution itself, the history of which I did not pretend to be master of. Mr Christie has half printed another and most excellent answer, containing more valuable information than even Mr Paine's work. There have been already about 25 answers to Mr Burke, and only one or two defences, so that you must not judge of the sense of the English nation, by that of the Court.

Earnestly wishing, for the sake of the noble example that you are setting to all nations, that you may go on with vigour and success in the great work of reformation, which [is] much greater than that of Hercules in cleansing the Augean stables. . . .

London Apl. 28, 1791.

No. 139.

FROM PRIESTLEY TO THOMAS WEDGWOOD

Birm., June 20, 1791.

Dear Sir

I like very much the plan of experiments that you mention, as they will very probably throw some new light on a very important subject, about which we as yet know very little. Indeed *Light* and *Heat* are little known, and yet I think they are as open to investigation as *air*. The experiments will no doubt be labourious, but nothing of value is to be had without labour, and in that long attention to our subject which they oblige us to new views will often arise, relating not only to that but to other things. I shall be very glad to hear of the progress you make.

You are very kind in inquiring after the subscription to the expence of my experiments. It is, of course, variable, both on account of deaths and caprice, but I am far from having reason to complain, and your father's uncommon generosity makes it impossible for me to receive anything more from the same family.

I should on several accounts be very happy to see you, and I hope if you can continue to come this way, you will be so good as to spend some time with me. . . .

No. 140.

THE CHEMISTS OF PARIS TO DOCTOR PRIESTLEY, GREETINGS

At the news of the dangers that you have run and the fury from which you have escaped, we, the Students of Chemistry, Medicine, and Pharmacy, join in addressing to you the testimony of their sensibility: it was your pupils who assembled; and all those who occupy themselves with the sciences in this Capital are proud to rank themselves among these.

You have, Sir, opened new directions in the sciences: you have honored the age and the country of your birth; you have been

[257]

wise, good, virtuous, and just; to have been persecuted miscarries to your glory and thus you acquire another point of resemblance with the most famous philosophers of antiquity.

As a Citizen, you belong to England, and it is to her to atone for your losses: as a Scholar and as a Philosopher you belong to the entire world; you belong, above all, to those who know how to appreciate you, and it is we, united in agreement, who vow to restore to you the instruments which you have employed so usefully in our instruction. We have therefore resolved to reestablish your Cabinet, to raise again the Temple which ignorance, barbarity, and supersition have dared profane. What more important service can we render to science than to place in your hands the instruments necessary for its cultivation?

Zealous defender of the liberty which our country aims to obtain, we have not been idle witnesses of the most astonishing of the revolutions of which the annals of the world have preserved the memory. We have followed its movements and progress with that spirit of observation which the study of science bestows and which we have imbibed from the works of our teacher. If, in the midst of the civic enthusiasm in which we have all repeatedly participated, the French people have been carried sometimes to blameworthy excess, it was always against oppression that they were armed: they defended the cause of tolerance, of liberty, and of philosophy. One cannot but expect that a people who declare themselves free and believe themselves enlightened would tend to excesses toward their opposers. We refrain from blaming them: the truly guilty are those who have misled them. We copy your virtue and we repeat with you that even the excesses which have been committed have done more in four days for the progress of reason, tolerance, and philosophy than the writings of wise men have been able to do in two centuries. . . .

[Another letter of the same type as the above, written by M. J. A. N. C. de Condorcet for the French Academy of Sciences and dated 30 July 1791, was printed in translation in Priestley's *An Appeal to the Public on the Subject of the Riots in Birmingham*, 2nd ed. (Birmingham, 1792), pp. 154–

156. A manuscript copy in the original French is preserved in the Bodleian Library, Oxford.]

No. 141.

FROM JOSIAH WEDGWOOD TO PRIESTLEY

Sep. 2. 1791.

Dear Sir,

I cannot refrain from expressing to you the high satisfaction I have received from the kind & very honourable attention paid to you on your late heavy misfortune by the Philosophers of Paris. I suppose their address will by this time have been presented to you, for the letter which mentioned it to me from Mr. Seguin is dated Aug: 10 though from a mistake in the direction it has been on the road till now, he says "We have all taken a great part in the misfortune which has fallen upon M. Priestley, we esteem him in every point of view; and we are employed at this moment in drawing up a letter which is to be addressed to him by all the Savants of the Capital." I persuade myself therefore that you will rise still more splendid & more respected from what was intended to sink you; and I am sure I am not mistaken in what I have said to Mr. Seguin, that your calmness & magnanimity on this trying occasion have put your enemies to shame.

I should not however have intruded upon you at present with a letter merely on this subject. Mess: Lavoisier & Seguin have requested some information from me, which I do not find myself very capable of supplying out of my own funds. They are constructing a furnace to be fed with vital air, in which they mean to melt 100 pounds of Platina, for the use of the Commissaires appointed by the Academy for the ascertaining of weights & measures.

It was natural enough for them to apply to me on this occasion for clay of the most unfusible nature, but I know of none which possess this property in a greater degree than the Stourbridge and I am confident that they have in France clays as refractory as this. Do you think Sir, that these or any clays can stand the action of a fire with dephlogisticated air? You have had some experience on this subject; I have not. I have recommended to them & sent them a specimen of a mixture of burnt alum earth with a proper quantity of the gelatinous precipitate of alum by alcali; this last giving the argillaceous tenacity which makes the mass fit for being formed into vessels, & the burnt earth serving to divide it & to prevent the great diminution & cracks to which the gelly alone is subject. I find vessels made of this composition to be reduced by a heat of 160° of my thermometer merely to the state of ordinary unbaked clay. —— and the interval must surely be very great between the heat which produces this effect only & that which would be necessary to bring them into fusion. Whether the difference is equally great between the effects of vital & atmospheric air, I cannot at all judge, but if at any time you should have occasion for a small vessel or lute to support any uncommonly intense heat I can venture to recommend such a composition to you. ——

Mr. Lavoisier has sent for two of my thermometers which I have accordingly forwarded to him. Mr. Seguin says "We find this instrument of the greatest use and at this moment feel more than ever its indispensibility; because we are occupying ourselves, Mr. Lavoisier & I in completing the theory of furnaces of fusion, but we are still in need of some instructions which we pray you to be pleased to give us." They want to know whether the degrees of this thermometer indicate the *real* comparative quantities of heat; I think it is not likely that they should; nor do I know that those even of the mercurial thermr. do. Have you ever made any observations on the thermor. pieces with this view?

They desire to know particularly what is the greatest degree of heat that has been given to the thermr. pieces either by myself or by any other person in England; & whether any new observations have been made upon this instrument. I shall therefore be glad to be informed what heat you have gone to or of any new facts which may have occurred to you in the use of the pieces. When I have the pleasure of knowing where I shall send you a new stock of tubes &c I shall take the liberty of including a thermr. with them.

Mr. Seguin wishes also to know what kind of fuel we have found in an equal rate to produce the most intense heat, —— Whether the greatest heat is in the middle of the burning fuel or at the extremity of the flame. Whether large bellows or very high chimneys produce the greatest effect. To what degree of heat they go in the iron furnaces and whether anyone has been able to bring iron into fusion when totally deprived of all contact of air. For the three last queries I have applied to Mr. Wm. Reynolds. I should be very thankful for any information that you could afford on these points either to me or immediately to Mr. Seguin himself in case you write to him.

I beg my best respects to Mrs. Priestley & shall be glad to hear & if you see Mr. Russell be so kind as to remember me to him most affectionately I have not troubled him with a letter on the present occasion, but I sympathize sincerely in his calamity and should be happy in having it in my power to give any alleviation to it . . . .

No. 142.

FROM PRIESTLEY TO JOSIAH WEDGWOOD

London, Sept. 7, 1791

Dear Sir

I am much obliged, and honored, by the attention that has been paid to me both at home and abroad. My answer to the Address of the Academy of Sciences was first published in a very awkward garb from a double translation, but yesterday a friend of mine got it inserted as I wrote it in the Morning Chronicle.

I am glad to hear of the intended experiment at Paris, but am not able to give them any particular assistance, from any experience that I have had of the kind. I know nothing so likely to stand the action of their fire as *magnesia*. Everything else I think has been melted. I forget the greatest degree of heat that I ever produced; but it did not much exceed what you have mentioned, except when the clay and case were so melted, that I could not take any measure.

Your thermometer can no more give the degree of *real heat* than any other, if by heat be meant the *fluid* that is supposed to be the cause of heat. But all causes are ascertained by their effects. On this subject I had intended to make some experiments, though with no great expectation of discovering anything, and had provided myself with Dr. Crawford's apparatus for the purpose, part of which you were so obliging as to supply me with, (viz., 4 vessels to heat acids in) when my laboratory was destroyed.

As what you generously gave to *me,* I am not obliged to give to the country, I shall be glad to know what I am to charge for the several articles you have furnished me with; viz., *retorts, tubes, mortars, evaporating vessels, levigators, Dr. Crawford's vessels,* and vessels 12 inches deep, with ground stoppers *for a sand heat.*

No attempt, I believe has been made to melt iron without the contact of air or steam. It is done with steel, but the fusion of iron converts it into finery cinder.

About the middle of next week I shall probably have the pleasure of calling on you at Etruria, if you will be at home, on my way to Castlehead, when I shall have much to say to you. My wife and son I hope will be with me. . . .

No. 143.

FROM PRIESTLEY TO SIR JOSEPH BANKS

Dear Sir

Having lost my whole stock of substances, ores, minerals, earths &c &c for the purpose of experiments, and being willing to replace them as expeditiously as possible, I shall be obliged to you if you will mention my situation to any of your friends whose laboratories are furnished, and who may have any thing to spare to set up a broken philosopher.

I shall take the first opportunity of doing myself the pleasure of waiting upon you. . . .

Clapton Jany. 10. 1792.

[On the verso page, in Banks's hand]

> offerd to him
> Black Lead
> Menecanite
> Sand)
>   from Sidney Cove
> Clay)
> Adamantine Spar
> Green Sand
> Garnet Sand from India
> do. from Greece
> Earth of Borax
> Tobasher

No. 144.

FROM PRIESTLEY TO ANTOINE LAVOISIER

[Hackney] June 2d, 1792

Dear Sir

I take the liberty to introduce to you Mr. Jones, who was lecturer in chemistry at the New College in Hackney, in which employment I now succeed him, and who is to be my successor at Birmingham. You will find him to be equally modest and sensible, and, as a philosopher, more inclined, I believe, to your system than to mine; but open, as we ought all to be, to conviction as new facts present themselves to us.

The late riots have interrupted my experiments near a whole year, but I am now refitting my apparatus and about to resume my usual pursuits, and I shall not fail to give due attention to what you may advance in reply to my last memoir on the subject, a copy of which I sent you; and for this purpose I shall be glad to be informed concerning them. Mr. Jones will convey your sentiments to me.

In case of more riots, of which we are not without apprehension, I shall be glad to take refuge in your country, the liberties of which I hope will be established notwithstanding the present combination against you. I also hope the issue will be as favourable to science as to liberty. . . .

No. 145.

FROM PRIESTLEY TO WILLIAM WITHERING

Clapton, Oct. 2, 1792

Dear Sir

I thank you for the third volume of your excellent Botanical work. I should now have the whole complete, but that the rioters have deprived me of the *first volume*. One of the most disagreeable circumstances attending the riot, with respect to my *books,* is that the sets are almost all broken, so that if they consisted of three volumes or more, hardly any of them are complete.

I have been much concerned to hear of the alarming return of your disorder, but I hope that report has magnified the danger. It was said that you would be under the necessity of removing to a warmer climate.

One of the things that I regret the most, in being expelled from Birmingham, is the loss of your company, and that of the rest of the Lunar Society. I feel I want the spur to constant exertion which I had with you. My philosophical friends here are cold and distant. Mr Cavendish never expressed the least concern on account of anything I had suffered, tho' I joined a party with which he was, and talked with them some time. I do not expect much intercourse with any of them.

I have, however, nearly replaced my apparatus, and intend not to be idle. I have already made some experiments relating to the *doctrine of phlogiston,* and when I have made a few more shall probably write something on the subject. I am surprised at the confidence with which the French chemists write; but I cannot yet learn what they have to object to my last Paper in the Philosophical Transactions. A friend at Paris, at my request, applied to

M. Lavoisier, and others, but got no satisfactory answer, but since the tenth of August he has absconded, and where he now is I cannot learn.

I was in hopes to have been able to pay my friends of Birm. a visit long before this time, but was always discouraged, so that I have now given up the thoughts of it, and must content myself with seeing as many of them as I can here. I should be very happy to see *you*, but fear I must dispair of that satisfaction. I do not, however, think I shall continue here long. Tho' unwillingly I shall some time hence follow my son to France. But as I can *do* nothing there I will stay here as long as I can. I shall be very happy to hear from you. . . .

No. 146.

FROM PRIESTLEY TO WILLIAM WITHERING

Clapton, April 15, 1793

Dear Sir

I take the opportunity of Mr Skey and Mr Russell's visit to Lisbon to congratulate you on the good accounts I have of your health. I hope now that with care it will be thoroughly established, so as to bear your native climate. Many times have your friends been alarmed for you, but you have always understood your own disorder, and have happily hit upon the proper remedy.

I wish the country was in a better state to invite your return to it, but it is far otherwise, at least with respect to myself and those who have generally passed for the friends of liberty. Such is the spirit of bigotry encouraged by the Court party, that great numbers are going to America, and among others all my sons, and my intention is, that when they are settled to follow them and end my days there. This will be a great mortification to me, after having replaced my apparatus, and recommenced my experiments, as I now have done. Indeed, to appearance, I have everything very comfortable about me, but I cannot get so much time to myself as I wish, and I have little intercourse with the members of the Royal Society. On both these accounts I do less in my laboratory than I wish to do. The Lunar Society was an unspeakable advantage to me, and I am unable to replace it here. I am not, however, quite idle, and some things that I have done tend to confirm the doctrine of phlogiston. I cannot yet learn what the French philosophers object to in my last paper, and I have repeatedly applied to them for the purpose, so that I think with you that their *charbon* or *hydrogene* will prove to be nothing more than another name for *phlogiston*. Still, however, the question will be whether either of them be contained in *metals,* or make an essential part of *water.*

Living in the neighbourhood of New College, I have given a course of lectures in chemistry, and have some thoughts of publishing the heads of my course for the students, and if I do, I shall add some observations on the new theory.

I send you a second part of my appeal to the public on the subject of the Riots, and some letters I have addressed to the Philosophers and Politicians of France. Neither of them, however, I fear, will have much effect. We have not yet received any indemnification for our losses. A petition is before Parliament for leave to borrow the money and raise it at different times, as it is found to be impracticable to collect the whole at once, as the law requires, but Mr Fox will oppose it as contrary to the intention of the law, and what will be done I cannot tell.

We have no intercourse now with France, and whether my son William has been able to leave it and go to America I cannot learn. Indeed, the prospect is very melancholy. The conduct of the French has been such as their best friends cannot approve; but certainly the present combination against them, which does not appear to have any other object than the restoration of the old arbitrary government, is as little to be justified.

Wishing, tho' hardly hoping, for better times. . . .

Although this correspondence contains but one letter from Priestley to Lavoisier (No. 144, of little importance but the only one so far uncovered) and specific references to him are scant, few of these letters can be read without seeing between their lines the shadow of the French systematist. The first letter (No. 90) sets the stage and also shows Priestley's resistance to ideas other than his own. Lavoisier had been outlining his growing objections to the theory of phlogiston at least since 1776 and had explicitly denied it in a series of publications of 1780. Yet this letter notes only his objections to Priestley's phlogistic theory of respiration. Not until the spring of 1782 (Nos. 93, 95) does Priestley recognize that a major attack has begun against the entire theory of phlogiston. From this time Priestley begins to display what Sir Philip Hartog has described as his "perverse ingenuity in adapting the phlogiston theory to fit every new fact."[2]

It is not immediately obvious, however, that his opposition to the theory of oxidation was a compulsive reaction which was to dominate Priestley's research until his death. Indeed, the first set of experiments described in these letters seems wholly unrelated to that controversy. There is some suggestion of a practical consideration (Nos. 90, 91) in his extraction of air from rocks and minerals, but the immediate motive appears to have been the geological interests of his fellow members in the Lunar Society. The earliest published report of his work is a prefixed note to William Withering's "Analysis of Two Mineral Substances, viz: The Rowley-Rag-Stone and the Toadstone," which appeared in the *Philosophical Transactions* for 1782. A later account with more detail in the 1786 volume of Priestley's *Experiments and Observations* reveals that he had joined the camp of "neptunist" geologists, in opposition to the "plutonist" majority of the Lunar Society, because in his opinion basalt and granite yield too much air on heating to be the product of volcanic action.[3]

[2] Hartog, "Newer Views of Priestley and Lavoisier," p. 46.
[3] Withering, "Analysis . . . ," *Philosophical Transactions*, 72 (1782), 327; Priestley, *Experiments and Observations relating to . . . Natural Philosophy* (Birmingham, 1786), vol. 3, pp. 215–222. We might note also that the reference (No. 91) to Keir's belief in the vitreous nature of basalt is described in more detail in James Keir, "On the Crystallizations observed on Glass," *Philosophical Transactions*, 66 (1776), 530–542.

It is, however, instructive for Priestley's many critics who argue his inability to conduct a connected pattern of research to examine the relationship of this investigation to his earlier work and to trace its progress into those studies on water and air which preempt so much of his research effort during this period. In his first important chemical paper, Priestley wrote:

> Considering this amazing consumption of air, by fires of all kinds, volcano's, &c. it becomes a great object of philosophical inquiry, to ascertain what change is made in the constitution of the air by flame, and to discover what provision there is in nature for remedying the injury which the atmosphere receives by this means.[4]

The connection between this statement and the attempt to recover air by heating volcanic substances is an obvious one. The supposed transforming of water into air by heating it in contact with calcareous substances has ultimately the same motivation (see Nos. 103, 104), though the progression to these experiments is not so directly to be seen, particularly because consideration of them becomes involved so quickly in what has since been called "the water controversy." Nonetheless, the elements in the progression are here to be noted. To the desire to find a natural origin of atmospheric air must be added Priestley's persistent conviction that mixture with water had a "revivifying" influence on airs rendered unfit for breathing, and also Watt's long-held belief (Nos. 101, 113, 114) that water might be converted into permanent air, if its latent heat was changed to sensible heat.[5] Finally, there was the inverse effect — first noted in a letter by John Warltire ap-

[4] Priestley, "Observations on different Kinds of Air," *Philosophical Transactions*, 62 (1772), 162.

[5] Details of this set of experiments and some of the motivation behind it are in Priestley, "Experiments relating to Phlogiston, and the seeming Conversion of Water into Air," *Philosophical Transactions*, 73 (1783), 398–434, particularly p. 416.

pended to the 1781 volume of Priestley's *Experiments and Observations* — showing that mixtures of inflammable and common airs repeatedly fired by electric spark produced water.[6] The sum of these influences resulted in a class of experiments which Priestley was repeatedly to perform throughout the remainder of his life, and in a delusion in which he was to persist to the ultimate detriment of his scientific reputation.

The extent to which Priestley committed himself in correspondence to his belief in the conversion of water to air by heating reflects his growing confidence in the accuracy of his experiments — in spite of the anomalies he noted (Nos. 105, 106, 109) and Wedgwood particularly queried (No. 107) — until the dénouement of April 1783 (No. 111), and not even the fact that his work represents the first significant notice of differential gaseous diffusion has saved Priestley from the obloquy which has followed on the discovery of his error. For, while Priestley was following the "wrong" clues, Cavendish, then Watt, and finally Lavoisier were on the "right" trail. The varying roles of Priestley, Cavendish, Watt, and Lavoisier in the discovery of the composition of water have been the subject of argument since Lavoisier announced that discovery in June and November of 1783.[7] In his letters to Sir Joseph Banks and Jean André DeLuc (Nos. 112–115), written during

---

[6] Priestley, *Experiments and Observations relating to . . . Natural Philosophy* (Birmingham, 1781), pp. *395–*398; Warltire's letter was added so late in the printing of the volume that some copies do not contain it. Priestley's comment on the letters appears to be the first published reference to the Lunar Society.

[7] The most extended treatment of the arguments can be found in James Patrick Muirhead, ed., *Correspondence of the Late James Watt on his Discovery of the Theory of the Composition of Water* (London, John Murray, 1846) and in George Wilson, *Life of the Honorable Henry Cavendish* (London, Cavendish Society, 1851). The more recent evidence in the letters included here is discussed in Sidney Edelstein, "Priestley Settles the Water Controversy," and R. E. Schofield, "Still More on the Water Controversy," *Chymia*, 1 (1948), 123–127; and 9 (1964), 71–76, respectively.

the earliest phase of the "controversy," Priestley defines his position: Cavendish performed the initial experiments, Priestley repeated them, and Watt interpreted them. What is not made clear is that Watt's letter, at first withheld from formal presentation to the Royal Society and subsequently released to De-Luc (Nos. 112, 114), interprets experiments which do not accord with those Priestley described to the Society in his paper of 1783, "on the seeming Conversion of Water into Air." Nor is there any suggestion in the correspondence between Priestley and Cavendish (Nos. 116–118, 122, 123) that Cavendish had read a paper on 15 January 1784, claiming:

. . . that water consists of dephlogisticated air united to phlogiston . . . [and] that dephlogisticated air is only water deprived of its phlogiston, and that inflammable air . . . is either phlogisticated water, or else pure phlogiston, but in all probability the former.[8]

Nor does that correspondence disclose that Watt had responded to both Lavoisier's and Cavendish's claims with the reading to the Royal Society in April 1784 of his 1783 letter and a supplement.[9]

Not the least remarkable aspect of this set of Priestley–Cavendish letters, for all their timeliness, is the complete absence of any reference to the composition of water, though the letter to Wilkinson (No. 119) written on the same date as one of those to Cavendish (No. 118) indicates Priestley's reservations about the notion of water as a unique compound, at least, of dephlogisticated and inflammable airs.[10] This corre-

8 Henry Cavendish, "Experiments on Air," *Philosophical Transactions,* 74 (1784), 137, 140.
9 James Watt, "Thoughts on the constituent parts of Water and of Dephlogisticated Air," and "Sequel to the Thoughts on the constituent Parts of Water," *Philosophical Transactions,* 74 (1784), 329–353, 354–357.
10 Priestley wrote another letter of the same date to Wedgwood, which is substantially the same as that to Wilkinson. Bolton, who prints the letter as No. 29 in his *Scientific Correspondence of Joseph Priestley,* misdates the letter as 26 January 1784, on the authority of George Wilson (*Life of Cavendish,* p. 95), who uses the letter to support Cavendish's claims.

spondence, perhaps particularly the letter to Cavendish (No. 123), in which Priestley with what seems almost typical perversity adopts the inverse option that "water is a necessary ingredient in inflammable air," reconfirms the view that it was Lavoisier alone who caught the significance of the discovery, recognizing in it the solution to the major unanswered problem of his theory of oxidation.[11] Neither Cavendish nor Watt quite understood the interpretation that Lavoisier gave their discovery; if Priestley understood, he soon found reason to oppose it.

Priestley's opposition to Lavoisier's concept of water became the most obvious block to his acceptance of the theory of oxidation as a whole. The reduction of metallic calces in inflammable air, which he cited (Nos. 92, 93, 95) in opposition to that theory could now, for example, have been fitted neatly into it — and was, by the Lavoisians — but Priestley resisted. The problem is to find why Priestley did not accept the Lavoisier view. On surface the answer is easy. Persistently, he offered his own conflicting experimental evidence to counter that of the antiphlogistic school. Yet it is here that his work seems least defensible, in spite of injunctions not to read back into history the obviousness of modern paradigms, for Priestley's experiments find easy interpretations within the frame of the oxidation theory. The two recurrent elements in his "bad" experiments are: the confusion of different inflammable airs — carbon monoxide and hydrogen, in particular — and the appearance of acidity in the product of water synthesis. The first of these also bothered the antiphlogistians and was only finally resolved by Cruickshank's positive identification of carbon monoxide in 1801; but there was ample previous indication of differences, and the chemical literature

[11] We may note that Cavendish's draft letter of December 1784 (No. 122) reveals to Priestley some five months before their publication those experiments on the analyses of atmospheric air which more than a century later inspired Rayleigh to the discovery of argon.

prior to Cruickshank had frequently referred to different kinds of inflammable airs. As for the second, Henry Cavendish had provided an explanation for the appearance of nitric acid in the nitrogen impurities which inevitably appeared either in preparation or use of the hydrogen or oxygen in synthesis experiments.[12]

In neither of these cases can the frequent accusation of ignorance of facts be accurately applied to Priestley. Not only does he publish accounts of various inflammable airs, but also in this series of letters he describes "a remarkable difference between the inflammable air from metals and that from *charcoal*" (Nos. 118, 119), while Keir specifically calls his attention to the "heterodox" possibility of different kinds of inflammable airs and what this might mean (No. 134).[13] And Priestley refers again and again to Cavendish's work on water synthesis and the production of nitric acid (e.g., Nos. 131, 138) without understanding (or perhaps "accepting" is the better term) the idea that the acid was more readily produced when the nitrogen impurity was present in small amounts.

Nor will the suggestion that Priestley somehow and suddenly had lost that skill in experimentation he had earlier shown bear examination. In this set of correspondence one can note the continuation of his experimental ability in the volumetric comparison of hydrogen and ammonia in the reduction of lead oxide (No. 93), in the analyses of ammonia and nitric oxide (Nos. 108, 120), in the ingenious application

12 See, for example, "Second Problème de Chymie à résoudre: Déterminer s'il y a plusieurs espèces de Gas inflammables, ou s'il n'y en a que d'une seule espèce," or ". . . sur l'Air des Marais & les différentes espèces de Gaz inflammable," [Rozier's] *Observations sur la Physique*, &c., 9 (1777), 321–322, and 19 (1782), 459–462, respectively; and Henry Cavendish, "Experiments on Air," *Philosophical Transactions*, 74 (1784), 119–153, and 75 (1785), 222–227.

13 See Priestley, *Experiments and Observations relating to . . . Natural Philosophy* (Birmingham, 1786), vol. 3, pp. 162–188; and *Experiments and Observations on Different Kinds of Air* (Birmingham, 1790), vol. 1, p. 205, where he even notes the different specific gravities of hydrogen and carbon monoxide.

of phlogistic principles to the understanding of the behavior of pyrolusite (No. 105), and particularly in the experiments (Nos. 118, 119, 120) in which he performs gravimetric analysis for the first (and only) time to significant purpose, and seems, to our ultimate frustration, to be on the point of confirming Lavoisier's views.[14] Obviously, Priestley was aware of the evidence and chose to ignore it, was capable of performing the apparently "crucial" experiments, and chose to interpret them in a different way.

Priestley's refusal to adopt the Lavoisian interpretations has given rise to accusations, the most sympathetic of which is Hartog's "perverse ingenuity." Yet it should be recognized that many of the specific interpretations though not the general ones) were "incorrect" and that they were all derived from a "crucial" conceptual scheme rather than being simple recitals of experimental "fact." The eighteenth-century neo-Baconian style of concealing theory under the recital of apparent fact makes it difficult, if not impossible, to determine from Priestley's published works what theory provided the rationalization for the seeming perversity of his ingenuity. These letters provide at least a clue to such a theory. The most revealing statement is that contained in the letter to Wedgwood of 8 December 1782 (No. 100), "I had also a general idea that if the parts of any bodies be rarefied beyond the sphere of *attraction* they will be in a sphere of repulsion to each other." This is the only indication in Priestley's writings of the direct application of Boscovich's theory of matter to his chemical speculations.[15] But with this as a guide, it is pos-

---

[14] For the pyrolusite experiments, see also *Experiments and Observations relating to ... Natural Philosophy* (Birmingham, 1786), vol. 3, p. 232; for the gravimetric experiments, see "Experiments and Observations relating to Air and Water," *Philosophical Transactions*, 75 (1785), 279–309, and for Hartog's comments, see his "Newer Views of Priestley and Lavoisier," p. 45.

[15] I have argued in "Joseph Priestley, the Theory of Oxidation and the Nature of Matter" (*op. cit.*) that Boscovich's theory of matter acted in a more subtle way to prevent Priestley's taking the theory of oxidation seriously.

sible to see the implications of the mechanistic terminology he so persistently employed in describing his work. The different "states" in which the phlogiston, contained in *precipitate per se* and mercury, existed (No. 95) may well be different spheres of attraction in the Boscovichian scheme. The *"aerial form"* lost by air in combination with the earth of retorts (No. 111) has the same connotation, which also goes far to explain Priestley's frequent references to the loss of elasticity and the decrease of volume as significant parameters in his experiments. The "different circumstances" or "different methods of combining airs" and the possibility that airs behaved differently if united after or during the act of their formation, as they are "dislodged" from the substances that "yield" them (Nos. 119, 133, 136, 137) — which Priestley thought might explain the varying production of water or fixed air from inflammable and dephlogisticated airs, or the differences between his results and those of Berthollet — suggest physical mechanisms for molecule formation which are best understood in a Boscovichian frame. This is seen still better when, in defiance of growing opinion and of our present understanding of chemical process, Priestley returns to the production, by physical means, of air from water. He ends the description of his experiments with the statement:

. . . the advances we are continually making in the analyses of natural substances into the *elements* of which they consist, bring us but one step nearer to their constitutional differences; since as much depends upon the *mode of arrangement,* concerning which we know nothing at all, as upon the elements themselves. For things the most different in their properties appear to consist of the very same elements. Thus the nitrous acid, nitrous air, fixed air, phlogisticated air, alkaline air, and probably all the kinds of air with which we are acquainted, except the dephlogisticated and inflammable, are all composed of dephlogisticated air and phlogiston.[16]

16 Priestley, *Experiments on the Generation of Air from Water, op. cit.,* p. 38.

Since we know that Priestley is here referring to inorganic and not organic chemistry, the emphasis on *"mode of arrangement"* seems excessively sophisticated, even when we know the Boscovichian origin of the idea. Without this knowledge — and few of his contemporaries (or subsequent critics) can have known — his work does appear simply perverse. Subsequent developments have shown that chemistry had a long way to develop, in terms of simple combinations of varying proportions of simple atoms, before it needed to worry about structural formulae and molecular models. Nonetheless, the new dimension to Priestley's thinking revealed by this analysis of his letters should add stature to his opposition to Lavoisier, making it wrong-headed rather than simple-minded.

Along with the insight these letters provide of greater scientific depths to Priestley's thinking, we obtain a reinforced respect for his rather bewildering integrity and courage. For these letters trace a personal tragedy as well as a scientific decline. Starting with that "situation . . . in all respects, a very agreeable one," Priestley ends this period of his life a lonely man on the verge of going into unwanted exile. From a well-stocked laboratory, patrons to supply research funds and equipment, and pupils to assist his labors, he goes to a makeshift laboratory painfully constructed by begging others' left-overs. Instead of a Lunar Society to encourage him, men seeking his advice, and societies honoring themselves by honoring him, he experiences the ostracism of his fellows of the Royal Society while his work is ignored rather than answered (Nos. 145, 146). Under such circumstances, the continuation of any research becomes a measure of personal merit; that he could do so with undiminished confidence, at the age of sixty, when on the verge of again removing his laboratory for reestablishment in the United States, may have been foolish, but it compels our admiration for its spirit.

CHAPTER SIX

Anticlimax
Northumberland, Pennsylvania
1794-1804

A LTHOUGH THE AMERICAN REVOLUTION occasioned the emigration of many intellectuals, including the scientists Dr. Alexander Garden and Benjamin Thompson, once the war was over a countercurrent set in. Priestley was but one of many such persons who early sought asylum in the United States from political or religious persecution. He was, however, the first distinguished scientist to do so, and thus he began a tradition of which Americans are justly proud. He also participated in another tradition, not so praiseworthy, in experiencing the differences between American pretensions and practice.

The Birmingham riots of 1791 had taught Priestley some of the folly of depending upon religious or political rationality in men. Moreover, early in 1793, his good friend Theophilus Lindsey had received a letter from the Reverend James Freeman of Boston, which surely Priestley saw before he sailed:

. . . bigotry is not yet extinct among us. Though it reflects disgrace upon some of my fellow citizens, I mention it freely because it gives me an opportunity of observing what I believe is not much attended to [in] England, that the people in America are much less liberal and enlightened than is generally imagined. . . . I have learned from various quarters that some liberal dissenters of England are migrating to this country. . . . I wish they may not be disappointed in their expectations.[1]

Priestley must therefore have been prepared for something less than the urbane tolerance of his late good friend Benjamin Franklin, but he cannot have known that his arrival would nearly coincide with that of an English journalist, uniquely talented for vituperation, who was to make attacks on Priestley a primary stock-in-trade over the next few years.

By these attacks, William Cobbett, passing through a conservative phase on the way to his later, more famous reactionary radicalism, injected Priestley into the midst of the bitter and protracted political campaign between Federalists and Jeffersonian democrats. Before the presidential election of Jefferson gave Priestley, for the first time in his memory, a friendly government under which to live, he had perforce to defend himself against the slander of "Peter Porcupine," he had seen one of his English companions arrested under the Sedition Act, and he himself had been threatened by the Alien Act of the Adams Administration.

Had Priestley settled in Philadelphia, the effects of such bigotry would surely have been less severe. Franklin's death four years earlier had deprived him of his only real American friend, but Franklin's influence remained, there were strong intellectual centers of liberalism in Philadelphia, and there was started the nearest thing to a Unitarian congregation Priestley was to see in his ten years in the United States. Instead he chose to move himself and family, baggage, books,

[1] James Freeman to the Reverend Mr. Lindsey, 16 June 1793; Dr. Williams's Library, London.

and laboratory apparatus a five-days' journey up the Susque-
hanna River to Northumberland, nearly one hundred and
fifty miles from Philadelphia and without any pretensions to
liberalism, intellectualism, or science. Though he may have
expected something nearer to the provincial culture of Birmingham, it is hard to believe he was totally unaware of the
primitive nature of an American backwoods settlement. This
condition, however, was to be changed. Somewhat north of
Northumberland, on nearly 700,000 acres of land optioned to
Priestley's sons, Thomas Cooper, and their friends, there was
to develop a new community of English liberal dissenters, of
which Priestley was to be the patriarch.

The colony failed to develop. Cooper's promotional pamphlet, *Some Information Respecting America* (London, 1794),
and some references to pantisocracy by Southey and Coleridge
are among the few extant reminders that it had ever been
planned, but it was not initially quite as visionary as it now
seems.[2] From the riots of 1791, through the transporting of
Thomas Palmer and Thomas Muir in 1793, to the indictment
of Thomas Hardy, John Horne Tooke, and John Thelwall
for high treason a month after Priestley sailed, it appeared that
the British government was determined to rid the country of
liberal dissent. Then heightened naval activities against
France made more difficult what the acquittal of Hardy,
Tooke, and Thelwall in December of 1794 made less pressing.
The stream of British settlers for the new community did not
materialize. This was probably just as well; few of the interested parties had the practical skills to sustain such an experiment in colonization; but their defection left Priestley virtually dependent upon himself and his family for intellectual
stimulation and without immediate access to the informed
criticism of his work that he had enjoyed in England.

2 The most complete story of this plan is in Mary Cathryne Park's "Joseph
Priestley and the Problem of Pantisocracy," *Proceedings of the Delaware
County Institute of Science*, 10 (1947), 1–60.

It is in fact not clear why he remained in Northumberland, though the unexpected expense of living in Philadelphia, Mrs. Priestley's forcibly acquired distaste for urban living, and the possibility of settling his sons on land nearby all presumably had a part in his decision. He built a house there and late in 1797 re-established his laboratory. Apparently, he attempted to pattern his life as much as possible after the one he had lived in provincial England, visiting Philadelphia annually as he had once visited London, submitting scientific papers to the American Philosophical Society as earlier he had to the Royal Society, and establishing a local printer to continue his career as a controversialist in theology. The circumstances were too unlike to make his new life more than a pale shadow of that in Leeds or Birmingham, but in spite of repeated illnesses, the death of his youngest son and his wife, and minor religious and political persecutions, he managed to carry on an active intellectual career until his death in 1804.

During his ten years at Northumberland he wrote more than a dozen theological works — including, as single items, the last four volumes of his *General History of the Christian Church*, the four volumes of *Notes on all the Books of Scripture*, and the *Index to the Bible*. During the same period he published two pamphlets and nearly forty papers on scientific experiments, many of the papers being printed in English journals as well as American.[3]

Nothing in Priestley's continuation of his *Memoirs* after settling in Northumberland refers to his scientific activities during this period, while his son's "completion" of the *Memoirs* mentions the pamphlets without giving details of the work in them. The published papers and his correspondence are therefore the only sources of information on Priestley's scientific thinking during these last ten years of his life.

[3] See Appendix III for a list of his scientific publications.

Fortunately for us, correspondence was Priestley's sole means during most of this time of keeping in touch with his friends and maintaining contact with the scientific world. There are more letters extant from this period than from any of the others. Most of these, unhappily, relate rather less to science than formerly, and a selection from their number gives substantially less information about his scientific work than earlier letters do. Equally unhappily, the published scientific writings of Priestley's American career have never been collected. Hence the letters printed here are neither complementary to easily available scientific works nor are they substitutions for them. The letters do, however, provide an impression of Priestley's final years as a natural philosopher, and serve to bring his scientific autobiography to a close.

No. 147.

FROM PRIESTLEY TO SAMUEL PARKER

Philadelphia June 27, 1794

Dear Sir

Your very obliging proposal to send me any philosophical instrument that I had occasion for, when I last had the pleasure of seeing you, emboldens me to request that, in addition to the glass vessels with which your father has always been so good as to supply me, you would be so good as to procure me a M. De Luc's hygrometer. When I was at New York, I saw one in the hands of Dr. Mitchill, professor of chemistry in the college there, made by Mr. Blunt, which I liked very much. Before the riots in Birmingham, I had one made by M. De Luc himself, and which he gave me. It is a most valuable instrument.

As far as I have seen of this country, I think I shall like it very well, and it promises to be a happy asylum during the troubles in Europe. But there is a great drawback in the expence of living here, which is higher than in London, the price of every thing having been doubled the last two years. On this account and with a view to having more leisure, I think I shall settle in the back part of this state, at Northumberland, near the place where my sons are making their establishment. I shall prefer the climate of this country to that of England very much, especially as I hope that here I shall be able to make much more use of the excellent *burning lens* with which your father supplied me, than I could ever have done in England.

People here are very anxious about the result of Mr. Jay's negociation. They wish for peace, but are every where preparing for war, and in the back country hostilities seem to be breaking out not only with the Indians, but with the British, who are universally considered as their instigators, and those who supply them with arms and ammunition. In these parts the people are eager for war. I am one who wish for peace, and hope that in this case I may some time hence visit my native country, for which I shall always feel a very strong attachment. . . .

No. 148.

From Priestley to Benjamin Rush

Northumberland, Sep. 14, 1794.

Dear Sir:

The Professorship of Chemistry in your College has, I own, some attractions for me, and one of the principal is the opportunity it would give me of having the advantage of your society, the loss of which [I o]ften speak of with regret. I have not in this country met with any person whose mind seems to be so congenial to my own. But I foresee several difficulties, and some of them, I fear, insuperable. 1. For the first year I could only give such a *general course* as I did at Hackney, the *Heads* of which you may have seen. I have not a copy here; but Mr. Vaughan can show you one, and as soon as a package arrives from New York I can present you with one. These would by no means supply so many lectures as your course would require. Again my apparatus is so packed up, and ready to be conveyed hither, that I could not make any use of it at present, and I fear yours would not sufficiently correspond to my course. 2. Being in *winter,* it would hardly be in my power to prepare the necessary experiments in the intervals of the lectures, even if I had an assistant. 3. My books too are so packed up, that I could not get at them for the composition of more lectures. Against another year I could be better prepared. In the meantime, could these defects be excused? for they cannot be wholly remedied.

Before I left England some fr[iends]
had a scheme of founding a Colleg[e where]
I shall settle on the idea tha[t it would]
be in a part of the Country
not provided with any. Would th[e legislature]
give any assistance or wou[ld they be opposed] [*torn*]
to it? This seems to be a promis[ing]
situation, and my library and Apparatus, might be of great use to it. [Can the]
leading men be consulted about it [?]
This I should prefer to anything in [Philadelphia where I]
could be employed. But this, I fear, i[s an un]
certain, as well as a distant, object.

I like this place much, but its [distance]
from Philadelphia, and want of an easy comm[u]
nication with it, are great objections to it. The latter may
in time be removed. . . .

[Could] I be comfortably boarded in a private family [*torn*]
[for the time] the College business would require?

Dr. Rush, Philadelphia

No. 149.

FROM PRIESTLEY TO BENJAMIN RUSH

Northumberland, Nov. 11, 1794.

Dear Sir:

I hope you will excuse my weakness (for such you will consider it), when, after giving you reason to expect that I would accept the professorship of Chemistry, if it was offered to me, I now inform you that I must decline it.

On the receipt of your obliging letter, I was determined to accept of it, and in my own mind had made every arrangement for that purpose. But when I began to consider the difficulty and irksomeness of a journey to Philadelphia at this time of the year, and especially the obligation I should be under of spending four months of every year from home, my wife in the house by herself, my heart failed me.

This, in fact, is my only objection, but it is an insuperable one. I am truly sensible of the honour that is done me by the invitation, and beg that you would express it for me to all the persons concerned. Nothing could have been so pleasing to me as the employment, and I should have been happy in your society, and that of other friends in the Capital, and, what I have much at heart, I should have had an opportunity of forming an Unitarian congregation in Philadelphia. But the considerations as mentioned, and that of my time of life, lead me to continue where I am, waiting for the opportunity of being of use to the College which I hope will be established here.

Had this proposal been made to me before the removal of my library and apparatus hither, the case would have been different; but this being now done, at a great risk and expence, I am, at all events, fixed for the remainder of my life.

If I had come, Mr. Henry would have assisted me in collecting materials, and making the preparations for the necessary experiments. As he is well qualified for the office, if you be not better provided, what should you think of *him*? At least, I think the students might, with advantage, attend his lectures, till the vacant professorship be filled. This I observe *in confidence,* wishing the hint to go no further, if you disapprove of it. . . .

No. 150.

FROM PRIESTLEY TO SAMUEL PARKER

Northumberland, Jan. 20, 1795

Dear Sir

Living, as I do, at a considerable distance from Philadelphia, and this being a time of the year in which all communication by water is cut off, I have not yet received your kind present of glass ware, which, however, I hear is safely arrived. I am sending a slay, which is our best method of conveyance in winter, to fetch them, and other things that are waiting for me. We shall soon have a stage-coach and stage-waggon to this place, which will remove one of the greatest inconveniences we labour under.

I shall very thankfully, by Mr. Johnson, pay for the *hygrometer*, or any thing else that you shall be so good as to purchase for me. And as you are pleased to say you will supply me with any vessel, for the use of my experiments, made of glass, I shall take the liberty to inform you, that that part of my apparatus (which was very complete) has suffered exceedingly in its conveyance hither, owing chiefly to injudicious packing, large thin glasses having been filled with smaller without sufficient stuffing, so that the *shades,* or *bell-glasses,* with which your father liberally supplied me, are almost all broken, and more than half of the *jars* of my electric *batteries.* If you will be so kind as to replace *these,* you will do me a most acceptable service. My jars were twelve inches deep and four wide; but others that will go within them will do just as well, and lessen the bulk of the package.

I have lost also the *receiver for the guinea and feather,* and a set of glass tubes with large bulbs at the end, which I used in the experiments I last published on the generation of air from water, the stems about half an inch wide, and thirty inches long, and the bulb made to hold a quart or two quarts of water. They were made for me at Russell's glass-house. Some of those with smaller bulbs are preserved.

This place is inconveniently situated for carrying on my experiments; but living here is cheap, and the climate, &c., uncommonly fine, and my sons are settling in farms about me. It is now the depth of winter, and the thermometer sometimes (though only in the night) below   of Fahrenheit. It is pleasanter in the day than your summer, and we had nothing like winter till the beginning of this month. But our great advantage arises from a happy constitution of government, and a state of *peace,* in consequence of which the country enjoys an unexampled state of prosperity, the advancement in population, and improvements of all kinds, being beyond any thing that the world ever saw before. I earnestly wish your situation and prospects were as good. For though I have found a happy *asylum* here, I consider it in no other light. I feel myself as in a state of *exile,* and my best wishes are for my native country and my friends there. . . .

No. 151.

FROM PRIESTLEY TO JOSIAH WEDGWOOD

Northumberland March 17, 1795

Dear Sir

I took the liberty to write to you on my arrival in this country, and hope you received the letter. I write now at the request of *Dr Barton,* who reads lectures in Chemistry in the College at Philadelphia, who will often want such vessels as I have made use of in my experiments, and desires my recommendation of him to you, that he may be supplied in the best manner, and on the best terms. For this I well know that [no re]commendation was necessary, but to oblige [him I] give you this trouble.

When I wrote last I expected to have been settled for some time in or near Philadelphia, and I was lately invited to accept of the office of Professor of chemistry in the College there. But I have declined it for the sake of living in a much more agreeable, and healthy situation, at one third of the expence, and where I can have more leisure for my pursuits. The greatest inconvenience I feel is the want of a ready communication with Philadelphia; but that will soon be removed. As to society, I have as much as I wish for, or nearly so, and I shall, when I am properly settled, spend some time every year in some of the larger towns.

The scheme of a large settlement for English emigrants, projected by Mr Cooper, you will before this time have heard is given up, and on the whole, tho it mortified me at the time, I am now not sorry for it. Great difficulty would have attended the carrying it into execution, and many would have been dissatisfied. Where I now am there is room for a few, as many as I wish to draw near me, and in a short time, as the place [has] uncommon natural advantages, it must [grow] considerable. Already it is determined to establish a College here, and we expect to raise the necessary buildings this very year. A handsome subscription has already been raised, and a petition is now before the Assembly of the State for a grant of lands for its support, and there is no doubt of its being duly attended to. Our State, I mean that of Pensilvania, is so far from being in debt, that it has a large and increasing sum in banks, which is annually expended in making roads, bridges, and improvements of all kinds.

My apparatus suffered exceedingly in its conveyance to this place, but all *your* articles are come very safe, and my stock is so ample, that it will not soon require any recruiting. When it does, I shall not fail to inform you. I have met with so many hindrances, that I have but just now been able to resume my experiments. Indeed, it will be some time before I can act to any advantage. [However] I have repeated my experiments on *the generation of air from water,* in such a manner as to remove, I think, every objection that can be made to them, and I am pursuing them still farther. In due time I shall not fail to inform you of the result.

Here we enjoy the great blessing of peace, and such a prospect of prosperity as no country ever had before. I sincerely wish you were in the same state; and live as I will here, I shall always feel as in a state of *exile.* But at my time of life it is of little consequence where I am. As long as I live I hope to be active and useful, and therefore happy. And as long as I live I shall retain a grateful of your kindness to me. My wife in grateful respects to your whole family. . . .

No. 152.

FROM PRIESTLEY TO WILLIAM WITHERING

Northumberland Oct. 27. 1795

Dear Sir

Your letter was peculiarly welcome to me, as, from the accounts I had received of the state of your health, I was apprehensive that our intercourse on this side the grave was at an end. I do indeed rejoice on hearing, and especially from yourself, so much better an account than I expected, and flatter myself that tho you may not get hardy, you may have tolerable enjoyment of life for many years to come. I am also happy to find that you are determined not to live useless, and that we may expect so much an improved edition of your Botanical Work. Mr Galton, in a letter I have received from him, since I had yours, mentions several of the improvements which please me much, tho I do not pretend to be a judge of those matters. Were I a young man, I should certainly, expecially in this new world, apply to Botany, and natural history in general; but it is too late in life for me to engage in new pursuits. It will be well if I be able to close some of the old ones, and in this I am now assidious, and happily have more leisure for them than ever I had, tho I have not the same advantages that I had in England. More than ever do I now regret the loss of the *Lunar Society,* where I spent so many happy hours, and for which I found no substitute even in London. Here I am quite insolated and I promise myself, when my house and laboratory shall be erected, to direct as much time to philosophical pursuits as ever I have done. Hitherto it has not been in my power to do much, as I have only one room in my son's house for my library and apparatus too. But I have done almost all that I can in the generation of air from water, and shall soon draw up a *Sequel* to my pamphlet on that subject for the Society at Philadelphia. I still find no end to the production of air from the same water, tho I can now torture it in more ways than I thought of before. That the air I get is not imbided in the course of the process, is demonstrable from its being at the last wholly phlogisticated air. The first that is extracted is always much purer than common air, and I presumed that it would continue to be so, tho, operating on a small scale, I could not ascertain it. I now do it with the greatest certainty. It is possible, however, that the air yielded by water may be that which it originally got from the atmosphere, retaining with the greatest obstinancy that which it is least apt to imbibe. I have many experiments, and some of them rather curious, on water deprived of air imbibing such as I present to it, which I do with great ease; but the particulars are too many for a letter.

I am now in a course of experiments by which I think I shall prove pretty decisively, that what I have called the *phlogistication of air* is really so, and not the mere absorption of the pure part of it, as the French chymists suppose. In many of the cases there is something emitted from the substance, as well as something imbibed by it, and this something which we have called *phlogiston,* uniting with the pure part of the air, makes phlogisticated air, so that originally it contains more pure air than they suppose. I hope to ascertain how much it really is, and how much is the produce of phlogistication. In other processes I think I make phlogisticated air by the union of dephlogisticated and inflammable air; but the processes are not yet completed. Having more opportunity for reading and writing than for anything else, I am now chiefly employed in the continuation of my *History of the christian church,* tasking myself, as I perceive you do, so much every day. By this means I reckon that I shall complete the whole in two years, and more than half of one is expired.

Soon, however, I expect to be employed in the instruction of youth, as a *College* is to be established in this place, and I am appointed the Principal. The next spring we begin to build; but at first our funds will be small. I wish we had a proper person for teaching *Natural History,* including Botany. Almost everything else I can, *pro tempor* in some measure, teach myself. When our common hall is erected, I shall also make use of it as a chapel. For such is the bigotry of the people in this part of the country that tho, in every other respect, my reception here has been very flattering, their pulpits are all shut to me. At Philadelphia I am assured I should raise a congregation of Unitarian christians, but, on several accounts, I could not live there. It is expensive, and disagreeable in the extreme. I was invited to the professorship of chemistry there, but I must have lived in the town, and more would have been expected of me than I could have performed, without more labor than, at my time of life, and interrupted as I should have been, I could well support. I intend however to spend a month or six weeks there every winter.

I am glad to hear of the fair trial that will be made of Dr Beddoes's theory at Birmingham. I want Mr Watts apparatus; I could use it for various purposes. Perhaps he will have the goodness to send it me, and might not be pleased if I propose to pay for it, as I gladly would do. I must get everything of much value from England — I am much pleased with your favorable account of Portugal. I had not heard of my election into their Society. . . .

No. 153.

FROM PRIESTLEY "TO MESSR. BERTHOLLET, DE LA PLACE, MONGES, MORVEAU, FOURCROY, AND HASENFRATZ, THE SURVIVING ANSWERERS OF MR. KIRWAN."

Northumberland June 15, 1796.

Gentlemen

Having drawn up a short defence of the doctrine of *phlogiston*, I take the liberty of inscribing it to *you*, as the principal advocates for the anti-phlogistic theory. My view in this, is, to draw your attention, once more, to the subject, and I request the favour of an answer to my objections. I hope I am not wanting in a proper deference to the opinion of men so justly eminent as yourselves and your friends in France and also of great numbers in England, and wherever chemistry is known, who have adopted your hypothesis. But you will agree with me, that no man ought to surrender his own judgement to any mere authority however respectable. Otherwise your own system would never have been advanced.

As you would not, I am persuaded, have your reign to resemble that of *Robespierre*, few as we are who remain disaffected, we hope you had rather gain us by persuasion, than silence us by power.

And, though we are all apt to flatter ourselves, we hope we are willing to be influenced by the former, as we are inflexible to the latter. If you gain as much by your answer to me, as you did by that to Mr. Kirwan, your power will be universally established, and there will be no *Vendée* in your dominions.

Differing as we do in this respect, we all agree in our wishes, for the prevalence of *truth,* and also, of peace, is wanted as much for the interests of philosophy as for those of humanity. . . .

No. 154.

From Priestley to Benjamin Smith Barton

Northumberland July 20 1796

Dear Sir

I think myself much obliged to you for correcting the press for my pamphlet. There are but two errata that I have observed and those of little moment. I desired Mr Adlum to mention them to Mr Dobson.

I read with much pleasure and instruction your paper on *fascination.* I had before thought that what was called fascination was the *terror* of the animal said to be fascinated, but you have set me right. I am fully convinced the fact is simply as you represent it. I wish you could trace other supposed instincts to their true source as well as this.

We have all had a great loss in the death of Dr Rittenhouse but you in particular. The more I saw of him the more I was pleased with him I feel for all his family, and lay my most affectionate respects to them on the mournful occasion.

I am glad to hear of the successful termination of your observations on the *Opossum,* and hope we shall soon a memoir of yours on this subject, as well as on that which you do me the honour to address to me.

I am glad that the *Nomenclature* arrived safe, and desire you would keep it as long as it is useful to you.

I shall be obliged to you if you will desire Mr Dobson to send me the numbers of the *Monthly Magazine,* lately published in

England. The first No was sent me, and I left it at Mr Russell's. If they can find it he may send me only those that follow. Please to see Mr Russell and ask him about it. But I ought not to give you so much trouble.

I want much to get the glass vessels that were to have been made for me by Mr Nicholson's people, and Mr Gatts, but begin to fear they are not to be procured from that quarter. These delays are a great obstruction to my experiments. I have but just received a box of articles from Mr Hunter which I saw packed and sent off while I was in Philadelphia.

I shall be glad to receive the seeds of [hirsutum] epilobium, and I imagine they will come well enough in a letter, if no better opportunity offers. Give me directions about setting them.

I shall thank you for the communication of any remarks your own or of others on my pamphlet on Phlogiston. . . .

P.S.   I have received a letter from *Mr Seymour* of Plimouth, inclosed in one of *Mr Davys* of that place, who writes from Philadelphia, and desires me to direct my answer to you, which accordingly I have done. Open the letter, if you please. You can probably give Mr Seymour more information than I can.

No. 155.

FROM PRIESTLEY TO BENJAMIN SMITH BARTON

Northumberland Oct 8. 1796

Dear Sir:

I am willing to hope that by this time something has been done with respect to the *glass vessels* I have wanted so long If they be made, my son, who will deliver this, will take the charge of conveying them If the whole vessel cannot be procured of one piece, perhaps you could assist him in getting a *large glass bulb* with a neck, which I could fasten with cement to tubes which I have here, or a large *decanter*.

I consider myself as sufficiently honoured by you and your friends, *thinking* of me as not improper for a president of the

Philosophical Society. But on many accounts you ought to prefer Mr Jefferson. It will be a reflection on the country not to chuse an American, and I am a foreigner. As to the President being much in Philadelphia, it is not of much consequence, as the business, the ordinary business, may be done by a Vice president, or any person who will attend to it.

I have just completed the arrangement of my new laboratory; but I cannot do much in it, till I live in the house with which it is connected, which will not be till the next summer. It is a house that my wife had planned; and just as it was advancing very fast, and promised to be everything that she wished, she is taken away. Having one tie to this place less than before, I shall probably spend some more time in Philadelphia, than I otherwise should have done. My son will endeavour to make some arrangement for that purpose.

When I come to Philadelphia, I shall be glad to see the Members of the Dublin [?] Society. . . .

P.S. I beg my respects to Mrs Rittenhouse and the family.

No. 156.

FROM PRIESTLEY TO SAMUEL L. MITCHILL

Dear Sir

I am very glad that your *Medical Repository* is extended to subjects of general philosophy and chemistry. Had I known this before, I should have taken the liberty to send you an account of some of my late experiments, especially those which have for their object the discussion of the question between the Phlogistians and the Antiphlogistians. I have not yet seen any part of the work, but shall not fail to procure it the first opportunity, and consider the history which you say it contains of the controversy between me and my opponents. In the mean time I beg you would communicate to the publishers the following account of an experiment which I wish Dr Maclean and other advocates of the new theory to consider, and endeavour to explain on their principles.

Our common object is the investigation of truth, and surely a question of this nature, purely philosophical, may be discussed in the most amicable manner. The pamphlet in which I replied to Dr Maclean and Mr Adet I presume he will answer in a separate pamphlet; and having waited for it some time, I am now in dayly expectation of it.

An argument on which, in my late publication, I laid some stress, is that when inflammable air is procured by the solution of iron in diluted acid of vitriol, there is no addition of oxygen found in the vessel in which the process is made, which ought to be the case if the inflammable air came from the decomposition of the water; and that *finery cinder,* called by the Antiphlogistians, *black oxide of iron,* cannot be proved to contain any oxygen at all, tho, according to their principles, it constitutes about one third of its weight. I have since this made a similar experiment with *zinc,* which is another metal by means of which inflammable air is easily procured, and which I think rather more decisive in favour of my hypothesis, which is that the inflammable air comes from the *metal,* and not from the *water* in which it is dissolved; and therefore that metals are compound substances, consisting of phlogiston and peculiar earths, and that water is not decomposed.

On throwing the focus of a burning lens on a quantity of zinc in common air, confined by water, in a glass vessel, the first effect is the production of *flowers of zinc,* which makes a beautiful appearance, by their dispersion within the vessel; and during this part of the process the air is diminished, the pure part of it, no doubt, entering the calx, while the phlogisticated part remains unaffected. After this, the application of the heat being continued, there is an increase of the quantity of air by the production of inflammable air; and instead of flowers of zinc, a *black powder* arises, and adheres to the inside of the vessel, and with care may be collected.

Now, since inflammable air is produced, the Antiphlogistians must say that part of the water over which the experiment was made was decomposed. But then I ask where is the oxygen which, according to them, constitutes the far greater part of the water?

I cannot find it any where. The *water* is intirely free from acidity, and the air expelled from it afterwards is even less pure than that which it yields before the process. And if I examine the *black powder* by heating it in confined common air, it becomes a whitish substance, the air is diminished, and rendered in a considerable degree impure; whereas, if it had contained any oxygen, the quantity would have been increased, and it would have been purer than common air; as when *red precipitate,* or *minium,* is treated in the same manner. It is evident, therefore, that it contained no oxygen, but a quantity of phlogiston, on the expulsion of which, and the imbibing of pure air, it became flowers of zinc.

This experiment is rather more decisive than the similar one with iron, because the black powder to which zinc is reduced can be affected by heat in common air, which finery cinder cannot.

I have been in expectation of hearing from Mr Bertholet, and the other chemists in France to whom my first publication on this subject was addressed; but as there is now no communication between this country and that, I shall be glad to proceed in the discussion of the question with Dr Maclean and other chemists on this continent. I shall attend with candour to any thing that they shall suggest, and freely acknowledge any mistakes or oversights into which I may have been betrayed; but I hope it will not be taken for granted, that where the results of experiments are differently reported by the French chemists and myself, they are always in the right. An impartial judge will see with his own eyes, and if he have not the means of doing this, he should not decide at all. . . .

Northumberland June 14. 1798

No. 157.

FROM PRIESTLEY TO BENJAMIN SMITH BARTON

Northumberland Aug. 8. 1798

Dear Sir:

I inclose my *Appendix,* and shall be much obliged to you if will get it inserted in the volume, and at the same time take off *a dozen copies* to send to me hither, by Mr Vaughan.

I rejoice to hear of the progress you make in your very important inquiry, and shall not fail to do as you wish with the copy you have sent me.

I could have sent several Articles, and some of considerable importance, if the publication of your *Transactions* had been more frequent; but as you manage matters, it does not answer the principle purpose of such publications; which is the speedy communication of philosophical discoveries. In want of this I am glad to find a resource in the *Medical Repository* at New York.

The letter I wrote to Dr Mitchill was not intended to be published. I did not wish to say anything in public to hurt Dr Maclean, tho he did not treat me as he ought to have done. It behoves him either to reply to my last pamphlet, or make some acknowledgment. . . .

P.S. Let me hear from you oftener. I beg my best respects to Mrs Rittenhouse and her daughters. I also wish you much happiness in your new connection. I depend upon you for correcting the press, and wish you would send me one copy by the post.

No. 158.

FROM PRIESTLEY TO BENJAMIN SMITH BARTON

In all my computations of the quantity of pure air contained in a portion of atmospherical air, I have of late years followed the example of others in *agitating* the mixture of nitrous air with it. But I have lately observed that this agitation only promotes the absorption of part of the nitrous air by the water, and not the union of the two kinds of air, as has generally been supposed. Consequently, my original method of mixing them *without agitation* is preferable to it, and this gives the proportion of pure air in atmospherical air more agreeable to the truth; viz about 27 parts in 100; whereas, if the computation be made after the agitation of equal quantities of the two kinds of air [exist?], the proportion will be about 33 in 100. After agitation one measure of atmospherical air and one of nitrous will generally occupy the space of 1.01 or 1.02 measures; when without agitation it will be about 1.25; and this also the result of forcing together an equal quantity of inflammable and atmospherical air. . . .

Northumberland Aug 16. 1798

Dear Sir:

I shall be obliged to you if you will get the above added to the article I sent you the last post, prefixing to it another number (7 I believe, or 8) but what the numbers in the copy I sent you were I do not recollect. I am much concerned to hear of the yellow fever being again in the city and shall be glad if you have leisure to hear your account of it. May God preserve you from it. . . .

Dr Ross is pretty well recovered Dr Woodhouse is also here.

No. 159.

From Priestley to John Vaughan

Northumberland March 21. 1799

Dear Sir

I sent to my son as particular an account as I could give of the *package of glass,* and did not doubt but he would have given it to you. It contained nothing but glasses of very various forms for philosophical purposes, and I have been told that philosophical instruments do not pay any duty. The value in England I believe to be *five* or *Six guineas,* but being a present to me, I do not know exactly. I have another box of philosophical instruments coming in the *Neptune,* about which I wish you to speak to the proper officers. If they be unpacked at the Custom house, they may almost as well remain there, as it will be impossible to replace them without great damage, for which I suppose nobody would be answerable. I was several hours in unpacking the glass that came last, and I could not have put half the things into the same box again. Many were broke in consequence of too close packing. My directions to my correspondents in England are always to acquaint you with the particulars of any package for me; but those who occasionally send me presents cannot always be apprized of this. There should be some better legal provisions in this case. Philosophical instruments, that are not made here, are much wanted in this country, and if your rules were strictly observed, it would amount to a prohibition of them. Without the packages being opened at the custom house, a very great proportion of the articles sent hither are broken or much damaged; and broken glass is of no use. If the packages must absolutely be opened, I should never order any thing more.

In a letter I lately received from Mr Lindsey, he mentions his having sent me a *parcell of Newspapers*; and a *box of books* is also sent from Johnson, but they do not mention the *ship* by which they were sent, so that I fear it will be not be easy to find them, and I know of no remedy.

The particulars of the last package were *retorts, phial with grind stoppered tubes, jars, evaporating dishes, tubes,* and things that have no names, and require drawings to give an idea of them. Nobody here could guess their value.

I am truly concerned for your situation, as I know no person better entitled to success in merchandise than you. But we must bear what, in the order of providence, cannot be avoided. You say that "as to money matters, my mind may be perfectly at ease." You mean that the security is good; but if be, as the lands mortgaged to me cannot be sold, and yield no revenue, tho they may be of use to my children, hereafter they are of none whatever to *me.* I lose the whole of my resources in this country, I [do] not get a farthing from France, and I consider my remittances from

England as very precarious. However, I cannot want anything long, and I have much to be thankful for. . . .

No. 160.

FROM PRIESTLEY TO ROBERT R. LIVINGSTON

Sir

I think myself much honoured by your letter, and should have thought myself singularly happy if my situation had been near to such a person as you. Persons engaged in scientifical pursuits are few in this country. Indeed, they are not very numerous any where. In other respects I think myself very happy where I am.

I have never given much attention to *machines* of any kind, and therefore cannot pretend to decide concerning your proposal for the improvement of the *fire engine*. It appears to me to deserve attention. But I do not for want of a *drawing* see in what manner the steam is to be let into the cylinder, or discharged from it. There would be, I fear, an objection to it from the force necessary to raise the column of mercury, and from the evaporation of the mercury in the requisite heat. I have found that it loses weight in 70° of Fahrenheit. If the mercury was pure, I should not apprehend much from the *calcination* of it, tho, as I have observed, the agitation of it in water converts a part of it into a *black* powder, which I propose to examine farther.

If travelling was attended to with no fewer inconveniences here than it is in England, I should certainly wait upon you and some other friends at New York. But this, and my age, render it impossible, and it would be unreasonable to expect many visitors in these *back woods*.

I shall be very happy to be favoured with your correspondence. . . .

Northumberland April 16. 1799

No. 161.

FROM PRIESTLEY TO BENJAMIN SMITH BARTON

Dear Sir

I send you a *fossil,* and wish you would inform me what natural substance it resembles. I have no knowledge of natural history; but if I were to begin life again, it would be a principal object with me.

I want much to see your *Oratson,* and also the 4th volume of your Transactions. I am, indeed, sadly behind hand in Philosophical intelli[gen]ce, which is a great disadvantage to me. I wish you and Mr Smith, to whom I have written, to spend some time with me this summer. I cannot go anywhither, and Philadelphia is a place that nobody is disposed to visit in the Summer.

Give my respects to Dr Woodhouse. I am pleased with the spirit and ingenuity of his defence of the *New System,* tho I have no doubt if its being a mere fallacy, as I am pretty confident I shall make appear before I have done. When they have printed all that I have sent to the Medical Repository I shall reduce all that I have written on this subject into one work, and reply to all my opponents, and in this I do not at present forsee much difficulty.

I have made several new experiments, and shall soon draw up an account of them for the *Medical Repository*; but I fear that publication does not go on well. I have only seen No. 3 of Vol. 2. . . .

Northumberland June 25. 1799.

No. 162.

FROM PRIESTLEY TO ROBERT R. LIVINGSTON

Dear Sir,

I hope you have received the letter I wrote to you the last post, making the best apology that I could for not writing before, and giving such an opinion as I could form, but certainly not worth sending you, of your engine.

I now congratulate you, and the world in general, on your most valuable discovery relating to the fabrication of *paper*; a thing of the greatest importance in the present state of the arts and of society. I have long thought that it might be made immediately from some plant or other, better than from rags, the collection of which is troublesome and uncertain; but what you have done is far beyond my most sanguine expectations. The specimen you were so obliging as to send me is of an admirable texture, and must answer every purpose of paper of that kind better, I should think, than any that has hitherto been made. If you can succeed in bleaching it, of which I have little doubt, you will produce a complete revolution in the whole manufacture. But it must not be called a *revolution* in these times. That alone would discredit it, tho ever so useful. It is not, however, the less acceptable to me.

Last night my thermometer was at 13, a degree of cold I have very seldom known exceeded in England. I dread your winters. They pinch old men like me, and are a great impediment to all my pursuits. I can do little more than sit by the fire, and read. Being a fine day, however, I have been making some use of my burning lens, and the middle of the day is tolerable enough.

The editors of your *Medical Repository* has three articles of mine, which I shall hope to see in their next number. but they relate to a subject that probably interests you much less than your engine does me. I wish for your sake that I were a better judge of *Mechanicks,* that my opinion might be of some little value to you.

My only doubt with respect to your *paper* is that there will not be found a sufficient quantity of the materials for it; but of this you know more than I do. . . .

Northumberland Oct. 24. 1799

No. 163.

FROM PRIESTLEY TO "A PHYSICIAN IN THIS BOROUGH"

December 26, '99

[Dear Sir]

I rejoice to hear of the Society you are about to form at Wilmington. It cannot fail to give great satisfaction to all the friends of science in your neighborhood; and contribute to the progress of science in the country. Though you may labor, at present, under some disadvantages with respect to instruments, &c., those evils will lessen every day. The resolution to make a beginning is every thing.

There are already, in my opinion, more lovers of science in this country, in proportion to the number of people, than in Europe.

I have been some time engaged in a controversy about the doctrine of *Phlogiston,* and having heard all that I imagine can be urged against it, I am printing my final defence of it, and a refutation of the *decomposition of water.*

I shall be glad to hear of the progress of your Society. . . .

No. 164.

FROM PRIESTLEY TO B. LYNDE OLIVER

Sir

I do not know whether you can forgive my neglecting to answer your obliging letter of so old a date as February, 1797; when I can only say that when I received it I was from home, and not at leisure to write, and that I afterwards forgot it, and when I recollected it I was ashamed to acknowledge it. If you can, please to accept a pamphlet I take the liberty to send you on a subject that is very interesting to chemists. I have since that completed a course of experiments in pursuance of those on the *generation of air from water,* the result of which is that, by repeated freezing of the same water, I always get from it a quantity of air, and to appearance without any limit; so that the whole might be converted into this kind of air as well as by previously converting it into vapour. By this means the atmosphere may constantly receive an addition to this ingredient in its constitution, as the other part, viz. dephlogisticated air, is recruited by the influence of light on plants.

I thought I had had the volume of the American Transactions to which you refer, but I find I have no more than the first volume; but I have somewhere seen it, and I think Mr. Holyoake makes the difference of heat to depend upon the difference of purity in the air in different seasons. If so, he must be mistaken, for I find no sensible difference in the purity of the air at any time, or, indeed, between the air of this country and that of England.

I am not very well acquainted with the doctrines of *Galvanism,* but it should seem that the different metals are in different states with respect to electricity, though it is very extraordinary that this should be the case. This is a curious and important subject just opening upon us.

I have always heard a good account of Mr. Tytler, both as a man and a philosopher, but I have no personal knowledge of him.

I rejoice to find that in you that philosophy is joined to Christianity, from which it is too much separated. With me this is a primary object, and philosophy, much as I have attended to it, only a secondary one, as my writings here as well as in Europe will show.

Please to remember me respectfully to your honoured father, if, as I hope, he be still living. He is very obliging to inquire after my situation, and assure him that I find in this country everything that I expected from it, or that I wish for in this world. I have convenience and leisure for my pursuits of every kind, and I shall endeavour to make as much use of them as I can. I want only such things as must be had from Europe, and more early intelligence of what philosophers are doing there. But this inconvenience will be removed after the present war, which cannot, I think, continue much longer, shall cease. . . .

Northumberland, April 3, 1800

No. 165.

From Priestley to Robert R. Livingston

Northumberland Apl. 17. 1800

Dear Sir

I am persuaded that the edition of my *Letters* at Albany was nothing more than a pretence that Mr Campbell made use of to cancell the agreement he had made, and therefore, if you still think that any good end would be answered by that edition, I have no objection to its being resumed. I only wish to be no great loser by my publications, and I am told that the sale in Philadelphia will sufficiently idemnify me —— These Letters, I find, have given the greatest offence to the Federalists, and to many, I hear, who are of the other party. They have, however, I have reason to think, been of some service to me in this neighbourhood, which was my principal object. Having said what I thought necessary, I shall hardly repeat the offence. I am sure I wrote without anger, or ill will to any body, and with a sincere respect for the constitution of the country.

I have no doubt of the priority of your very valuable discovery, and am glad it will be so easy to ascertain it. I wish much to see it reduced to practice, and hope you will take proper measures for that purpose. You will oblige me much by favouring me with your observations on the process of *distillation*. I know but little of it.

Tho almost singular in my defence of *phlogiston,* and in my opinion of the fallacy of the decomposition of water, I am pretty confident of success. The *facts* I have advanced I have no doubt will bear the strictest examination, and the *reasoning* from them is easy enough. What I have done in last frost is a great confirmation of what I have advanced concerning water. By freezing the same water repeatedly I get from it a quantity of *phlogisticated air,* and this production is equable after at least nine processes; so that, to appearances, the whole of it might be converted into this species of air. If any kind of air ought to be termed *hydrogene,* it is this, and not inflammable air. I have sent the full account of the

[303]

experiments to the Philosophical society at Philadelphia, and another copy to England.

I should think myself singularly happy to shew you and Dr Mitchill, or any other of your friends, the conveniences that my *shed* affords for making experiments &c. as well other advantages of my situation. Perhaps, if your employment leaves any leisure (as I think it ought to do) to make an excursion in the summer season, you may turn your faces this way as well as any other. I hope you will contrive it if you can, be the time longer or shorter. As I do not write to Dr Mitchill this post, please to signify my wishes to him. I do not know that I shall have any other visitors.

I am not at all anxious about Mr Campbell's fulfilling his agreement. The sale of the work will be chiefly in England. However, if it come in your way to make any favourable mention of it to your friends, you will oblige me.

I have not received the kind present you make me of the *Transactions of your Agricultural Society,* and the letter sent with them came to hand about a month after its date. . . .

No. 166.

FROM PRIESTLEY TO B. LYNDE OLIVER

Northumberland, Aug. 8, 1800

Dear Sir

I thank you for the valuable present of Mr. Tytler's treatise. It is a very interesting work, and I shall read it with particular attention, not only on account of the principal object of it, the investigation of the nature of pestilential disorders, but on account of the great mass of collateral subjects that I perceive he discusses, especially the doctrine of *heat,* concerning which I have long been unable to form any satisfactory opinion. When I have perused the work, I shall take the liberty to propose to him, or to you any question that may occur to me on that subject, or any other that he has introduced. I see that in his account of the plague in the Appendix, he has not mentioned the most extensive and fatal of any that we read of, in that of 1348, in the time of Petrarch, which seems to have swept off one-third of the human race.

Mr. Tytler's opinion in favour of my objections to the new theory, I think of much value, and I am well persuaded that the more attention is given to the subject, the more groundless that system will appear. Many I hear suspect it in England, and there has been a serious attack made upon it in France, but by whom I have not learned. We shall soon, I hope, have a communication opened with that country, and then I shall know more particulars. The want of it at present is a great obstruction to the progress of science, but this is no object with politicians.

My experiments on the perpetual production of phlogisticated air from water, both by means of a vacuum and by freezing, I think absolutely subversive of the hypothesis of the resolution of water into inflammable and pure air. I have made both with the greatest care, and do not at present foresee that any sufficient objection can be made to either of them; their agreement with each other is a striking circumstance. Your objections to the new nomenclature are certainly very just.

The objections that Mr. Tytler makes to Count Rumford's experiments did not strike me at the time that I read them, but I shall now attend to it more particularly. I have not yet seen Noah Webster's book on the plague, but intend to procure it. What do you and Mr. Tytler think of it? I wish we were nearer to each other. . . .

P.S.   I have printed at my own expense *a comparison of the institutions of the Hindoos and other nations with those of Moses.* Could you assist me in the disposal of a few copies in your neighbourhood?

No. 167.

FROM PRIESTLEY TO WILLIAM PARKER

Dear Sir

I have to thank you for a quantity of valuable glass vessels which I received, in two casks, some time ago, and I desired a friend to call upon you, and inform you that they were arrived at Philadelphia. The value of such articles, in my present situation, is above all estimation. For this country cannot supply anything of the kind. Owing, I believe, to the roughness of our roads, not less than 20 of the largest vessels, which inclosed the rest, were broken, but we shall have better roads in time, and then I shall think my situation at Northumberland preferable on the whole to any other on this continent. In a former package many of the vessels were broken in consequence of being too closely [stowed], and some of them thrust too hard one within another.

Thro your kindness, and that of your father, I think I am now furnished with all the glass vessels in the usual forms, that I can want of many years. But I must accept your kind offer of assistance occasionally, for vessels in new forms, and adapted to particular purposes; and at present a set for *Mr Humphrey Davy's Experiments*. What they are I do not know, but I hear they all require particular exactness in stoppering. Tho I think it probable that you make them for him, I shall write to him, or to Dr Beddoes, to give you instructions on the subject.

I have desired a copy of my late *treatise on phlogiston* to be delivered to you; and by this, and various other publications, you will find I am not idle. I am now engaged in a set of interesting experiments with the excellent *lens* with which your father furnished me, and in my account of them, shall speak with pleasure of the great obligation I am under to him and you for the assistance you so generously afford me.

I have not yet seen the relation of yours that I was led to expect would come this way last summer.

My son, who is safely arrived, speaks with much pleasure of the civilities he received from you in England and desires to be remembered to you. . . .

Northumberland Aug. 13. 1800

No. 168.

From Priestley to Benjamin Smith Barton

Northumberland Nov. 27. 1800

Dear Sir

I thank you for your *Fragments* and think them deserving of a more respectable title. They have afforded me much instruction. Were I to begin life again, I would apply to *Natural History,* and should rejoice to have such a guide, and such an example as you have set. *"Trammelled"* as you are in a profession, I am astonished that you have found time to do so much, and so well. The first Naturalist in Europe must owe you great obligations. If you do nothing more, you will have established a lasting reputation.

The excellent use you have made of the *Russian Nomenclature* fully intitles you to it. At least it shall always remain in your custody. If ever I want it (which is not very probable) I know where it is.

I am very little of a Naturalist, but I own I cannot help think that if the great body of *European swallows* crossed the Mediterranean, they would be found in great numbers in Africa, and this is not found to be the case. A servant of the Marquis of Lansdown told me that on the falling in of the bank of a river in Ireland he found a large hole full of swallows. He carried away a basket full of them, and several of them came to life in a warm room. These could not all have been sickly ones, unable to fly away.

What think you of my *treatise on phlogiston?* You are more of a chemist, than I am of a Naturalist. I desired a copy of the work to be given to you, and hope you received it.

I have been much interested in reading *Tytler on the plague.* Can you get me the loan of *Webster* on that subject. I cannot buy every thing I wish to read, and if you can assist me in this way now and then you will lay me under very great obligation. Mr Vaughan will convey anything to me, and we have now waggons frequently going from this place to Philadelphia.

Mr Cooper, I find, was recommended to your Philosophical

Society, and rejected. Can you explain it to me? I fear that *Politics* had something to do in it. . . .

P.S. None of the seeds of the *epilobicum hirsutum* that you were so good as to send me would vegetate.

No. 169.

FROM PRIESTLEY TO BENJAMIN SMITH BARTON

Northd. July 7. 1801

Dear Sir

I have received, and read with much pleasure (I do not *conviction,* for that was complete before,) your additional observation on *fascination.* I am glad to find by the *Medical Repository* that you intend to give us a new *Introduction to Botany.* It is what I very much want, for old as I am, I intend to give some time to the study of Natural History. I have just read, and with much improvement, works which you will look down upon with a smile of Superiority, *Smellie* and *Goldsmith's.* But I see that I shall never get more than a general knowledge of the subject. You will extend the bounds of this branch of science. I am, indeed, astonished that you should have done so much as you have done, occupied as you are in such various pursuits.

Your account of the discovery of the *Chinese coin* is very curious, as well as that of the *Chinese words* in the language of the Siaun Indians. Your discovery with respect to this subject are equally new and interesting. You have placed the subject beyond all possibility of doubt.

I have communicated your request to Mr Cooper, who, I doubt not, will attend to it.

I find by letters from England, and also in the Philosophical Magazine, and Nicholsons Journal, accounts of experiments on the *pile of Volta* or Galvanism, inconsistent with the theory of *decomposition of water.* Many have begun to suspect the truth of the new system, and I am confident that in a few years it will be universally exploded.

Do not fail to put my name among the subscribers to your *Travels,* or any thing else that you chuse to publish in that manner. . . .

No. 170.

FROM PRIESTLEY TO SAMUEL L. MITCHILL

Dear Sir

I do not recollect, any more than you, which of us wrote last, but I should not, on that account, have deferred writing to you, if I had had anything to communicate; and but that I fear you will think me unmindful of you, and indifferent about our correspondence, I should have deferred writing one week long, when I hope to have something of value in its way to send for your Repository. I am flattered by your thinking my communications of any use to such a work, which I think does credit to the conductors, and to the country. If I have a few days more sun shine, I shall finish what I am about, and write the next post. Happily, we are never long without sun-shine; whereas in England I have often waited months, and the days in which I could use a burning-lens to advantage have not, I am confident, exceeded one fortnight in one whole year, and I have often watched every gleam the year thro. In all respects I think the climate of this country greatly preferable to that of England; and its government still more so. Here we have *peace* and *plenty,* and in England they have neither, nor do I see that a revolution can be warded off much longer. Peace, in my opinion, will only be the beginning of internal troubles.

I have lately received many Nos of *Nicholson's Journal,* and also of the *Philosophical Magazine,* in which I see an account of experiments with the *pile of Volta* absolutely inconsistent with the doctrine of the *decomposition of water.* There are other symptoms of its decline in point of credit, and I doubt not that in a few years it will be universally exploded. *Sic transit gloria mundi.*

I thank you for the manner in which you noticed my Articles in your Review. They are so dilatory in the publication of the

Transactions of the society at Philadelphia, that I think your Repository greatly preferable to it. The principal use of these publications is the speedy communication of philosophical intelligence, and your quarterly publication is excellent in that respect; and it circulates I believe thro the whole of Europe.

On your recommendation I shall not fail to order the *American Review and Literary Journal.* This country is rising very fast in literary and philosophical reputation. Considering its age, it has done wonders, and you have had a great share in it. What think you of the cure of putrid fevers by *yeast?* How does it accord with your doctrine of alkaline remedies; concerning which I am disposed to think of highly; but I have not given any very particular attention to the subject.

Expect to hear from me again the next post, with an article for your Repository. . . .

Northd. July 16. 1801

No. 171.

FROM PRIESTLEY TO THEOPHILUS LINDSEY

No. 79 Northumberland Oct. 2, 1801

Dear friend,

Having sent to Mr. Nicholson a paper of *experiments on the pile of Volta,* I beg you would send him the above P.S. to it, and ask whether he has received the paper itself. I this day send him another article in reply to what Mr Cruikshank has advanced in the Journal on the subject of the *new theory;* so that you see I am not altogether idle, tho circumstances do not favour the publication of any *theological* compositions. These, however, are continually improving under my hands, so that the delay will not be of any disservice to either of the works, provided they be printed while I am capable of giving due attention to them. I shall not fail to continue my labours but the disposal of them is not with myself. Whatever become of them, I have no doubt will be for the best, and I could not have done anything with more satisfaction to myself. Having had great success in my experiments in this country, as well as in England, I shall never desert *philosophy*; but I have much more satisfaction in theological studies; and I find they greatly aid one another. I have lately given more attention than I had done before to *Natural history* and am exceedingly interested in it. Several conclusions of a higher nature are strongly suggested by this study. In a plan abounding with such marks of infinite wisdom, nothing surely can ultimately go wrong, and observations with a microscope convince us that the smallest things are attended to as much as the greatest. The smallest *events*, therefore, as well as the greater and more striking. This consideration tends to reconcile us to small troubles, and disappointments, as well as to those of greater magnitude. All are equally from the same hand.

The view of the creation and the *connection of its parts,* must convince any attentive person of the folly of Arianism. No Being but he that planned and executed the whole could execute or superintend any part of the system.

It must appear impossible that a Being of such unusual wisdom and power can bear the least ill will to any of his creatures, whose conduct, be it what it may, was a necessary part of his benevolent plan. It follows with a force that gives me, in my present situation, a satisfaction I cannot describe. The most refractory tempers must be [rectified] some time or other, and in the mean time they are not without their use here; and the worst dispositions must be reclaimed. You will know to what I refer.

I am glad that you have received the copy of *Mr Jefferson's letters* to me, and also, as I find by Mr Belsham's letter, the copies of the second edition of my *Letters to the Inhabitants of Northumberland* including my notes of Mr *Liancourt's* strange conduct. —— You wish me to visit Mr Jefferson, and I have no objection but the length of the journey and the difficulties in the conveyance, of which I cannot give you an idea. However, if Mr Jefferson's views succeed, I am rather inclined to go, especially as I shall preach to some advantage. But I fear that the bigotry of some, and the federalism of others, will defeat the scheme, and my own wishes are nearly balanced. I shall be much more com-

[311]

fortable at home, and will [be in] the winter, and can employ myself to more advantage.

I have the *Cambridge paper* to June 27, but I want those for March. They perhaps were those that you sent by a private hand, which I have generally found the most uncertain conveyance. The account of the debates in parliament interest me much, and we have seldom anything of this in the American papers. —— So careless is Mr Johnson, that in 3 volumes and an half of the *Monthly Review* he has sent *eight duplicates,* several copies of the same No in the same packet, and many articles that I ordered near two years ago he has not sent yet. But I hope there may be a package from him at Philadelphia, or on the way thither —— In your parcel I have received *Mr Morgan's pamphlet,* which interests me much. Give my compliments and thanks to him. . . .

P.S. I hope you see the *Medical Repository.* It will generally contain some article of mine, and on many accounts it is worth having. We have had an uncommonly sickly season in all these parts, tho very few have died. You will see that I fortold it. I have had a slight ague, and not one in the family has intirely escaped. The youngest child (Lindsey) is now the only one that ails any thing and he is recovering.

I have long wished to see Gale's Ansr to Wall, and Wall's reply. I wish you would assist Mr Johnson in procuring them for me as also Crosly's history of the English Baptists. I read with much attention Wall on Infant baptism and also Mr Robinson's publication on that subject. He is a most unfair, deceitful writer. I think I could with some advantage address a *Letter to a Learned Baptist.* I have hints for it, but I want the books mentioned above. —— I thank God continually for your health and spirits, and hope that our lamps will go out nearly together. I am not what I was before my fever in Philadelphia. I have lost flesh and strength, but in other respects I feel very well. But bodily labour, either in the garden, in which I take much pleasure, or in the laboratory, is now irksome to me, and I read more than I did.

No. 172.

FROM PRIESTLEY TO HUMPHRY DAVY

Northumberland, October 31, 1801

Sir

I have read with admiration your excellent publications, and have received much instruction from them. It gives me peculiar satisfaction, that as I am now far advanced in life, and cannot expect to do much more, I shall leave so able a fellow-labourer of my own country in the great field of experimental philosophy. As old an experimenter as I am, I was near forty before I made any experiments on the subject of *air,* and then without, in a manner, any previous knowledge of chemistry. This I picked up as I could, and as I found occasion for it, from books. I was also without apparatus, and laboured under many other disadvantages. But my unexpected success induced the friends of science to assist me, and then I wanted for nothing. I rejoice that you are so young a man, and perceiving the ardour with which you begin your Career, I have no doubt of your success. My son, for whom you express a friendship, and which he warmly returns, encourages me to think it may not be disagreeable to you to give me information occasionally of what is passing in the philosophical world now that I am at so great a distance from it, and yet interested, as you may suppose, in what is passing in it. Indeed, I shall take it as a great favour. But you must not expect any thing in return. I am here perfectly insulated, and this country furnishes but few fellow-labourers, and these are so scattered that we can have but little communication with each other; and they are equally in want of information with myself. Unfortunately our correspondence with England is very slow and uncertain, and with France we have not, as yet, any intercourse at all, though we hope to have it soon.

As Dr. Nicholson was so obliging as to give a place in his Journal to the account that I sent him of my experiments on the freezing of water, I have sent him two other articles, one containing experiments with the pile of Volta, to which I sent a P.S. by my friend, Mr. Lindsey, in Essex Street, and another in reply to

Mr. Cruickshank's observations on finery cinder. I also sent him a copy of several articles that are printed for the fifth volume of the Philosophical Transactions of Philadelphia, which are not yet published. The more important of these I hope he will insert in his Journal. In some of them you will find an account of facts of an extraordinary nature, such as I am far from being able to account for. I wish you would give some attention to them, especially to the transmission of air through some air-tight vessels and bladders, and the total absorption of air after long standing in water. I see in the "Annales de Chimie," that Dr. Guyton has considered the former of these in the Encyclopedie, but I have not that work. You can see it and tell me what he says of it.

I thank you for the favourable mention you so frequently make of my experiments, and have only to remark, that in Dr. Nicholson's Journal you say that the conducting power of charcoal was first observed by those who make experiments on the pile of Volta, whereas it was one of the earliest I made and gave an account of in my history of electricity and in the Philosophical Transactions. And in your excellent Treatise on the Nitrous Oxide, p. 90, you say, and justly, that I concluded the air to be lighter than that of the atmosphere. This, however, was an error in the printing that I cannot account for. It should have been *alkaline air,* as you will see the experiment necessarily requires.
. . .

No. 173.

From Priestley to Samuel L. Mitchill

Dear Sir

I think myself much obliged to you and Dr Miller for so early an admission of my Paper on *Galvanism* into the *Medical Repository.* I have sent another article, in answer to Mr Cruickshank in *Nicholson's Journal* to Dr Woodhouse, to be forwarded to the *Repository,* which I hope you will insert when it is convenient. I am very glad to hear of the extensive circulation of that valuable work, which does so much credit to the conductors, and the country. I shall always think myself honoured by the publication of any article of mine in it.

I wish much to see this new No, especially on account of the article of your own on the colour of *black,* and the other contents that you mention. Dr Woodhouse is so good as to forward the Nos to me the first opportunity after their arrival in Philadelphia, and therefore I hope I shall not be long without it.

My bookseller in London having disappointed me I am at present much behindhand in philosophical intelligence, by which I suffer much.

In winter also I am not fond of going much into my laboratory, so that I do very little in the way of experiments, at present, tho in other respects I am not quite idle. I feel, however, the effect of years, and am by no means so active as I have been. Neither have I recovered from the effects of the fever that I had in Philadelphia. I am much thinner and weaker, and this I fancy has been in some measure the cause of the ague which I have had lately, and which I never had before.

You will oblige me if you will call on Mr Smith the printer, and desire him to send me not the *National,* but the *Universal Intelligencer.* As I do not want the advertisements, and the *Universal* contains everything of value besides. Also I wish he would let me know how I am to pay him. It must be to some person in Philadelphia, as we have no direct communication with Washington.

I should be glad to know how you are accommodated this winter, and what is the price of boarding and lodging, &c. The last winter I heard the members of Congress complained much. In what state is the *building* of the city, and the *paving,* &c. What matters of importance have you in discussion?

As I know your time must be fully occupied, I ought not to give you this trouble, but if you have leisure to notice these queries, you will oblige me very much. . . .

Northumberland Jan. 5, 1802

No. 174.

FROM PRIESTLEY TO WILLIAM MORGAN

Northumberland, Oct. 23, 1802.

Dear Sir

I thank you for your kind letter, and though it was directed to Virginia, some postmaster, I suppose, in this country had changed that word for Pennsylvania, and it came safe.

Though my philosophical labours are nearly over, I am glad to hear what is passing in that region in which I once moved, though what I then did seems for the present to be overlooked and forgotten. I am confident, however, as much as I can be of any thing, that notwithstanding the almost universal reception of the new theory, which is the cause of it, it is purely chimerical, and cannot keep its ground after a sufficient scrutiny, which may be deferred, but which must take place in time. I am glad to find that Mr Cruickshank in England, as well as the chemists in France, begin to attend to my objections, though the principal of them have been published many years; but, as you say, many will not read, and therefore cannot know any thing that makes against the opinions they have once adopted. Bigotry is not confined to theology. It seems to be as conspicuous among philosophers, who disclaim every thing of the kind. We see that envy, jealousy, and every bad passion, may be excited by any thing that is interesting to us, even in the *belles lettres*. Pope and Swift, and too many others of that class, had as much pride and malevolence as any divines.

Your experiment on inflammable air is curious; but our opponents will say, that though water be decomposed in order to form it, it will at the same time take up more water undecomposed, and hold it in solution; though, when condensed, it must part with some of it; the quantity of the water thus being in proportion to its dimensions.

Mr Cruickshank, I find, promised an answer to my reply to him, and I suppose it has been published in Nicholson's Journal some time, but I have not yet seen it. In this respect I work and write to great disadvantage. It is much to be wished that some able advocate for the old doctrine might arise in England or France. They would engage more attention than any person situated as I am. Some time ago I sent Mr Phillips, for his Magazine, a general answer to all the objections that I had heard of to the argument attacked by Mr Cruickshank; and it appears to me that of three principles on which that argument has been assailed, that adopted by him is the most unfortunate, directly militating against the system that he endeavours to support.

You surprise me with your account of the effect of the new apparatus for the Galvanic experiment. I have the very apparatus you describe, and have not been able to make it answer so well as the old one, and I find it exceedingly difficult to make so many cells quite separate by means of cement. Your account, however, encourages me to try again.

I thank you for your hint of politics. How different is our situation from yours! Our debt is trifling, and will to appearance soon be discharged, though almost all our taxes are done away. Our particular state has a fund, out of which all the expences of government are difrayed; so that we hear of nothing but county taxes for the repair of roads, &c. We in this place have only been called upon to pay a poor's rate, and in both cases on account of single insane persons, and we hardly ever see a beggar, except for accidental fires, &c., and these are soon relieved, every body contributing with great cheerfulness. There being no church establishment, we have no tithe, or any expences beside voluntary ones, on account of religion, and yet there is full as much attention given to it as with you. I do not think that any country in the world was ever in a state of greater improvement, in all respects, or had fairer prospects, than this has at present. It is a great pleasure to look round and see this: and yet we have many grumblers and discontented persons.

I rejoice to hear of the good state of your family, and hope that this will continue a source of happiness to you, when you cannot derive any from the state of public affairs; for which, however, we cannot but have a feeling. I have, though at this distance, and am a sincere well-wisher of Old England. All the friends of liberty must have been disappointed with respect to France. But, perhaps, a state of less political liberty may suit that nation. If they do not complain, why should we? though it is unpleasant to see public liberty make a retrograde motion in any part of the world. . . .

No. 175.

PRINTED INVITATION

Philadelphia, March 2d, 1803.

Sir:

You are hereby invited to join the other members of the American Philosophical Society, in giving a testimony of respect, to their venerable associate Dr. Joseph Priestley, who dines with them on Saturday next at Francis' Hotel — Dinner on table at 3 o'clock.

C. Wistar,
J. Williams,
J. R. Smith,
T. T. Hewson,
J. Vaughan,
} Committee

An answer will be called for to-morrow morning.
Dr. Rush.

No. 176.

FROM PRIESTLEY TO THE MEMBERS OF THE AMERICAN PHILOSOPHICAL SOCIETY

Gentlemen,

I think myself honoured, indeed too much so, by your kind invitation to dine with you, and shall with much pleasure comply with it.

Having been obliged to leave a country which has been long distinguished by discoveries in science, I think myself happy by my reception in another which is following its example, and which already affords a prospect of its arriving at equal eminence. . . .

Wednesday March 2d. [*1803*]

No. 177.

FROM PRIESTLEY TO BENJAMIN SMITH BARTON

Dear Sir

I have received both of your very acceptable letters, the last by Dr Mitchel, with whom I am much pleased, and wish I could encourage him to settle with us. I hope however, he will be at Sunbury, which is near. Another physician has been here some time (Dr. Latby from England) and seems to gain ground in the esteem of the people.

I have read with great satisfaction your *Elements of Botany*, and have learned from it much more than I ever knew before, especially by a careful attention to your well chosen and well engraved *Plates*. I have observed one erratum in the references to them, which is H for F, in the description of Plate 23 p 32. I shall soon peruse the whole a second time. I read every thing of yours with admiration of the extent of your reading, and the variety and importance of your original observations, notwithstanding your manifold avocations, and bad health. It is consequence to the world that you take more care of it, and I hope your projected tour will in some measure answer that purpose, as well as that of science, of which I am confident you will never lose sight go where you will.

I am glad to hear that you have another volume of *philosophical Transactions* ready for the press. This I was far from expecting, after seen that the volume preceding took, I think, five or six years. However, I have nothing to communicate. Indeed, I am, as Mr Wilks used to say, *an exhausted volcano*. My time is over, and my poor state of health, and my age together, warn me to quit all laborious pursuits. Indeed, I feel a languor creeping upon me that I am not able to shake off. A little, however, I am doing, but not much, or of much importance, in philosophy; but I am not idle other ways, where bodily exertion is not wanted. Call on Mr Byrne, and he will give you every [thing] that he publishes of mine. I shall long to see your *Second part*. Though I cannot *do* much, I have more pleasure in reading than ever. . . .

Northumberland July 12. 1803.

No. 178.

FROM ANDREW ELLICOTT TO ROBERT R. LIVINGSTON

Lancaster Jany. 20th. 1804

Dear Sir

Your agreeable favour of the 30th of September last has been duly received. —— Those parts relative to the fall of stones from the Sky, and Count Rumford's experiments upon cold, I have copied, and sent to Doctr. Priestley; but I fear his bad state of health will prevent his making any more experiments. —— A few weeks ago he was attacked with a difficulty of swallowing, (particularly any solid food,) by which he was reduced so low, that his life was despaired of; —— he has however got about again, but there appears very little probability of a complete restoration to health.

I confess my scepticism with respect to the fall of stones from the sky, of course, the arguments concerning their generation in our atmosphere, or being the effects of volcanic eruptions in the moon, appear useless, unless the fact of their fall be placed beyond all doubt. —— Notwithstanding my present scepticism, which arises from the very dubious statement of all the cases which have come to my knowledge, my mind is open to conviction on such evidence as ought to satisfy a mathematician. —— If there have been any new publications on this subject in france, you will do me a particular favour by transmitting them to me. ——

Count Rumford's experiments relative to heat, and cold, are

ingenious and plausible, but they are far from convincing me that cold is a body as well as heat. —— The conclusions drawn from the experiments of Lavoisier on the *calorique liber, & calorique combiné, quantité spécifique de calorique,* appear to have too much weight, to be quickly abandoned.

I have written to Mr. Delambre for a few Books, the price may be 8, or 10 dollars, which I must request the favour of you to pay; the money shall be immediately repaid to your order in this country. —— I would have enclosed a bank note for the purpose of paying for those articles, had I been certain that it would have answered your purpose in france. . . .

No. 179.

FROM THOMAS COOPER TO BENJAMIN SMITH BARTON

Northumberland Feb. 6. 1804

Dear Sir

I have to acquaint you with the melancholy news of the Death of Doctor Jos. Priestley this morning about 11 oClock. He wd. have been 71 had he lived till the 24th of next month.

Mr Priestley would have taken upon himself to inform you of this loss to himself, and to the literary world, but the event has been so recent, that he has not the Spirits to take the opportunity of todays post for the purpose. I wish it had fallen to my lot to communicate intelligence less unpleasant.

The Doctor died without pain, and seemingly from mere debility. His faculties of mind, his composure, and his good temper continued to the last.

I am sure you will grieve not only at the loss the philosophical world has sustained, but at the Death of an eminent man who highly respected your person and Character. . . .

No. 180.

Memorial Service Announcement

The *American Philosophical Society* request the favour of your attendance at the Presbyterian Church in Market-Street, on Thursday next, at eleven o'Clock in the forenoon; when an Eulogium to the memory of their late Associate, Doctor JOSEPH PRIESTLEY, will be delivered by Doctor Benjamin Smith Barton.

Decr. 29th, 1804.

A. Seybert
J. R. Coxe
T. C. James   ⎱———— Secretaries
T. T. Hewson

J. Vaughan   ———— Librarian

Pews, in the body of the Church, will be reserved for those Gentlemen and publick bodies, that are specially invited.

The number of scientific papers Priestley published during these last ten years of his life is more than twice that for the whole of his earlier career, and the total number of their pages nearly equals that of one of his volumes of *Experiments and Observations on Air*. But one cannot argue from numbers that Priestley's scientific productivity in America was at a high level. Indeed, if one examines the papers themselves, the paucity of new ideas and original experiments is at once apparent. When read in conjunction with this correspondence, however, one cannot but be impressed with the effort they represent in overcoming the most adverse of working conditions.

Priestley's initial optimism that he could continue his "philosophical studies" to advantage (Nos. 147, 152) was soon tempered. Part of the trouble was poor facilities. Though some of the necessary apparatus could apparently be obtained in the United States (Nos. 154, 155), the continuing correspondence with the Parkers and Wedgwood (Nos. 147, 150, 151, 167) shows that the greater part of his equipment had to be imported from England. That this method of supply had its own problems is indicated by the letter to Vaughan (No. 159). Inadequate physical facilities were not, however, a severe or lasting handicap. Priestley carried on some experimentation before the summer of 1797, when he first could make full use of his new laboratory (No. 155) and, when finally installed, he could honestly write his friend Lindsey that his library was "far the best in all America, and my Apparatus the most complete."[4]

More pressing was the problem of maintaining a continuous and speedy communication of scientific news. Because of his insistence on the most rapid transmission of knowledge, Priestley committed his scientific papers to the relatively obscure *New York Medical Repository* rather than submit to the halting publication pace of the *Transactions of the American Philosophical Society* (No. 157). His letters repeatedly complain of failures in the communication of "philosophical news" (e.g., No. 172). The serial numbering of his letters abroad suggests something of the uncertainty of transatlantic mail, and on several occasions it appears that as many as seven months passed before he received material sent him. Nevertheless, his correspondence shows that, in addition to the scien-

---

[4] Priestley to Theophilus Lindsey, 6 March 1800; Dr. Williams's Library, London. Priestley's library, when sold at auction in 1816, contained more than 4,000 volumes. In 1800, when he made his boast to Lindsey, only Harvard of the ten principle colleges in the country had a larger collection. See the *Catalogue of the Library of the late Dr. Priestley . . . for sale by Thomas Dobson* (Philadelphia, 1816), and Theodore Hornberger, *Scientific Thought in the American College, 1638–1800* (Austin, University of Texas Press, 1945). Priestley's laboratory supplied the basis of Thomas Cooper's teaching apparatus for his chemistry course at Dickinson College.

tists represented in this collection, he heard from Richard Kirwan and the Royal Dublin Society, and from von Marum, and that he received copies of the *Philosophical Transactions,* Nicholson's *Journal,* and the *Annales de Chimie;* he knew of the work of Beddoes, Davy, Volta, Rumford, Nicholson, Carlisle, and Cruickshank within a year of publication.

Unhappily for Priestley, with but few exceptions the sum of these communications does not represent an exchange of scientific views. For all his experimentation and writing, and though he sent duplicate accounts of his work to Nicholson's *Journal* or Phillips' *Monthly Magazine* to insure that they would be read abroad (Nos. 171, 172), he could elicit little dialogue from European scientists. Even the direct challenge of a public letter to the French chemists (No. 153) was not answered.[5] He appears to have believed that this intellectual isolation was a consequence of his physical remoteness from the scientific world (e.g., No. 174). In fact, his work had increasingly been ignored in Europe since the mid-1780's, and one might well argue that his unique reputation in the United States earned his opinions a more extended hearing there than they ever could have received had he remained in England. So far as his general scientific reputation was concerned, it would have been far better had Priestley ceased to write on chemical subjects, like such other continuing adherents to phlogiston as Keir, Cavendish, Watt, de la Métherie, or Senebier. He was not read in Europe because, for all his protests that he "should rather feel a pride in making the most public acknowledgement" of any change in opinion, he continued to be a vigorous opponent of the new chemistry.[6]

---

[5] This letter seems to be his only extant reference, oblique though it is, to Lavoisier's fate. It is difficult to believe that Priestley never commented elsewhere and more fully on that subject, but if he did so, the documents have not been found.

[6] In a letter to Theophilus Lindsey, 29 May 1797; Dr. Williams's Library, London.

There were many specific grounds on which parts of the Lavoisian theory of oxidation might usefully have been attacked: its protean role for oxygen as the unique supporter of combustion, the cause of acidity, but also of basicity; its failure to account for the production of heat and light; its confusion about the relation between water and the production of inflammable air. Only the last of these points did Priestley question in any detail. Like most die-hard phlogistonists, he had gradually shifted his line of argument and accepted some of the interpretations of the new chemistry. He now agreed that substances "imbibe" oxygen, as well as emitting phlogiston in becoming calces (No. 152); occasionally and reluctantly he adopted parts of the new nomenclature (Nos. 156, 166); he even admitted oxygen as the principle of acidity in his argument against the antiphlogistic explanation for the production of inflammable air from metals in acid solutions (No. 156). But to one of the strongest links in the new chemistry — the compound nature of water — he remained adamantly opposed (No. 165).

It was not that he denied the role of water in the production of gases. Indeed, the point of most of his late experiments was to demonstrate the direct transformation of water into various airs, by the physical processes for "torturing" water that he devised (No. 152). He continued for the American Philosophical Society his experiments on heating water in tubes, begun as early as 1782 and reported again in his last European paper of 1793.[7] Later he developed a new version of the same argument, subjecting water to a vacuum or to repeated freezing (Nos. 164, 165, 166). In retrospect, the only historical significance of this work is as another demonstration that unique interpretations of experimental results do not exist. The fact

---

[7] See Joseph Priestley, *Experiments on the Generation of Air from Water* . . . (London, J. Johnson, 1793); and his "Farther experiments relating to the generation of air from water," *Transactions of the American Philosophical Society*, 4 (1799), 11–20.

that Priestley's own work on gaseous diffusion provides an explanation for most of his water-to-air experiments is almost irrelevant. Characteristically, he remained unaware that gaseous diffusion, investigated again in an ingenious series of experiments for the American Philosophical Society, had any connection with his other researches.[8] But the European supporters of the new chemistry did not as a rule bother to use this explanation either. The compound nature of water was essential to the coherence of interpretation of Lavoisier's system; Priestley's experiments were necessarily wrong, without the necessity of disproof.

The attitude of the European supporters of the new chemistry toward Priestley's experiments with finery cinder was much the same. When he heated ferrosoferric oxide (Fe_3O_4) with charcoal, he obtained an inflammable air which he defined as phlogiston. His opponents promptly argued that the charcoal, or the finery cinder, or both, must contain hydrogen or water which decomposed in contact with the hot iron — this in spite of Priestley's having heated both to a near-red heat before the experiment. A satisfactory explanation was first found by William Cruickshank in 1801, when he identified this inflammable air as an oxide of carbon, i.e., carbon monoxide. Priestley is quite correct, however, when he declares that Cruickshank's explanation militates against the system it endeavors to support (No. 174). That system had declared that the production of inflammable air necessarily required the previous decomposition of water. It also declared that oxides were the end product of combustion. This first position the antiphlogistonists now abandoned, and how, asks Priestley, can one expect something which has already burned to burn again?[9]

[8] For example, see Priestley, "Experiments on the change of Place in different kinds of Air through several interposing Substances," *Transactions of the American Philosophical Society*, 5 (1802), 14–21.

[9] Priestley, "Remarks on Mr. Cruickshank's Experiments upon Finery cinder and Charcoal," *New York Medical Repository*, 6 (1803), 24–26.

Priestley's confidence that Cruickshank's explanation represented the beginning of the end for the new chemistry reveals how little he understood the significance of Lavoisier's revolution. Neither this nor succeeding corrections could shake the essentials of that work, for the new chemistry rested less on a a particular set of experimental justifications than it did on a radical reinterpretation of what chemistry was all about. Priestley never adjusts his scientific interests to the confines of a chemistry increasingly better defined as a study of the proportional constituents of compounds. As earlier he had insisted on the importance of the mode, rather than the proportion, of combination, so he repeats the same sentiments in one of his last scientific papers:

Indeed, a knowledge of the *elements* which enter into the composition of natural substances, is but a small part of what is desirable to investigate with respect to them, the principle, and the mode of their combination; as how it is that they become hard or soft, elastic or non-elastic, solid or fluid, &c. &c. &c. is quite another subject, of which we have, as yet, very little knowledge, or rather none at all.[10]

The essentially mechanistic preconceptions of Priestley's work remain clear, though the precise influence of this view on his experimental observations is frequently less so. It turns out, indeed, that the prolixity of his experimental papers is considerably less revealing than one might suppose. Being unaware of his "errors," he frequently fails, as for example in the experiments on freezing water, to give sufficient detail on those "crucial" aspects which might permit intelligent criticism of the causes of his mistakes.[11] One of his series of experi-

---

[10] Priestley, "Miscellaneous Observations relating to the Doctrine of Air," *New York Medical Repository,* 5 (1802), 266; see also chapter 5, *supra,* footnote 12.

[11] Priestley, "Experiments on the production of Air by the Freezing of Water," *New York Medical Repository,* 4 (1801, 2nd ed. 1808), 17–21.

ments is a harking back to Stephen Hales and the concept of "fixing" airs by changing their elasticities, combined with later discoveries in heat. In his essay, "Of the proportion of latent heat in some kinds of Air," Priestley attempts to measure the release of latent heat by airs (HCl, SO_2, NH_3) becoming liquid in solution with water.[12] It is only by inference from the context of his scientific career, however, that the significance of such an experimental design is revealed.

It is in the interpretation of the experiments of others that his biases show most distinctly. By July 1801 (Nos. 169, 170, 173, 174), Priestley had read in the *Philosophical Magazine* and Nicholson's *Journal of Natural Philosophy* sketchy accounts of the voltaic experiments of Johann Ritter (misspelled "Richter" in the *Philosophical Magazine* report). This work, following the discovery by Nicholson and Carlisle of the electrolysis of water, opened the subject of electro-chemistry, providing just those connections between electricity and chemistry which Priestley had begun his career by seeking; in the hands of Davy and Faraday electro-chemistry would ultimately force some modifications on Lavoisian chemistry, and by just that concentration on "the principle, and the mode of . . . combination" which Priestley had emphasized. But he failed to note any of this.

Ignoring the question of voltaic action, Priestley missed the molecular transport anomaly that later inspired Faraday's researches and concentrated instead (as admittedly Ritter and his commentators were doing) on the apparent disproof of the composition of water. Essentially repeating, with minor variations, the experiments of others, Priestley apparently promoted the polarization of the electrolytic cell by preventing the escape of the liberated gases, and then asserts that production of these gases depends upon their absorption from

[12] Sec. 6, in his "Experiments on the Transmission of Acids and other Liquors in the form of Vapour . . . ," *Transactions of the American Philosophical Society*, 5 (1802), 10–11.

the atmosphere.[13] Once again the mechanism of his outlook prevented him from appreciating the significance of his own experiments. But no one else appreciated it either. In the debate over the meaning of voltaic experiments, Priestley's work was not mentioned. It is doubtful if anyone had bothered to read the papers which presumably were republished in England more out of respect for the person than for the ideas of the writer. By concentrating on the composition of water, Priestley repelled the supporters of Lavoisian chemistry while he deflected attention which might have been given him by the new school of electro-chemists. He continued to be ignored.

Fortunately, perhaps, for his peace of mind, Priestley began to take an interest in scientific subjects previously outside his serious concern. He was hardly settled in Northumberland before he began to express an interest in botany, which he repeatedly mentions in numerous letters to Benjamin Smith Barton (Nos. 152, 154, 157, 161, 168, 169, 177). Priestley was too old and his knowledge too superficial for much in the way of original experiments or observations in areas far from the physical sciences. His observations on hearing and on dreams are isolated instances which remain little more than curiosities.[14] Even in botany, in which his interests were most en-

[13] Priestley, "Observations and Experiments relating to the Pile of Volta," *New York Medical Repository*, 5 (1802), 152–159. See also: a correspondent (probably Dr. George S. Gibbes), "On the Chemical Effects of the Pile of Volta"; "Extract of a Letter from Doctor G. M. to Dr. William Babington . . . On the State of Galvanism and other Scientific Pursuits in Germany"; and a correspondent, "On the Chemical Effects of the Pile of Volta," [Nicholson's] *Journal of Natural Philosophy, Chemistry and the Arts*, 4 (January–February 1801), 472–473, 511–513, and 514–515, respectively; and "Account of Experiments made in Germany with Volta's Galvanic Apparatus, communicated to the French National Institute . . . ," *Philosophical Magazine*, 9 (April 1801), 221–226. For a discussion of Ritter's work and early electrochemical speculation (not including Priestley's), see L. Pearce Williams, *Michael Faraday* (London, Chapman and Hall, 1965), pp. 227–231.

[14] Priestley, "Some Observations relating to the Sense of Hearing," and "Some Thoughts concerning Dreams," *New York Medical Repository*, 4 (1801), 247–248, and 5 (1802), 125–129, respectively.

gaged, his studies might have been confined to reading had his religious beliefs not been challenged by Erasmus Darwin's arguments in support of spontaneous generation, for which Priestley's earlier inadvertent contributions to the study of photosynthesis were used as supporting evidence. In one of his last scientific papers, Priestley reports the results of some ingenious experiments designed to prove that the "green matter" (*conferva fontinalis*) of his early observations was not spontaneously generated. The experiments are reminiscent of Redi's and Spallanzani's, and there is little indication that they were read with anything more than the morbid curiosity reserved for posthumous publications.[15]

His final years were not, however, completely frustrating. Though new scientific discoveries and reactionary politics had combined to ruin his reputation in Europe, he remained a distinguished elder statesman of science to Americans. Although he rejected both the professorship of chemistry at the University of Pennsylvania (Nos. 148, 149), and the presidency of the American Philosophical Society (No. 155), the offers must have been balm to his lacerated pride. Probably neither invitation would have been given during the height of anti-Federalist prejudice; but highly placed persons of his political persuasion continued to consult him on technical problems (Nos. 160, 162) and, with the election of Jefferson, Priestley could relax in an atmosphere of friendliness and admiration. Robert R. Livingston, when American Minister in Paris, sent him scientific news (No. 178) and Jefferson himself wrote letters (see No. 171) and asked his advice on curricula for the projected University of Virginia.[16] The

15 Priestley, "Observations and Experiments relating to equivocal, or spontaneous Generation," *Transactions of the American Philosophical Society*, 6 (1809), 119–129. See also Harold J. Abrahams, "Priestley answers the Proponents of Abiogenesis," *Ambix*, 12 (1964), 44–71.

16 See R. J. Honeywell, *The Educational Work of Thomas Jefferson*, vol. 16, Harvard Studies in Education (Cambridge, Harvard University Press, 1931), pp. 121, 172–173; and, for a general study of Priestley's influence on

testimonial dinner held in his honor by the American Philosophical Society (Nos. 175, 176) might well have prompted
Priestley to a reappraisal of his exile. At Priestley's death the
Baron Georges Cuvier read the traditional éloge for a foreign
member before the reconstituted Institut Royal de France,
while Benjamin Smith Barton, representing the American
Philosophical Society, delivered an elogium of Priestley at the
Presbyterian Church in Philadelphia (No. 180). Regardless of
their content, of the two there can be little doubt that Priestley
would have felt the more honored by the recognition from his
American friends and colleagues.

American education, R. E. Schofield, "Joseph Priestley's American Education,"
in *Early Dickinsoniana, The Boyd Lee Spahr Lectures in Americana, 1957–
1961* (Carlisle, Pennsylvania, Dickinson College, 1961), pp. 117–138.

APPENDIX I

Sources of Letters
in the Collection

Correspondence, vol. 2, no. 66," Archives, Royal Society, London.

No. 9.   Priestley to John Canton, 30 June 1766; Edgar Fahs Smith Library, University of Pennsylvania, Philadelphia.

No. 10.   Priestley to Benjamin Franklin, 21 September 1766; Franklin Papers II, 1, 42, American Philosophical Society, Philadelphia.

No. 11.   John Canton to Priestley, 10 January 1767; "Canton Papers, Correspondence, vol. 2, no. 69," Archives, Royal Society, London.

No. 12.   Priestley to Richard Price, 21 January 1767; Bodleian Library, Oxford University.

No. 13.   Priestley to John Canton, 28 January 1767; "Canton Papers, Correspondence, vol. 3, no. 29," Archives, Royal Society, London.

No. 14.   Priestley to John Canton, 21 April 1767; "Canton Papers, Correspondence, vol. 2, no. 72," Archives, Royal Society, London.

CHAPTER 3

No. 15.   Priestley to John Canton, 27 September 1767; "Canton Papers, Correspondence. vol. 2, no. 74," Archives, Royal Society, London.

No. 16.   Priestley to John Canton, 12 November 1767; "Canton Papers, Correspondence, vol. 2, no. 75," Archives, Royal Society, London.

No. 17.   Priestley to John Canton, 17 November 1767; "Canton Papers, Correspondence, vol. 2, no. 76," Archives, Royal Society, London.

No. 17a.   Advertisement for Electrical Machines, verso of Half-Title, Joseph Priestley's *Familiar Introduction to the Study of Electricity*, 1st ed. (London, J. Dodsley, T. Cadell, and J. Johnson, 1768).

No. 18.   Benjamin Franklin to Lord [Morton, *c.* 1767]; Franklin Papers XLVI (1), 22, American Philosophical Society, Philadelphia.

No. 19.   Benjamin Franklin to John Canton, 27 November [1767]; "Canton Papers, Correspondence, vol. 3, no. 4," Archives, Royal Society, London.

No. 20.   Priestley to Richard Price, 16 January 1768; Bodleian Library, Oxford University.

No. 21.   Benjamin Franklin, unpublished paper, read to the Royal Society, 10 March 1768; Record Books of the Royal Society, Decade V, vol. 41, no. 12, Archives, Royal Society, London.

No. 22.   Priestley to John Canton, 24 May 1768; "Canton Papers, Correspondence, vol. 2, no. 78," Archives, Royal Society, London.

No. 23.   Priestley to John Canton, 11 August 1768; "Canton Papers, Correspondence, vol. 2, no. 79," Archives, Royal Society, London.

No. 24.   Priestley to Benjamin Franklin, [1 November 1768]; Franklin Papers II, 2, 146, American Philosophical Society, Philadelphia.

No. 25.   Priestley to Benjamin Franklin, 28 November 1768; Franklin Papers II, 2, 151, American Philosophical Society, Philadelphia.

No. 26.   Priestley to John Canton, 28 February 1770; "Canton Papers, Correspondence, vol. 3, no. 31," Archives, Royal Society, London.

No. 27.   Copy: Memorandum, Priestley to [the Duke of Northumberland], *c.* 1770; the Fay-Priestley Collection, Dickinson College Library, Carlisle, Pennsylvania.

No. 28.   Priestley to Benjamin Franklin, 2 June 1770; Massachusetts Historical Society, Boston.

No. 28a. *Proposal for Printing by Subscription . . ., c.* 1770.

No. 29.   Priestley to Theophilus Lindsey, 30 July 1770; Dr. Williams's Library, London.

No. 30.   Priestley to Benjamin Franklin, 21 November 1770; Franklin Papers III, 1, 33, American Philosophical Society, Philadelphia.

No. 31.   Priestley to Theophilus Lindsey, 23 December 1770; Dr. Williams's Library, London.

No. 32.   Priestley to Benjamin Franklin, 19 April 1771; Charles Roberts Autograph Collection, Haverford College Library, Haverford, Pennsylvania.

No. 33.   Benjamin Franklin to John Canton, 15 August 1771; "Canton Papers, Correspondence, vol. 3, no. 6," Archives, Royal Society, London.

No. 34. Priestley to Richard Price, 3 October 1771; Bodleian Library, Oxford University.

No. 35. Priestley to John Canton, 9 October 1771; "Canton Papers, Correspondence, vol. 2, no. 90 (1)," Archives, Royal Society, London.

No. 36. Priestley to Richard Price, 12 October 1771; Bodleian Library, Oxford University.

No. 37. Priestley to Richard Price, 19 October 1771; Bodleian Library, Oxford University.

No. 38. Priestley to John Canton, 22 October 1771; "Canton Papers, Correspondence, vol. 2, no. 90 (2)," Archives, Royal Society, London.

No. 39. Priestley to John Canton, 18 November 1771; "Canton Papers, Correspondence, vol. 3, no. 33," Archives, Royal Society, London.

No. 40. Priestley to Richard Price, 23 November 1771; Bodleian Library, Oxford University.

No. 41. Priestley to [William Eden], 4 December 1771; Add. MSS 34, 412, British Museum, London.

No. 42. Priestley to Richard Price, 5 December 1771; Bodleian Library, Oxford University.

No. 43. Priestley to [William Eden], 10 December 1771; American Philosophical Society, Philadelphia.

No. 44. Priestley to Joseph Banks, 10 December 1771; C. R. Weld, *History of the Royal Society*, vol. 2, pp. 56–57.

No. 45. Priestley to Alessandro Volta, 14 March 1772; *Epistolario di Alessandro Volta*, National edition (Bologna, 1949), vol. 1, pp. 59-60; freely translated from the French.

No. 46. Priestley to Thorbern Bergman, 14 March 1772; Handskriftsavdelnigen, Universitetsbiblioteket, Uppsala, Sweden, freely translated from the Latin.

No. 47. Benjamin Franklin to Priestley, 4 May 1772; Franklin Papers XLV, 58, American Philosophical Society, Philadelphia.

No. 48. Priestley to Benjamin Franklin, 13 June 1772; Franklin Papers III, 2, $103\frac{1}{2}$, American Philosophical Society, Philadelphia.

No. 49. Priestley to Benjamin Franklin, 1 July 1772; Franklin Papers III, 1, 65, American Philosophical Society, Philadelphia.

No. 50. Priestley to Richard Price, 21 July 1772; Bodleian Library, Oxford University.

No. 51.   Priestley to Richard Price, 27 September 1772; Bodleian Library, Oxford University.

No. 52.   Priestley to Thorbern Bergman, 21 October 1772; Handskriftsavdelnigen, Universitetsbiblioteket, Uppsala, Sweden; freely translated from the Latin.

No. 53.   Priestley to Richard Price, 11 November 1772; Bodleian Library, Oxford University.

No. 54.   Priestley to Richard Price, 26 November 1772; Bodleian Library, Oxford University.

No. 55.   John Winthrop to Benjamin Franklin, 4 March 1773; Jared Sparks, *Works of Benjamin Franklin*, vol. 6, pp. 375–378.

No. 56.   Priestley to Joseph Bretland, 7 March 1773; J. T. Rutt, *Life and Correspondence of Joseph Priestley*, vol. 1, pp. 189–191.

CHAPTER 4

No. 57.   Priestley to Benjamin Franklin, 26 September 1773; Franklin Papers III, 2, 167, American Philosophical Society, Philadelphia.

No. 58.   Priestley to Benjamin Franklin, 14 October 1773; Franklin Papers III, 2, 168, American Philosophical Society, Philadelphia.

No. 59.   Priestley to Alessandro Volta, 10 November 1773; *Epistolario di Alessandro Volta*, vol. 1, p. 63; freely translated from the French.

No. 60.   Priestley to Caleb Rotheram, 31 May 1774; J. T. Rutt, *Life and Correspondence of Joseph Priestley*, vol. 1, 231–233.

No. 61.   Priestley to Jeremy Bentham, 16 December 1774; Add. MSS 36, 524, British Museum, London.

No. 62.   Priestley to Andrew Oliver, 12 February 1775; *Proceedings of the Massachusetts Historical Society*, 3 (2nd series, 1886–1887), 13–14.

No. 63.   Priestley to George Walker, n.d. (about 6 April 1775); extract in George Walker, *Essays on Various Subjects, to which is prefixed a Life of the Author* (London, J. Johnson, 1809), vol. 1, pp. lxviii–lxx.

No. 64.   Priestley to Newcome Cappe, 28 August 1775; J. T. Rutt, *Life and Correspondence of Joseph Priestley*, vol. 1, pp. 274–275.

No. 65.   Priestley to Matthew Boulton, 22 October 1775; Boulton and Watt Papers, Assay Office, Birmingham.

No. 66.   Priestley to Matthew Boulton, 6 November 1775; Boulton and Watt Papers, Assay Office, Birmingham.

No. 67.   Priestley to Thomas Henry, 31 December 1775; extract in W. Henry, *An Estimate of the Philosophical Character of Dr. Priestley* (York, 1832), p. 15.

No. 68.   Priestley to Caleb Rotheram, 9 February 1776; J. T. Rutt, *Life and Correspondence of Joseph Priestley*, vol. 1, pp. 288–290.

No. 69.   Priestley to Benjamin Franklin, 13 February 1776; Franklin Papers IV, 2, 79, American Philosophical Society, Philadelphia.

No. 70.   Priestley to Alessandro Volta, 25 April 1776; *Epistolario di Alessandro Volta*, vol. 1, pp. 122–123.

No. 71.   Priestley to Matthew Boulton, 28 September 1776; Boulton and Watt Papers, Assay Office, Birmingham.

No. 72.   Priestley to Alessandro Volta, 6 June 1777; *Epistolario di Alessandro Volta*, vol. 1, pp. 170–171.

No. 73.   Antoine Lavoisier to Benjamin Franklin, 8 June 1777; Franklin Papers V, 1, $55\frac{1}{2}$, American Philosophical Society, Philadelphia; freely translated from the French.

No. 74.   Priestley to [Newcome Cappe], 14 September 1777; Wellcome Medical Historical Library, London, A1892.

No. 75.   Priestley to Matthew Boulton, n.d. (about October 1777); Boulton and Watt Papers, Assay Office, Birmingham.

No. 76.   Priestley to Matthew Boulton, 25 November 1777; Boulton and Watt Papers, Assay Office, Birmingham.

No. 77.   Priestley to James Keir, 4 February 1778; Wellcome Historical Medical Library, London.

No. 78.   Priestley to Marsilio Landriani, 24 July 1778; *Opuscoli Scelti sulle Scienze e sulle Arti* 1 (1778), pp. 271-272, freely translated from the Italian.

No. 79.   Priestley to the Abbé Roger Joseph Boscovich, 14 August 1778; Boscovich Archive, General Library, University of California, Berkeley.

No. 80.   Roger Joseph Boscovich to Priestley, 17 October 1778; complete draft, Boscovich Archive, General Library, University of California, Berkeley; freely translated from the French.

No. 81.   Priestley to Giovanni Fabroni, 20 June 1779; American

Philosophical Society, Philadelphia, plus fragment, Biblioteca Nazionale Centrale, Firenze.

No. 82. Priestley to Alessandro Volta, 5 August 1779; *Epistolario di Alessandro Volta*, vol. 1, pp. 357–358.

No. 83. Priestley to Giovanni Fabroni, 5 September 1779; American Philosophical Society, Philadelphia.

No. 84. Priestley to Radcliffe Scholefield, 14 September 1779; J. T. Rutt, *Life and Correspondence of Joseph Priestley*, vol. 1, pp. 324–326.

No. 85. Priestley to Benjamin Franklin, 27 September 1779; Franklin Papers XV, 224, American Philosophical Society, Philadelphia.

No. 86. Priestley to Giovanni Fabroni, 17 October 1779; American Philosophical Society, Philadelphia.

No. 87. Priestley to Benjamin Vaughan, 26 March 1780; American Philosophical Society, Philadelphia.

No. 88. Priestley to Richard Kirwan, August 1780; in J. R. Forster, transl., Charles William Scheele, *Chemical Observations and Experiments on Air and Fire* (London, 1780), pp. 250–259.

No. 89. Priestley to William Herschel, 12 August 1780; J. L. E. Dreyer, ed., *Scientific Papers of Sir William Herschel*, vol. 1, p. xxxi.

CHAPTER 5

No. 90. Priestley to Josiah Wedgwood, 26 May 1781; Misc. MSS V–VI, No. 2, Archives, Royal Society, London.

No. 91. Priestley to Josiah Wedgwood, 8 August 1781; Misc. MSS V–VI, No. 5, Archives, Royal Society, London.

No. 92. Priestley to Josiah Wedgwood, 6 March 1782; Misc. MSS V–VI, No. 7, Archives, Royal Society, London.

No. 93. Priestley to Josiah Wedgwood, 21 March 1782; Misc. MSS V–VI, No. 8, Archives, Royal Society, London.

No. 94. Priestley to Samuel Vaughan, Jr., 17 April 1782; Franklin Institute, Philadelphia.

No. 95. Priestley to Benjamin Franklin, 24 June 1782; lithographed facsimile, Library of Congress, Washington, D. C.

No. 96. Priestley to Arthur Young, 1 July 1782; Add. MSS 35, 126; British Museum, London.

No. 97.   Samuel Vaughan, Jr. to Priestley, 9 September 1782; draft, Franklin Institute, Philadelphia.

No. 98.   Priestley to Josiah Wedgwood, 16 September 1782; Misc. MSS V–VI, No. 9, Archives, Royal Society, London.

No. 99.   Priestley to Josiah Wedgwood, 10 October 1782; Misc. MSS V–VI, No. 10, Archives, Royal Society, London.

No. 100.   Priestley to Josiah Wedgwood, 8 December 1782; Misc. MSS V–VI, No. 11, Archives, Royal Society, London.

No. 101.   Priestley to James Watt, 8 December 1782; H. C. Bolton, *Scientific Correspondence of Joseph Priestley,* No. 15.

No. 102.   Priestley to Edmund Burke, 11 December 1782; Burke Correspondence, Wentworth Woodhouse Muniments, Sheffield City Libraries, Sheffield, England.

No. 103.   Priestley to Jean André DeLuc, 11 December 1782; History of Medicine Library, Yale University, New Haven, Connecticut.

No. 104.   Priestley to Arthur Young, 12 December 1782; Add. MSS 35, 126; British Museum, London.

No. 105.   Priestley to Sir Joseph Banks, 28 December 1782; Burndy Library, Norwalk, Connecticut.

No. 106.   Priestley to Jean André DeLuc [January 1783]; DeLuc, *Idées sur la Météorologie* (Paris, 1787), vol. 2, pp. 208–210; freely translated from the French.

No. 107.   Priestley to Josiah Wedgwood, 23 January 1783; Misc. MSS V–VI, No. 14, Archives, Royal Society, London.

No. 108.   Priestley to Arthur Young, 27 January 1783; Add. MSS 35, 126; British Museum, London.

No. 109.   Priestley to Josiah Wedgwood, 7 March 1783; Misc. MSS V–VI, No. 15, Archives, Royal Society, London.

No. 110.   Priestley to Arthur Young, 31 March 1783; Add. MSS 35, 126; British Museum, London.

No. 111.   Priestley to Josiah Wedgwood, 6 May 1783; lithographed facsimile, Library of Congress, Washington, D. C.

No. 112.   Priestley to Sir Joseph Banks, 23 June 1783; Burndy Library, Norwalk, Connecticut.

No. 113.   Priestley to Jean André DeLuc, 13 December 1782 [3]; Yale Medical Historical Library, Yale University, New Haven, Connecticut.

No. 114.   Priestley to Sir Joseph Banks, 14 December 1783; Collection of Sidney Edelstein, Dexter Chemical Company, New York City.

No. 115. Priestley to Jean André DeLuc, 27 December 1783; Yale Medical Historical Library, Yale University, New Haven, Connecticut.

No. 116. Priestley to Henry Cavendish, 13 May 1784; Devonshire Collections, Chatsworth, Bakewell, England.

No. 117. Henry Cavendish to Priestley, undated draft letter, after 13 May and probably before 16 June 1784; Devonshire Collections, Chatsworth, Bakewell.

No. 118. Priestley to Henry Cavendish, 16 June 1784; Devonshire Collections, Chatsworth, Bakewell.

No. 119. Priestley to William Wilkinson, 16 June 1784; MSS/Add. 4251, University Library, Cambridge.

No. 120. Priestley to Jean André DeLuc, 9 September 1784; Yale Medical Historical Library, Yale University, New Haven, Connecticut.

No. 121. Priestley to Josiah Wedgwood, 8 November 1784; H. C. Bolton, *Scientific Correspondence of Joseph Priestley*, No. 33.

No. 122. Henry Cavendish to Priestley, draft letter, 20 December 1784; Devonshire Collections, Chatsworth, Bakewell.

No. 123. Priestley to Henry Cavendish, 30 December 1784; Devonshire Collections, Chatsworth, Bakewell.

No. 124. Priestley to the Philosophical Society at Orléans, 12 May 1785; Bibliothèque Publique, Archives du Loiret, Orléans, France.

No. 125. American Philosophical Society Certificate, 22 January 1785; Archives, American Philosophical Society, Philadelphia; another copy, engrossed on parchment, dated 17 June 1785, Historical Society of Pennsylvania, Philadelphia.

No. 126. Priestley to the Secretary, American Academy of Arts and Sciences, 23 June 1785; Archives, American Academy of Arts and Sciences, Boston.

No. 127. Priestley to Martin von Marum, 14 September 1785; Hollandsche Maatschappij der Wetenschappen, Haarlem.

No. 128. Priestley to Arthur Young, 11 November 1785; Add. MSS 35, 126; British Museum, London.

No. 129. Priestley to Martin von Marum, 9 June 1786; Hollandsche Maatschappij der Wetenschappen, Haarlem.

No. 130. Priestley to Jan IngenHousz, 24 November 1787; Handschriftensammlung Österreichische Nationalbibliothek (Autogr. 50/5), Vienna.

No. 131. Priestley to Josiah Wedgwood, 8 January 1788; H. C. Bolton, *Scientific Correspondence of Joseph Priestley*, No. 44.

No. 132. Priestley to Josiah Wedgwood, 18 August 1788; H. C. Bolton, *Scientific Correspondence of Joseph Priestley*, No. 47.

No. 133. Priestley to Martin von Marum, 12 December 1788; Hollandsche Maatschappij der Wetenschappen, Haarlem.

No. 134. James Keir to Priestley, n.d. but supposedly of 1789; [A. Moilliet], *Sketch of the Life of James Keir*, pp. 93–94.

No. 135. Priestley to John Parker, 8 June 1789; File 989, Musée de Mariemont, Belgium.

No. 136. Priestley to Martin von Marum, 21 August 1790; Hollandsche Maatschappij der Wetenschappen, Haarlem.

No. 137. Priestley to Josiah Wedgwood, 26 February 1791; H. C. Bolton, *Scientific Correspondence of Joseph Priestley*, No. 58.

No. 138. Priestley to the Duc de La Rochefoucauld ["Mr De Rochfocault"], 28 April 1791; Bibliothèque Mantes Municipale, Mantes, France.

No. 139. Priestley to Thomas Wedgwood, 20 June 1791; H. C. Bolton, *Scientific Correspondence of Joseph Priestley*, No. 59.

No. 140. Chemists of Paris [Lavoisier?] to Priestley, n.d. but probably July 1791; Burndy Library, Norwalk, Connecticut.

No. 141. Josiah Wedgwood to Priestley, 2 September 1791; draft, the John Rylands Library, Manchester.

No. 142. Priestley to Josiah Wedgwood, 7 September 1791; H. C. Bolton, *Scientific Correspondence of Joseph Priestley*, No. 65.

No. 143. Priestley to Sir Joseph Banks, 10 January 1792; Burndy Library, Norwalk, Connecticut.

No. 144. Priestley to Antoine Lavoisier, 2 June 1792; H. C. Bolton, *Scientific Correspondence of Joseph Priestley*, No. 77.

No. 145. Priestley to William Withering, 2 October 1792; Birmingham Reference Library, Birmingham, England.

No. 146. Priestley to William Withering, 15 April 1793; Birmingham Reference Library, Birmingham, England.

CHAPTER 6

No. 147. Priestley to Samuel Parker, 27 June 1794; J. T. Rutt, *Life and Correspondence of Joseph Priestley*, vol. 2, p. 267.

No. 148. Priestley to Benjamin Rush, 14 September 1794; H. C. Bolton, *Scientific Correspondence of Joseph Priestley*, No. 83.

No. 149. Priestley to Benjamin Rush, 11 November 1794; H. C. Bolton, *Scientific Correspondence of Joseph Priestley*, No. 86.

No. 150. Priestley to Samuel Parker, 20 January 1795; J. T. Rutt, *Life and Correspondence of Joseph Priestley*, vol. 2, p. 292.

No. 151. Priestley to Josiah Wedgwood, 17 March 1795; Gratz Autograph Collection, Historical Society of Pennsylvania, Philadelphia.

No. 152. Priestley to William Withering, 27 October 1795; American Philosophical Society, Philadelphia.

No. 153. Priestley to the French Chemists, 15 June 1796; MS Copy, Dr. Williams's Library, London, printed as preface to Priestley's *Doctrine of Phlogiston* (1800).

No. 154. Priestley to Benjamin Smith Barton, 20 July 1796; Historical Society of Pennsylvania, Philadelphia.

No. 155. Priestley to Benjamin Smith Barton, 8 October 1796; Historical Society of Pennsylvania, Philadelphia.

No. 156. Priestley to Samuel L. Mitchill, 14 June 1798; Edgar Fahs Smith Library, University of Pennsylvania, Philadelphia.

No. 157. Priestley to Benjamin Smith Barton, 8 August 1798; Historical Society of Pennsylvania, Philadelphia.

No. 158. Priestley to Benjamin Smith Barton, 16 August 1798; Historical Society of Pennsylvania, Philadelphia.

No. 159. Priestley to John Vaughan, 21 March 1799; American Philosophical Society, Philadelphia.

No. 160. Priestley to Robert R. Livingston, 16 April 1799; Pennsylvania Historical and Museum Commission, Division of Public Records, Harrisburg.

No. 161. Priestley to Benjamin Smith Barton, 25 June 1799; Historical Society of Pennsylvania, Philadelphia.

No. 162. Priestley to Robert R. Livingston, 24 October 1799; Charles Roberts Autograph Collection, Haverford College Library, Haverford, Pennsylvania.

No. 163. Priestley to "a Physician in this Borough [Dr. John

Vaughan]," 26 December 1799; extract from *Mirror of the Times* (Wilmington, Delaware), 11 January 1800. This letter was called to my attention by Carroll Pursell, Jr., University of California, Santa Barbara, California.

No. 164. Priestley to B. Lynde Oliver, 3 April 1800; *Proceedings of the Massachusetts Historical Society*, 3 (2nd series, 1886–1887), 34–35.

No. 165. Priestley to Robert R. Livingston, 17 April 1800; Historical Society of Pennsylvania, Philadelphia.

No. 166. Priestley to B. Lynde Oliver, 8 August 1800; *Proceedings of the Massachusetts Historical Society*, 3 (2nd series, 1886–1887), 38–39.

No. 167. Priestley to William Parker, 13 August 1800; MSS Collections, New York Public Library, New York.

No. 168. Priestley to Benjamin Smith Barton, 27 November 1800; Historical Society of Pennsylvania, Philadelphia.

No. 169. Priestley to Benjamin Smith Barton, 7 July 1801; Historical Society of Pennsylvania, Philadelphia.

No. 170. Priestley to Samuel L. Mitchill, 16 July 1801; Historical Society of Pennsylvania, Philadelphia.

No. 171. Priestley to Theophilus Lindsey, 2 October 1801; Dr. Williams's Library, London.

No. 172. Priestley to Humphry Davy, 31 October 1801; John Davy, ed., *Fragmentary Remains, Literary and Scientific, of Sir Humphry Davy*, p. 51.

No. 173. Priestley to Samuel L. Mitchill, 5 January 1802; MS Copy, Edgar Fahs Smith Library, University of Pennsylvania, Philadelphia. Original given by E. F. Smith to Rice Institute, to be placed in the cornerstone of a new chemical laboratory.

No. 174. Priestley to William Morgan, 23 October 1802; J. T. Rutt, *Life and Correspondence of Joseph Priestley*, vol. 2, pp. 495–497.

No. 175. Printed Invitation, 2 March 1803, H. C. Bolton, *Scientific Correspondence of Joseph Priestley*, p. 161.

No. 176. Priestley to American Philosophical Society, 2 March [1803]; American Philosophical Society, Philadelphia.

No. 177. Priestley to Benjamin Smith Barton, 12 July 1803; Historical Society of Pennsylvania, Philadelphia.

APPENDIX II

Biographical Sketches
of Correspondents

M OST OF THE PERSONS with whom Priestley exchanged letters of scientific interest are well known for one or more areas of achievement as scientists, industrialists, statesmen, educators, or writers. Many of them are the subject of at least one full-length biography, and accounts of almost all are to be found in their respective national biographical dictionaries. At the other end of the scale, a few of his scientific correspondents are so little known that for them even the barest of biographical information is next to unobtainable.

For both the famous and the obscure, however, the intention here has been the same — merely to provide in these sketches sufficient information to identify the correspondents and establish their relationship to Priestley and the occasion of their correspondence.

Where the sources of information are not cited, the material has been extracted from the *Dictionary of National Biography* and the *Dictionary of American Biography* for British and American nationals, respectively. Members of the Lunar Society of Birmingham are also discussed, with particular attention to their scientific accomplishments and their relations with Priestley in my book, *The Lunar Society of Birmingham*. Any other references used are specifically cited in the notes to individual sketches.

[346]

BANKS, SIR JOSEPH (1743–1820)
President, Royal Society, 1778–1820
and patron of science

Educated at Harrow, Eton, and Christ Church, Oxford, he early showed an interest in botanical studies. He became a Fellow of the Royal Society in 1766, and accompanied Captain James Cook on the first voyage of the "Endeavour" from 1768 to 1771. His plans to go on Cook's second voyage were canceled when the accommodations for his party and scientific stores were altered. He succeeded Sir John Pringle as President of the Royal Society, where his long term in office (1778–1820) was marred by repeated dissension and somewhat justified accusations of autocratic rule. He was a munificent patron of botanists, and his great library was freely used by them.

His associations with Priestley were almost entirely within the Royal Society, and their correspondence primarily relates to scientific and organizational problems arising out of this connection. Banks was a high Tory and undoubtedly did not approve of Priestley's political and religious views. The "coldness" Priestley complained of in the Society after the Birmington riots of 1791 probably originated in Banks, but the latter's aid in re-establishing Priestley's laboratory shows him in a favorable light.

BARTON, BENJAMIN SMITH (1766–1815)
physician, botanist, and mineralogist

Born at Lancaster, Pennsylvania, and educated at York Academy, Pennsylvania; and the College of Philadelphia; he studied medicine in Edinburgh and London, and obtained his M.D. degree at Göttingen in 1789. On his return to the United States, he practiced medicine, became successively professor of natural history and botany, of *materia medica* and, on the death of Benjamin Rush, of the theory and practice of medicine at the University of Pennsylvania. He was a member of the American Philosophical Society and the American Academy of Arts and Sciences.

He became one of Priestley's foremost scientific friends when the latter came to the United States in 1794, and read his memorial eulogy before the American Philosophical Society. The two men corresponded chiefly on botanical and chemical subjects, but it was from Priestley that Barton obtained the *Vocabularia Comparativa* of Peter Simon Pallas, which he used in his study of the languages of American Indians.

BENTHAM, JEREMY (1748–1832)
social philosopher and author

Educated at Westminster and Queen's College, Oxford, he received his B.A. degree in 1763, and his M.A. in 1768; he kept terms at Lincoln's Inn, was called to the bar in 1767, and became a member of Lincoln's Inn in 1817. He dabbled in chemistry and natural philosophy, and in 1783 he translated an essay by Thorbern Bergman on the usefulness of chemistry. He published his *Fragment on Government* in 1776, which marked the beginning of a career of writing on jurisprudence, politics, and social philosophy. He became a protégé of Lord Shelburne after 1776.

He probably met Priestley through their mutual association with Shelburne. The letter published here (No. 61) is a slight indication of a shared interest in science, while Bentham's famous formula for good government, "the greatest happiness to the greatest number," was admittedly derived from a similar phrase in Priestley's *An Essay on the First Principles of Government* (London, 1768).[1]

[1] Mary Peter Mack, *Jeremy Bentham* (New York, Columbia University Press, 1963), particularly p. 103. There is another Priestley-Bentham letter, of 19 March 1775, which briefly refers to some of the same topics as in the published letter of 16 December 1774 in the Fay–Priestley Collection, Dickinson College Library, Carlisle, Pennsylvania.

BERGMAN, THORBERN (1735–1784)
*natural philosopher, professor at
the University of Uppsala*

Educated at Uppsala, where he studied mathematics, physics, chemistry, botany, entomology, he was a member of the Swedish Academy of Sciences, and became a Fellow of the Royal Society in 1765. He published work on electricity, physical geography, mineralogy, chemistry and pharmacy. He became professor of chemistry and pharmacy at Uppsala in 1767. Known for his development of methods in qualitative and quantitative analyses, and for his work on the chemical classifications of minerals and the study of elective affinitives, he introduced a new chemical nomenclature which was to influence later French labors, but remained a supporter of phlogiston all his life.[2] He was a patron of Carl W. Scheele.

His first communication to Priestley was apparently prompted by the publication of Priestley's *History of Electricity,* which in the first edition had not mentioned some of the work of the Scandinavians. It was probably in this letter that Priestley also learned of Bergman's identification of the acidic nature of an aqueous solution of "fixed air." Bergman was surely one of the earliest of Priestley's foreign correspondents on chemical subjects.

BOSCOVICH, ROGER JOSEPH, S.J. (1711–1787)
mathematician, astronomer, natural philosopher

He was educated first at the Jesuit College in Ragusa, now Dubrovnik, Yugoslavia, then at the Collegium in Rome, where he passed his doctorate and entered the Jesuit priesthood in 1744. He then commenced his distinguished career as teacher, poet, diplomat, astronomer, natural philosopher, and writer. In 1748 he became a corresponding member of the Royal Academy of Sciences, Paris; he was elected member of the Russian Academy

[2] J. R. Partington, *A History of Chemistry* (London, 1962), vol. 3, pp. 179–199.

of Sciences and Fellow of the Royal Society in 1760. He traveled in Austria, France, the Netherlands, England, and the German states. Professor of mathematics at the University of Pavia in 1764, he was director of Milan Observatory, 1765–1773. On the suppression of the Jesuit order in 1773, he became Director of Naval Optics of the Franch Navy. He returned to Italy in 1782, and died there.[3]

Priestley probably first learned of Boscovich's work from John Michell, while working on the *History of Optics* in 1772. Boscovich's famous *Theoria Naturalis Philosophiae* (Vienna, 1758; second edition 1763), which described an elaborate mechanistic philosophy of nature combining elements of Leibniz' and Newton's views, was a major influence on Priestley's beliefs. Priestley and Boscovich discussed the latter's work during Priestley's visit to Paris in 1774. These letters, presumably the only ones exchanged by the two, were prompted by the publication of Priestley's *Disquisitions on Matter and Spirit* (London, 1777), in which Priestley defended a peculiar mechanistic and quasi-materialistic yet theistic view of the soul based on Boscovich's atomism. Boscovich's reaction was predictably critical, but the harsh tone of the letters is probably also the result of Boscovich's growing melancholia, from which he died in 1787, and of Priestley's automatically pugnacious response to slighting criticism.

BOULTON, MATTHEW (1728–1809)
merchant, manufacturer, entrepreneur, and engineer

Born in Birmingham and educated in grammar school there, he was early a partner of his father's, a manufacturer of buttons and buckles. Boulton was a developer of the Soho Works, long one of the major industrial complexes in England, and a partner of James Watt's in perfecting and distributing Watt's steam engines. Patron of the arts and sciences, he became a Fellow of the Royal Society in 1785, was a member of the Society of Arts, a

[3] Lancelot Law Whyte, ed., *Roger Joseph Boscovich*. London, George Allen & Unwin, 1961.

founding member of the Lunar Society of Birmingham, and a "Proprietor" of the Royal Institution. He was friendly with Benjamin Franklin and with Samuel Garbett, financial advisor to Lord Shelburne.

Probably he first met Priestley when the latter visited Birmingham in the company of Lord Shelburne. Their early correspondence reflects Boulton's interest in chemistry and mineralogy. They presumably became friendly when Priestley joined the Lunar Society on his move to Birmingham in 1780. The friendship ceased with Priestley's political difficulties after the riots of 1791.

BRETLAND, JOSEPH (1742–1819)
dissenting minister (Unitarian) and teacher

He kept a classical school at Exeter and ministered at dissenting (Unitarian) chapels there till 1797; he ran a dissenting academy in the west of England until its dissolution in 1805. There is little evidence that he was interested in science, and his connection with Priestley was evidently the result of their mutual concerns with education and theology. Priestley sent Bretland an early copy of the *Disquisitions on Matter and Spirit,* and Bretland edited an edition of Priestley's *Rudiments of English Grammar.*

BURKE, EDMUND (1729–1797)
statesman, political philosopher, author

Born in Ireland, he was educated at a Quaker school and at Trinity College, Dublin. He received his B.A. degree in 1748. He read for the bar at the Middle Temple, and was the first editor of the *Annual Register* until about 1788. He entered politics through his attachment to Rockingham interests, was friendly with Garrick, Reynolds, Johnson, and for a time with Benjamin Franklin and Charles James Fox. He was a member of Parliament after 1766, and after 1768 he attempted to apply science to agriculture on his estate.

[351]

Burke was at first friendly with Priestley during the American revolutionary period. He courted the support of the liberal dissenting interests until the outbreak of the French Revolution, when he became the leader of English political reaction. His public attacks on Priestley were in large measure responsible for the violence and suspicion leading to Priestley's emigration to the United States.

CANTON, JOHN (1718–1772)
schoolmaster, natural philosopher

Initially apprenticed to a cloth weaver, he articled himself to a schoolmaster in Spital Square, London, and subsequently became partner and then head of the school. He wrote scientific articles for the *Ladies' Diary* and the *Gentleman's Magazine*. He became a Fellow of the Royal Society in 1749, a member of its Council in 1751, and a Copley medalist in 1751 and again in 1765. He was the first Englishman to confirm Franklin's hypothesis of the electrical nature of lightning, and was one of the foremost "electricians" of mid-eighteenth-century England. He was introduced to Priestley by John Seddon, a fellow schoolmaster; in turn Canton introduced Priestley to Franklin. During the writing of the *History of Electricity* Canton was one of Priestley's mentors, and thus he helped guide Priestley's early scientific career.

CAPPE, NEWCOME (1733–1800)
dissenting clergyman

Educated at Kibworth Academy, Northampton Academy, and in Glasgow, he became minister to a dissenting chapel in York, where he remained all his life. He took a prominent role in the literary and political life of the community, and founded a York Literary Society, which lasted nearly twenty years. He was not well known beyond his own borders.

His acquaintance with Priestley resulted from shared theological interests, and from Cappe's early association with Aikin and

Doddridge, whose educational influence Priestley also felt. Their correspondence primarily relates to theology and metaphysics, particularly Hartleyian physiological psychology, with only occasional and casual scientific references.

CAVENDISH, HENRY (1731–1810)
natural philosopher

He was educated at Peterhouse, Cambridge, and by his father, Lord Charles Cavendish. In straitened circumstances early in life, he inherited a fortune in middle age, by which time he had become something of an eccentric and a recluse. He was probably the most eminent natural philosopher in England in the late eighteenth-century. The major part of his scientific work remains unpublished, but it appears to have ranged from mathematics through heat and electricity to chemistry and geology. He became a Fellow of the Royal Society in 1760; and a Corresponding Member of the Institut de France in 1802.

He apparently knew Priestley by the 1770's, when the two discussed electrical experiments, and from then until their communications cease in the 1790's the work of each so complements and supplements that of the other that it is impossible to determine which more greatly influenced the other. Priestley was the greater discoverer, while Cavendish was clearly the more exact and penetrating thinker and experimenter. The letters here are unfortunately all that seem to have survived a long and mutually fruitful correspondence.

COOPER, THOMAS (1759–1839)
political agitator, scientist, educator

Born in Westminster, England, he was educated at University College, Oxford, and studied anatomy and clinical medicine at London. He practiced medicine in Manchester, was a member of a firm of calico printers, and a barrister on the Northern Circuit. A member of the Manchester Literary and Philosophical Society, he was twice rejected by the Royal Society, probably for his radical political beliefs. Member of the Manchester Constitutional Society, he visited Paris in 1792. He was attacked by Burke in the House of Commons. In 1794 he emigrated with Priestley's sons to the United States.

He practiced law and medicine in Northumberland, Pennsylvania, joined the Jeffersonian opposition to Federalists and was convicted under the Sedition Act in 1800. He was a commissioner and judge in Pennsylvania, a chemistry teacher at Dickinson College (Carlisle, Pennsylvania), a professor of chemistry and mineralogy at the University of Pennsylvania, professor and ultimately president at South Carolina College. He was extravagantly praised by Jefferson, but he never achieved the results possible to his native abilities because of the unmanageable range of his concerns, and his personality, which excited animosities.

His association with Priestley was probably first brought about through his friendship with Joseph Priestley, Jr., in Manchester. Cooper was one of the organizers of the abortive colonization scheme involving the Priestley family and later lived in the Priestley household in Northumberland. He was a literary executor and assistant editor of Priestley's *Memoirs* and arranged for the transfer of a substantial portion of Priestley's scientific apparatus to Dickinson College after Priestley's death.

DAVY, SIR HUMPHRY (1778–1829)
natural philosopher

Educated in grammar schools at Penzance and Truro, he was first introduced to science by an itinerant laborer and amateur scientist; in 1794 he was apprenticed to a Penzance surgeon and apothecary. He became a protégé of Davies Giddy (afterwards Gilbert), Dr. Edwards, chemical lecturer at St. Bartholomew's Hospital, Gregory Watt, and the Wedgwoods. In 1798 he became superintendent of the laboratory of Dr. Thomas Beddoes' Pneumatic Medical Institute, Bristol; in 1801 he went to the Royal Institution, London, ultimately as professor of chemistry and director of the chemical laboratory. He became a Fellow of the

Royal Society in 1803, Copley medalist in 1805, secretary of the Royal Society in 1807, member of the Council in 1806, was knighted in 1812, was Rumford medalist in 1817, and succeeded Banks as president of the Royal Society in 1820. He discovered potassium and sodium by the electrolytic decomposition of potash and soda, he proved chlorine was an element, and invented a mine safety lamp. Davy was Michael Faraday's patron.

Priestley may first have learned of Davy through the latter's association with Lunar Society members or their sons. Joseph Priestley, Jr., was at any rate a party along with Gregory and James Watt, Jr., Tom Wedgwood, and Matthew Robinson Boulton in Davy's early experiments with laughing gas. Priestley read and admired Davy's early publications (Davy afterwards regretted the publication of these "immature hypotheses") and began a correspondence that was shortly to be ended with Priestley's death.

DeLuc, Jean André (1727–1817)
geologist and meteorologist

Born in Geneva, Switzerland, he was tutored by his father, and early showed an ability in mathematics and the natural sciences. He became a merchant and politician in Geneva until the failure of his business in 1773, when he settled in England. He became Reader to Queen Charlotte; a Fellow of the Royal Society; honorary professor of geology at Göttingen; and corresponding member of the Academy of Sciences at Paris. He designed meteorological instruments (he invented the "dry pile"); his anti-Hutton, conservative views on geology were admired by Cuvier. DeLuc was an opponent of the "new chemistry of Lavoisier." DeLuc first met Priestley in 1773, and the association was continued because of a shared interest in the behavior of gases and in theological metaphysics.

[355]

Douglas, James, Earl of Morton (1702–1768)
patron of science, President of the Royal Society
1764–1768

Graduate of Kings College, Cambridge, where he received his master's degree in 1722. A student of mathematics and natural philosophy, he was a friend of Maclaurin and other Scottish scientists. He represented Scotland in the House of Lords, 1739–1768. He was the contributor of several astronomical papers to the Royal Society, and became president (1764–1768) after thirty years as Fellow. He attended assiduously to his duties, he imposed a needed restraint on the election of new Fellows, and promoted the transit of Venus expedition of 1769.

Morton was president of the Royal Society the year Priestley was elected Fellow, but there appears to have been no other connection between them except the indirect one represented by the letter from Franklin and the references to him (as "Moreton") by Franklin in relation to the abortive attempt to gain the Copley Medal for Priestley's electrical researches.

Eden, William (1744–1814)
the first Baron Auckland, statesman and diplomat

Educated at Eton and Christ Church, Oxford, he received his B.A. degree in 1765, and his M.A. in 1768. He was called to the Middle Bar in 1769. In 1772 he was named undersecretary of state; in 1776 he became a member of the Board of Trade and Plantations. From the first he devoted himself to legal and economic questions; he served in administrative positions in Ireland, accepted office under Pitt in 1785, and turned to diplomatic concerns. He helped negotiate a commercial treaty with France in 1785, and was sent on special ambassadorial missions to Madrid, Paris, The Hague, etc., until 1793, when he returned to England. He was raised to the peerage in 1789. His friendship with Pitt gave him much political influence until they split in 1804. Eden was president of the Board of Trade, 1806–1807.

Priestley's letters to Eden give an impression of friendship not otherwise supported by any evidence and negated by Auckland's conservative political opinions. Their correspondence, indeed, seems limited to the proposed appointment of Priestley to the second voyage of Captain James Cook, a proposal that may be attributed to Eden's position on the Board of Trade and Plantations.

ELLICOTT, ANDREW (1754–1820)
surveyor and mathematician

Son of a prosperous Pennsylvania miller and mechanic, Ellicott had a scanty formal education, but early turned to surveying and instrument making. He served as a major during the American Revolution; after the war he published almanacs, and acted on a number of official state surveying parties, e.g., in Virginia, Pennsylvania, New York, and the District of Columbia. He revised L'Enfant's design for Washington, D.C. In 1813 he was appointed professor of mathematics at West Point. Although his correspondence and diaries indicate that he was friendly with Priestley, we here see him only as a medium of scientific communication between Robert Livingston and Priestley.

FABRONI, BARON GIOVANNI (1752–1822)
natural philosopher

First an assistant to Felice Fontana, director of physics and chemistry at the laboratory of Leopold, Grand Duke of Tuscany, Fabroni became director on Fontana's death. The author of many minor works on agriculture, natural history, chemistry, physics, medicine, physiology, and political economy, he became a scientific and political functionary in the various local governments established in relationship with the French empire.[4]

Fabroni met Priestley when in Fontana's company he toured France and England to study recent discoveries in natural philosophy. His skill in German, English, and French as well as Italian

---

[4] F. Hoefer, ed., *Nouvelle Biographie Générale* (Paris, 1872), vol. 16.

made him a useful medium for the transmission of scientific information to the continent, while Priestley appears also to have had a high regard for Fabroni's chemical knowledge.

FRANKLIN, BENJAMIN (1706–1790)
printer, natural philosopher, statesman, etc., etc.

Born in Boston, Massachusetts, he was self-educated, except for two years in grammar schools and his apprenticeship to his brother, a printer. He established himself in Philadelphia as an author, printer, and civic leader. He went to England in 1757 and, with one brief return to the colonies, remained there until 1775 as representative of various colonial assemblies. He worked to reconcile political differences until this became futile, and then committed himself thoroughly to the cause of American independence. He was a member of the Second Continental Congress, of the committee to draft the Declaration of Independence, the major emissary of the United States to France until the conclusion of peace negotiations in 1785, when he returned to the United States. He was the first president of the executive council of Pennsylvania, and a member of the Constitutional Convention, 1787.

He commenced his electrical studies in Pennsylvania in the mid-1740's; he became Copley medalist in 1753, a Fellow of the Royal Society in 1756, and foreign associate of the Royal Academy of Sciences in 1772. When he arrived in England, he was already one of the most distinguished of British scientists. His work on electrical theory and his invention of the lightning rod had earned him an international reputation. He met Priestley for the first time in 1765, through the courtesy of John Canton and at the request of John Seddon, and at once became Priestley's mentor. Franklin's influence is evident in Priestley's research, writing, and political beliefs. Their correspondence was extensive, continuing through the American Revolution and beyond, and covering personal, political, and religious subjects as well as scientific.

HENRY, THOMAS (1734–1816)
chemist, surgeon–apothecary

Educated at a grammar school kept by his father at Wrexham, he was apprenticed to an apothecary. He attended anatomical lectures while an apothecary's assistant at Oxford, and then established himself successfully in Manchester, manufacturing calcined magnesia as a medicine. Writer and lecturer on chemical subjects, he also translated some of Lavoisier's early works. He became a Fellow of the Royal Society in 1775, on the recommendation of Sir John Pringle and Priestley; a member of the American Philosophical Society on Franklin's recommendation; he was a secretary and subsequently a president of the Manchester Literary and Philosophical Society.

Henry's friendship with Priestley predates the publication of the latter's first volume of *Experiments and Observations on Air,* which contains an extract of a letter from Henry; subsequent volumes of that work attest the continued friendship, which probably commenced through their mutual friend, Dr. Thomas Percival. The manuscript letters from Priestley to Henry seem to have disappeared. Thomas Henry's son, William, wrote one of the earliest scientific biographical sketches of Priestley.

HERSCHEL, SIR WILLIAM (1732–1822)
astronomer, natural philosopher, musician

Born in Hanover and trained as a musician, Herschel went to England in 1756, where he held a series of posts as a musician until 1766, when he became organist at the Octagon Chapel, Bath. Self-educated in mathematics, optics, and astronomy, in 1773 he constructed his own astronomical instruments, and so far succeeded that his telescopes became the means for major astronomical discoveries, including that of the planet Uranus in 1781. In 1780 he became a member of the Philosophical Society of Bath, on the invitation of Sir William Watson; he was made Copley medalist and Fellow of the Royal Society in 1781; in 1782 he became Court Astronomer to George III. He was virtually the

[359]

founder of sidereal astronomy and he discovered infrared radiation.

There is no evidence that Priestley and Herschel had met before Herschel's visits to Birmingham and the Lunar Society. His early writings indicate that Herschel was familiar with Priestley's *History of Electricity* and *History of Optics,* while a mutual friendship with Watson may have encouraged Herschel to request Priestley's aid in approaching John Michell for advice. The Priestley letter included here is obviously a response to such a request from Herschel. No other Priestley-Herschel letters apparently exist.

INGENHOUSZ, JAN (1730–1799)
physician and natural philosopher

Born in Breda, he was educated for the medical profession in Breda, Louvain, London, Paris, and Edinburgh. He practiced for several years in the Netherlands, moved to London in 1766, and to Vienna in 1768, where he was personal physician to the family of Maria Theresa. In 1779 he returned to London and became a Fellow of the Royal Society. He replaced Priestley as Shelburne's scientific protégé. He was a conformist in social and religious matters and possessed the genial manners and social graces that Priestley lacked. IngenHousz wrote papers and books on electricity and magnetism, the electric torpedo, and atmospheric gases; his pamphlet, *Experiments on Vegetables* (London, 1779), contains the first published account of the influence of light on the production of oxygen by plants.[5]

His personal acquaintance with Priestley probably began in 1779, but, though Franklin was a mutual friend, it is unlikely that IngenHousz and Priestley ever really became friendly. Their work was too much along the same lines to avoid misunderstandings on priorities, as the letter printed here indicates. It is probably true that Priestley should have been more generous in his

[5] Howard Reed, "Jan IngenHousz, Plant Physiologist," *Chronica Botanica,* 11 (1949), 285–396.

description of IngenHousz's work, though other letters in this correspondence show that Priestley had observed the agency of light in photosynthesis before the publication of IngenHousz's book.

KEIR, JAMES (1735–1820)
chemist, manufacturer

Educated at the University of Edinburgh, he became a member of the Lunar Society of Birmingham and in 1785 a Fellow of the Royal Society. He translated and annotated Macquer's *Dictionary of Chemistry,* in two editions; to the second is added a *Treatise on Different Kinds of Elastic Fluids or Gases,* also published separately. For a brief time he managed a glass works near Stourbridge; then he directed manufacturing operations at Soho for Matthew Boulton; and finally he operated a chemical works at Tipton, one of the largest such plants in Britain. He wrote articles and pamphlets on geology, chemistry, politics, and military strategy. He was toastmaster at the 14 July 1791 dinner in Birmingham which was made the excuse for the Birmingham riots.

His acquaintance with Priestley probably began through Matthew Boulton and continued after Priestley's move to Birmingham and his joining the Lunar Society. Their correspondence primarily relates to matters of common scientific interest, though Keir was one of the friends who tried to moderate Priestley's *Appeal to the Public on the Subject of the Riots in Birmingham.*

KIRWAN, RICHARD (1733–1812)
geologist and chemist

Born in Ireland, he was educated in France (Poictiers), England, and Germany. Called to the Irish bar in 1766, he practiced without success. He returned to London in 1777, where he studied and wrote on mineralogy, meteorology, geology and chemistry. He became a Fellow of the Royal Society in 1780, and a Copley medalist in 1782. He went to Dublin in 1787, and was president of the Royal Irish Academy from 1799 until his death.

He was regarded as a brilliant but eccentric scholar by his contemporaries. His opposition to Lavoisier's new chemistry was publicly retracted in 1791 after the refutation of Kirwan's *Essay on Phlogiston* by French chemists. Kirwan's views on geology were consistently conservative, and he attacked Hutton's *Theory of the Earth* on theological as well as scientific grounds.

He presumably met Priestley for the first time in 1777, and they pursued the acquaintance from mutual admiration and a shared interest in scientific and theological questions. Kirwan was one of the few British scientists who continued corresponding with Priestley after his exile to the United States. No traces of the manuscript correspondence have been found.

LA ROCHEFOUCAULD D'ENVILLE, LOUIS-ALEXANDRE
DUC DE LA ROCHE-GUYON ET DE (1743–1792)
["DUC DE ROCHFOCAULT"]
soldier, liberal statesman, natural philosopher

After serving as a soldier, Rochefoucauld became interested in the sciences and expended both time and money in astronomical and chemical investigations. He was elected member of the Royal Academy of Sciences in Paris in 1782, and published articles in its *Mémoires* on astronomy and on metallurgical and agricultural chemistry. A friend of Franklin and La Fayette, he was a member of the Assembly of Notables in 1787, and a deputy of the nobles to the Estates-General in 1789; a moderate liberal, he was stoned to death by a Revolutionary mob in 1792.

Priestley may have met Rochefoucauld during his visit to Paris in 1774, but it is more likely that Franklin called Priestley's attention to him when Franklin was in Paris during the American Revolution. It is ironic that the only letter located of what seems to have been a moderately steady correspondence should be primarily devoted to praising the Revolution, which shortly was to result in Rochefoucauld's death.[6]

6 Hoefer, *op. cit.*, vol. 29–30.

LANDRIANI, COUNT MARSILIO (*c.* 1751–*c.* 1827)
*Lord Chamberlain to Albert, Duke of Saxony-Teschen
natural philosopher*

Landriani lived in various places, in Vienna and in Italy. He published voluminously on air, electricity, magnetism, heat, meteorology, and machines. He was a corresponding member of the Royal Academy of Sciences in Paris. Though he was one of Priestley's many Italian correspondents, it is unlikely that the two were friends. Their correspondence appears to have been intended for public scientific communication; no manuscript copies have been found.[7]

LAVOISIER, ANTOINE LAURENT (1743–1794)
chemist, tax farmer

Educated at the Collège Mazarin, Paris, he was made Bachelor of Law in 1763 and licentiate in 1764. He received private lessons in mathematics and astronomy from La Caille, in botany from Jussieu, in chemistry from Rouelle, and in geology from Guettard. He was named "assistant" in the Royal Academy of Sciences in 1769, became associate in 1772, *pensionnaire* in 1778, and director in 1785. In 1788 he was made a Fellow of the Royal Society. He published more than sixty papers in the *Mémoires* of the Academy of Sciences from 1768 to 1790; he worked primarily in chemistry, but his reports, either as personal papers or for commissions of the Academy, ranged from agriculture and geology to the metric system, the manufacture of gunpowder, street lighting, water supply, and animal magnetism. In 1768 he became assistant to, and in 1780, himself a member of, the Fermier Général. He was executed in 1794 by order of the Revolutionary Tribunal.[8]

From the beginning of Priestley's career as a "chemist" in 1772, Lavoisier was his major protagonist, though it was not until 1782 that Priestley recognized the opposition and not really until Lavoisier, de Morveau, Berthollet, and Fourcroy published the

[7] *Dizionario Enciclopedico Italiano* (Roma, 1957), vol. 6; J. C. Poggendorff, *Biographisch-Literarisches Handwörterbuch Zur Geschichte der Exacten Wissenschaften* (Leipzig, 1863), vol. 1.

[8] Douglas McKie, *Antoine Lavoisier* (Philadelphia, J. B. Lippincott [1935]).

Méthode de Nomenclature Chimique in 1787, that it became clear that Lavoisier's new chemistry was to win the day. The two men met on Priestley's trip to Paris in 1774. It is hard to believe that they did not correspond, but no letters other than the one printed here have been located. It is still harder to believe that Priestley left no comment on the execution of Lavoisier, but, except for the oblique reference in Letter 153, none has been found.

LINDSEY, THEOPHILUS (1723–1808)
Unitarian clergyman

Educated at St. Johns College, Cambridge, where he received his bachelor's degree and became a Fellow (1747). He held several livings in the established church until 1773, when he resigned his post at Catterick, Yorkshire, to open the first avowedly Unitarian chapel, on Essex Street, London. Lindsey was the author of many works on dogmatic theology and apologetics, and of many sermons. He met Priestley in 1772 as a result of the "Feathers Tavern Petition" for clerical relief from obligatory subscription to the Thirty-nine Articles. He became Priestley's warmest personal friend, his editorial advisor and supporter. They corresponded extensively, and, though few of their letters relate to science, Priestley's to Lindsey (the bulk of which are preserved at the Dr. Williams's Library, London) give a more continuous picture of his personal life than does any other source available.

LIVINGSTON, ROBERT R. (1746–1813)
Chancellor of New York, statesman, diplomat, agriculturist and experimenter

Born in New York city, he was educated at King's College (Columbia), from which he graduated in 1765. He was a delegate to the Continental Congress and secretary of the Department of Foreign Affairs. Initially second only to Hamilton as a New York Federalist, Livingston switched to support Jefferson in about 1791. Appointed minister to France in 1801 by Jefferson, he negotiated the Louisiana Purchase. He resigned in 1804. He pioneered in scientific agriculture on his considerable family estates on the Hudson River, was an early importer of Merino sheep, and in 1791 organized the Society for the Promotion of Useful Arts. He worked with his brother-in-law, John Stevens, and with Nicolas Roosevelt, and later lent technical as well as financial assistance to Robert Fulton in the development of the steamboat as a practical mode of transportation.

He apparently opened correspondence with Priestley soon after the latter settled in Northumberland, in hope of obtaining practical advice on steam engines. Their correspondence continued on topics of mutual interest in practical science and politics, and Livingston attempted to transmit to Priestley the latest scientific intelligence from Paris.

MITCHILL, SAMUEL LATHAM (1764–1831)
physician, natural philosopher, editor
U.S. Senator and Representative

First educated in local grammar schools, Mitchill was then apprenticed to Dr. Samuel Bard of New York City. He received his medical degree (M.D.) at the University of Edinburgh in 1786. He was professor of natural history, chemistry, and agriculture at Columbia College, 1792-1801. From 1807 to 1826, he was professor of chemistry, natural history or botany, and materia medica at the New York College of Physicians and Surgeons. From 1826 to 1830 he was vice-president of Rutgers Medical College. He helped establish the Society for the Promotion of Agriculture, Arts and Manufactures (1796); in 1814 he was a founding member of the New York Literary and Philosophical Society; in 1817 he helped establish the Lyceum of Natural History. With Edward Miller and Elihu H. Smith, he established the *New York Medical Repository,* for which he was principal editor for twenty-three years. His major scientific interests were mineralogy and chemistry, particularly applied and medical chemistry. He served in the United States House of Representatives (1801–1804), and in

[365]

the United States Senate (1804–1809), and again in the House (1810–1813).

Mitchill was one of the New York City scientists who welcomed Priestley on the latter's arrival in the United States, and remained one of his firmest scientific friends, though Mitchill was an early supporter of Lavoisier's new chemistry. Priestley published the majority of his United States scientific papers in Mitchill's journal, the *New York Medical Repository*.

MORGAN, WILLIAM (1750–1833)
actuary, nephew of Richard Price

He was apprenticed to a London apothecary until 1772, when he became a protégé of his uncle Richard Price. He was assistant actuary and (after 1775) chief actuary for the Equitable Assurance Society, where his work was distinguished by his careful administration and sound actuarial advice; he resigned in 1830. He was a Copley medalist and became a Fellow of the Royal Society in 1783. He wrote many papers on annuities and actuarial mathematics, as well as the "Examination of Dr. Crawford's Theory of Heat and Combustion." His home was a meeting place for such liberal reformers as Horne Tooke, Sir Francis Burdett, and Tom Paine. His brother was George Cadogan Morgan, scientific writer, Unitarian minister and teacher, and phlogistonist chemist (died in 1798).

Morgan undoubtedly first met Priestley through Richard Price, a good friend of Priestley's. Their religious, political, and (as the letter here shows) scientific beliefs were similar, but there is no indication that they corresponded very much.

OLIVER, ANDREW (1731–1799)
jurist, natural philosopher

Though he was the son of the Tory Lieutenant–Governor of Massachusetts at the time of the American Revolution, he remained quietly in Salem when the remainder of the family went into exile. He graduated from Harvard in 1749. He was a founding member of the American Academy of Arts and Sciences, and a member of the American Philosophical Society. He was the author of articles on electricity and on water spouts, and published an *Essay on Comets*. His life was darkened by illness and he lived in seclusion for nearly thirty years before his death.

OLIVER, B. LYNDE (1760–1835)

Son of Andrew Oliver, Benjamin Lynde studied medicine privately and practiced in both Williamsburg, Virginia, and Salem, Massachusetts. He was a Fellow of the Massachusetts Medical Society and the American Academy of Arts and Sciences, and received an honorary degree from Harvard in 1808. Greatly interested in optics and other branches of natural philosophy, he is known to have corresponded with William Herschel and David Brewster as well as with Priestley. The latter's correspondence with the Olivers began with Andrew's communication of his *Essay on Comets,* and it apparently continued intermittently, on a variety of subjects, at least through 1800; but the letters here are the sole surviving examples.[9]

PARKER, JOHN, SAMUEL, AND WILLIAM
(n.d.), *glassmakers*

These three were variously listed in London directories as "cut glass" manufacturers of 69 Fleet Street, under the firm name of "William Parker and Sons" (from 1774 to 1794), and (in 1798) as "Samuel Parker." They regularly supplied Priestley with glass articles for his researches, including burning lenses and in particular the twelve-inch lens he used in the famous experiment in which he isolated "dephlogisticated air." Priestley refers to their generosity in his *Memoirs* and in the volumes of his *Experiments and Observations,* as well as in his correspondence.[10]

[9] "Benjamin Lynde Oliver, M.D.," *Essex Institute Historical Collections,* 68 (1932), 1–4.
[10] Douglas McKie, "An Unpublished Letter from Priestley to John Parker," *Archives Internationales d'Histoire des Sciences,* No. 35 (1956), 117–124.

Percy, Hugh (Smithson) (1715–1786)
Duke of Northumberland
statesman, improving landlord

Born Hugh Smithson, he changed his name to Percy in 1750, on succession through his wife to the estates of the Percy family; he was created Duke of Northumberland in 1766. Father-in-law of Lord Bute, and a member of George III's private junto and a "king's friend," he nevertheless opposed the Stamp Act and voted for its repeal.

He was interested in art, science, and literature; in 1736 he became a Fellow of the Royal Society; he ran unsuccessfully against Lord Morton (1764) for the presidency of the Royal Society. He was made a trustee of the British Museum in 1753. He was the father of James Smithson, whose bequest to the United States was used to establish the Smithsonian Institution.

His only known connection with Priestley is as a suggested patron for the *History of Optics* — a suggestion presumably based on his known interest in science. Though the *Optics* is dedicated to him, there is little evidence that he lent its publication much assistance, and it was ultimately issued by subscription.

Price, Richard (1723–1791)
Arian minister, teacher, political economist, actuary

Price was educated at various dissenting academies, and finally at Fund Academy, London. He received his divinity degree from Marischal College, Aberdeen, and became simultaneously minister at Old Jewry, Newington Green, and Hackney Chapels. He was the author of many works on public morals and on the national debt, and his *"Observations on Civil Liberty and the Justice and Policy of the War with America"* attracted substantial and favorable attention, particularly in America. He became a Fellow of the Royal Society in 1765, to whose *Philosophical Transactions* he contributed several papers on actuarial mathematics and population figures. He was a good friend of Benjamin Franklin and Lord Shelburne, to whom he recommended Priestley. His sermon of 1789, "On the Love of Our Country," incited Burke's rage because of its praise of the early stages of the French Revolution.

Price was one of Priestley's earliest scientific friends and gave him sound (if cautious) advice on scientific topics, ranging from electricity, optics, and chemistry to metaphysics and the theory of matter. They disagreed on many subjects and carried on a friendly debate on free will and materialism which, as published, is a rare example of even-tempered, rational disagreement in the eighteenth-century public press.

ROTHERAM, CALEB (1738–1796)
Unitarian clergyman

Educated at Kendal and Daventry academies, he was ordained minister at Kendal and served there most of his life. He met Priestley when both were students at Daventry, and they maintained a correspondence at least until Priestley sailed for the United States. Rotheram acquired an interest in the sciences from his father, who headed the academy at Kendal, but most of his correspondence with Priestley was related to theological matters.[11]

RUSH, BENJAMIN (1745–1813)
physician, statesman

Educated at the College of New Jersey (Princeton), he received his bachelor's degree in 1760. He studied medicine under Dr. John Redman, from lectures at the College of Philadelphia, and at Edinburgh, where he received the M.D. degree in 1768. He practiced medicine in Philadelphia, and became a member of the American Philosophical Society in 1774. An associate of Tom Paine, John Adams, and Thomas Jefferson, he was a delegate to the Continental Congress, a signer of the Declaration of Inde-

---

[11] *Dictionary of National Biography;* and J. W. Ashley Smith, *Birth of Modern Education* (London, 1954), pp. 107–109.

pendence, and for a time served in the Revolutionary Army as Surgeon-General of the Middle Department. He worked for the adoption of the Constitution of the United States, and also to establish a liberal and effective constitution for the state of Pennsylvania. In 1783 he led in the founding of Dickinson College.

He lectured successively at the College of Philadelphia, the University of the State of Pennsylvania, and the University of Pennsylvania on chemistry, medical institutes and on the theory and clinical practice of medicine. Though admired as a teacher, he was inclined to fanciful medical theories, but was an accurate observer in the special areas of his interest. He early contributed to an understanding of mental-health problems.

Rush met Priestley when the latter first passed through Philadelphia on his way to Northumberland; and he may have been associated with the Priestley-Cooper colonization scheme. In any event, the two became friends, Rush attempting to get Priestley a teaching position at the University of Pennsylvania and serving as his physician whenever Priestley was in Philadelphia. They corresponded on theology, politics, and the establishment of Northumberland Academy, as well as on scientific subjects.

SCHOLEFIELD, RADCLIFFE (d. 1803)
dissenting clergyman

Priestley and Scholefield were friends and fellow students at Daventry Academy. Scholefield was minister of the Old Meeting House at Birmingham when Priestley moved there in 1780 and became a member of the fortnightly theological discussion groups Priestley organized in Birmingham. He assisted Priestley in the editing of the *Theological Repository,* and his meetinghouse, like Priestley's, was destroyed in the riots of 1791. No record of an extensive correspondence has survived and there is no indication, beyond the letter printed here, that Scholefield was at all interested in science.[12]

12 Priestley's *Memoirs;* and the *Gentleman's Magazine,* 73 (1803), 603.

SEDDON, JOHN (1725–1770)
Arian minister, rector of Warrington Academy

Educated at Kendal Academy and Glasgow University, he was ordained minister of Cairo Street Chapel, Warrington, in 1747. He was promoter, first secretary, and librarian of Warrington Academy (1757); rector and successor to Priestley as lecturer in belles lettres (1767), and founder and first president of the Warrington Library. He met and befriended Priestley when the latter accepted a post at Warrington. Their extant correspondence relates to fund-raising and to the administrative problems of Warrington. He was responsible, as his letter to John Canton shows, for introducing Priestley into London scientific circles.

VAUGHAN, BENJAMIN (1751–1835)
merchant, politician

Educated at Hackney Academy, Warrington Academy, and Cambridge University, he read law at the Temple and studied medicine at Edinburgh, but later engaged in mercantile pursuits when not serving Shelburne as private secretary, and in confidential political business. He was a friend of Price, Horne Tooke, Franklin, and Paine, and acted unofficially in peace negotiations with Franklin. He was chosen by Shelburne as Member for Calne, 1792; but his known friendship with French revolutionaries and his opposition to Pitt and his French policy ended his political career. He fled into exile, first to France and then to the United States, where he settled on his mother's estates in Maine. He was editor of Franklin's collected *Works*, published in London in 1779 and again in 1806.

VAUGHAN, JOHN (n.d.)

A brother of Benjamin Vaughan, John was educated at Warrington Academy. He went on to study the wine-importing trade in France, and then settled in Philadelphia in 1782 as a merchant and land speculator. He became a member of the American Philosophical Society in 1784 and later "almost merged" himself with the Society on becoming its long-time secretary. He was one of the earliest members and a lay reader of the Unitarian congregation Priestley helped to establish in Philadelphia.[13]

VAUGHAN, SAMUEL, JR. (n.d.)

Youngest brother of Benjamin and John Vaughan, Samuel, Jr., attended Warrington Academy (*c.* 1777). In 1814, he was living in Cork, dealing "in the victualling business."[14] Benjamin, John, and Samuel, Jr., were three of the five sons of Samuel Vaughan, all of whom attended Warrington Academy. The Vaughan family became very friendly with Priestley when Benjamin and William Vaughan were student-boarders in Priestley's home in Warrington. Though John, Charles, and Samuel, Jr., enrolled at Warrington after Priestley had left, Samuel, Jr., appears, from the letters printed here, to have studied chemistry privately under Priestley in Birmingham. William Vaughan provided a London refuge for Priestley after the 1791 riots in Birmingham, and John was Priestley's business agent after the latter's emigration. There was extensive correspondence between Priestley and the Vaughan family, much of which has been preserved, but little of it relates to science, in which only John seems really to have had much interest, and that only in an organizational sense.

VOLTA, ALESSANDRO (1745–1827)
natural philosopher

Classically educated in schools at Como, at sixteen he entered the Royal Seminary there and became its rector in 1775. A student of languages, chemistry and physics, by 1778 he was professor of

---

[13] Sarah P. Stetson, "The Philadelphia Sojourn of Samuel Vaughan," *Pennsylvania Magazine of History and Biography,* 73 (1949), 459–474.
[14] William Turner, *Warrington Academy,* with an introduction by G. A. Carter (Warrington, Library and Museum Committee, 1957), p. 73.

physics at the University of Pavia. He traveled in Europe and England, became a corresponding member of the Royal Academy of Sciences (Paris) in 1782, a Fellow of the Royal Society in 1791, and Copley medalist in 1794. As a foreign member of the Institut de France, he was one of the scientists patronized by Napoleon, but after 1815, under Francis, Emperor of Austria, he became director of the Faculty of Philosophy at the University of Padua.[15]

Best known for his work elucidating Galvani's discovery of electric current, he first corresponded with Priestley on static electricity after reading the *History of Electricity* and continued the correspondence on chemical matters. Through his correspondence with Volta, Priestley had access to the best scientific thought in Italy, but Volta's observations in Lavoisier's laboratory in the early 1780's appear to have convinced him of Priestley's errors, and their correspondence ceased. No letters have been found that are dated after the formal attack on the phlogistonists was launched.

VON MARUM, MARTIN (1750-1837)

physician, natural philosopher

Born in Delft, he was educated by his father, who had scientific interests, and at the University of Groningen, where he received the bachelor's degree in 1773, and his doctor's degrees in medicine and philosophy in 1776, with a dissertation on the motion of fluids in plants. Author of a treatise on electricity in 1776, and a popular lecturer on natural philosophy, he became permanent secretary of the Society of Science in Haarlem, director of the science division, librarian, and chief experimenter of the physical laboratory of the Teylerian Institution. His scientific reputation is primarily based on electrical experiments performed with a static electrical machine which was the largest known until the construction of the Van der Graaf generator.[16]

His first communication with Priestley was as secretary of the

---

[15] Bern Dibner, *Alessandro Volta and the Electric Battery*. New York, Franklin Watts, Inc., 1964.

[16] (Michaud) *Biographie Universelle* (Paris, 1843–1865), vol. 42.

Haarlem Society, but the correspondence continued on the basis of their shared scientific and theological interests. There is no indication that von Marum adopted any of Priestley's or Withering's suggestions for experiments with his machine, and after 1787 he clearly was interpreting some of his experiments on the basis of Lavoisier's new chemistry.

WALKER, GEORGE (1734?–1807)
dissenting minister, mathematician, teacher

Educated at Kendal Academy and the University of Glasgow, he became a dissenting minister at Durham, Filby, Great Yarmouth, Nottingham, and Manchester, successively. He taught mathematics and navigation to private pupils, and succeeded John Holt as mathematics tutor at Warrington Academy in 1772; later he became professor of theology at Manchester College. A Fellow of the Royal Society, he also became member and president (in 1804) of the Manchester Literary and Philosophical Society. He contributed mathematical articles to the *Ladies' Diary,* and wrote a treatise on the sphere and on conic sections. He probably met Priestley through Richard Price, who recommended Walker's election to the Royal Society, and suggested him for the post as Lord Shelburne's librarian that Priestley afterwards filled. The only extant examples of what appears to have been an extensive correspondence are the extracts in Walker's *Life,* cited in Appendix I.

WATT, JAMES (1736–1819)
inventor, engineer, and chemist

Watt was educated in the Greenoch, Scotland, grammar school, in his father's carpentry shop, and as apprentice to instrument makers in Glasgow and London. He opened an instrument shop in the University of Glasgow, where he invented the separate-condenser steam engine. He worked as surveyor and engineer for canals, rivers, and harbors until 1774, when he moved to Birmingham as partner of Matthew Boulton in the development and distribution of his improved engine. He was a friend of Joseph Black, John Robison, and Adam Smith in Scotland, and became a member of the Lunar Society of Birmingham, a Fellow of the Royal Society, foreign member of the Academy of Sciences in Paris, etc.

Watt first met Priestley when the latter moved to Birmingham and became a member of the Lunar Society. Priestley assisted Watt's steam-engine work with experiments on "airs," and Watt joined Priestley in "chemical" experiments — the most significant of which led to his enunciation of the compound nature of water. Their correspondence primarily relates to their shared interest in chemistry, but Watt also corresponded with Priestley after the Birmingham riots, and sent scientific instruments as well as advice to aid the continuation of Priestley's scientific career.

WEDGWOOD, JOSIAH (1730–1795)
potter, applied scientist

Son, nephew, and brother of potters, Josiah Wedgwood was briefly educated at a local grammar school until he was apprenticed to his brother. He opened his own pottery in 1759, and became a partner of Thomas Bentley in 1762; his most famous pottery works, called "Etruria," opened in 1769; it was a showplace and the greatest British pottery of the age. He attempted to apply scientific theories to the improvement of his product, particularly in the control of quality and in this connection invented a ceramic pyrometer which he described to the Royal Society and which was widely used. A member of the Society of Arts, he became a Fellow of the Royal Society in 1783.

Wedgwood probably met Priestley through Bentley and the latter's associations with Warrington Academy. Wedgwood corresponded regularly with Priestley on matters of science and politics and supplied him with gifts of apparatus and with financial support for his scientific work.

WEDGWOOD, THOMAS (1771–1805)

On Josiah's death, his sons, particularly Thomas, continued this assistance until Priestley's death. Thomas Wedgwood, the most scientific of the sons, was educated at home under the supervision of Alexander Chisholm and for a term or two at the University of Edinburgh. Best known, though incorrectly, as the "father of photography," he did perform experiments on the copying of pictures on materials moistened with silver nitrate, experiments which were reported by his friend, Humphry Davy. He had earlier experimented on the radiation of heated solids, about which he corresponded with Priestley. He was ill most of his last years, during which he used a portion of the substantial fortune left him by his father toward the support of Coleridge, John Leslie, and others in need of assistance.

WILKINSON, WILLIAM (1738–1808)
iron master, brother of John Wilkinson

Educated at Warrington Academy, he worked for and with his brother John at the Wrexham and Bersham Iron Foundries. Put in charge of John Wilkinson's foreign business, he established and managed a state iron foundry and coke furnace at Indret, near Nantes, 1777–1780. About 1787 he broke with his brother, who was a difficult man. He helped design the Soho foundry for Boulton and Watt. He first met Priestley when a student at Warrington; Priestley married Mary Wilkinson, his sister, and later attempted to enlist the support of John and William to establish his sons. Both the brothers appear to have been imaginative empiricists, but neither was interested in science. In the feud between them, the Priestleys tended to side with John, perhaps because they were dependent upon him for a substantial part of their American income.[17]

[17] H. R. Schubert, "Iron and Steel," Chapter 4, Part I, of Charles Singer *et al.*, eds., *The History of Technology*, Volume IV, "The Industrial Revolution, *c.* 1750–*c.* 1850" (New York, and London, Oxford University Press, 1958), pp. 99–117.

WINTHROP, JOHN (1714–1779)
astronomer, physicist, mathematician, teacher

Born in Boston, Massachusetts, he was educated under his father, who had scientific interests, and at Harvard where he received his B.A. degree in 1732. In 1738 he became Hollis Professor of Mathematics at Harvard. He received his LL.D. degree at Edinburgh in 1771 and at Harvard in 1773; he was made a Fellow of the Royal Society in 1766, and was also a member of the American Philosophical Society. He published articles in the *Philosophical Transactions,* mostly on astronomical subjects, and kept a record of his magnetic and meteorological observations over a twenty-year period.

His initial connections with Priestley were made through their mutual friend, Benjamin Franklin, who sent Harvard a copy of Priestley's *History of Optics.* Although Priestley and Winthrop corresponded directly, no part of their correspondence seems to have survived.

WITHERING, WILLIAM (1741–1799)
physician, botanist, mineralogist

Born in Shropshire, he was educated privately and at the University of Edinburgh, where he took his medical doctorate in 1766. He became a major provincial physician of his period, with a practice centered in Birmingham. Author of articles on minerals and gases, he is most famous for his Linnean botany of English plants, which went through three editions during his life, and for his *Account of the Foxglove* (1785), a classic clinical study of digitalis. He became a Fellow of the Royal Society in 1785, and was an early member of the Lunar Society of Birmingham.

His first association with Priestley came through Dr. Thomas Percival, but as fellow Lunar Society members their friendship grew. They corresponded on chemical and political subjects, Withering having also suffered during the Birmingham riots.

YOUNG, ARTHUR (1741–1820)
agricultural writer

Educated at local grammar schools, he was apprenticed to a merchant, then began writing political pamphlets and novels in 1758, the year he began farming. In 1767 he published his first collection of agricultural writings, and from that time on he was the major British publicist for agricultural reform, though he himself was indifferently successful as a farmer. He became a Fellow of the Royal Society in 1774. In 1785 he began his influential journal, the *Annals of Agriculture,* in 1793 he was appointed secretary of the Board of Agriculture. He was most famous for his *Tour* books describing his agricultural and social observations made on trips throughout England and in France.

He first wrote to Priestley regarding the use of "airs" in promoting plant growth, following Priestley's initial work on photosynthesis. The correspondence continued as he attempted to develop a scientific basis for agriculture, and, though his early agrarian liberalism turned to conservatism, he never rejected Priestley and continued to acknowledge with pride the assistance Priestley had given him.

The Scientific Writings of Joseph Priestley in Order of Publication

Bibliographic Note: The following, so far as I know, is the most nearly complete listing of Priestley's scientific writings — including their varying editions, translations, and reprintings — available anywhere. Nevertheless, it is virtually impossible to insure completeness. The proliferation of periodical publications which reprinted extensively (often without seeking permission of the author), the translation of all, or parts, of various Priestley writings in many different languages, and the continuing interest in Priestley as a subject of scholarly investigation — all these virtually guarantee that many items that should be included here have been omitted. Suggestions for additions to this list will be gratefully received, to be included in a bio–bibliography of Priestley gradually being compiled by the writer in collaboration with Eric Osborne, of London.

1767

The History and Present State of Electricity, with Original Experiments. London, J. Dodsley, J. Johnson, B. Davenport, and T. Cadell, 1767, 4to.

1768

A Familiar Introduction to the Study of Electricity. London, J. Dodsley, T. Cadell and J. Johnson, 1768. 4to.

[379]

"An Account of Rings consisting of all the Prismatic Colours, made by Electrical Explosions on the Surface of Pieces of Metal," read 10 March 1768, *Philosophical Transactions*, 58 (1768), 68–74.

1769

The History and Present State of Electricity. 2nd ed., corrected and enlarged. London, J. Dodsley, J. Johnson and J. Payne, and T. Cadell, 1769. 4to.

A Familiar Introduction to the Study of Electricity. 2nd ed. London, J. Dodsley, T. Cadell, Johnson and Payne, 1769. 8vo.

"Experiments on the lateral Force of Electrical Explosions," read 23 February 1769, *Philosophical Transactions*, 59 (1769), 57–62.

"Various Experiments on the Force of Electrical Explosions," read 2 March 1769, *Philosophical Transactions*, 59 (1769), 63–70.

1770

A Familiar Introduction to the Theory and Practice of Perspective. London, Johnson and Payne, 1770. 8vo.

"An Investigation of the lateral Explosion, and of the Electricity communicated to the electrical Circuit, in a Discharge," read 29 March 1770, *Philosophical Transactions*, 60 (1770), 192–210.

"Experiments and Observations on Charcoal," read 5 April 1770, *Philosophical Transactions*, 60 (1770), 211–227.

1771

Histoire de l'Électricité, traduite de l'Anglois, 3 vols. Paris, Hérissant, 1771. 12mo. (First French edition of the *History of Electricity*, translated by M. J. Brisson).

1772

Directions for Impregnating Water with Fixed Air; in order to Communicate to it the Peculiar Spirit and Virtues of Pyrmont Water, and other Mineral Waters of a similar Nature. London, J. Johnson, 1772. 8vo.

————. (This pamphlet was reprinted in its essentials in Priestley's second volume of *Experiments and Observations on Air* [1775], pp.

277–292, and a photo-facsimile copy was published by the American Bottlers of Carbonated Beverages, Washington, D.C., 1945.)

The History and Present State of Discoveries relating to Vision, Light, and Colours. London, J. Johnson, 1772. 4to.

Observations on Different Kinds of Air. Printed for the *Philosophical Transactions*, 1773, vol. LXII (London, W. Bowyer and J. Nichols, 1772), 4to. (This appears to be a "pre-print" of Priestley's first paper on chemistry, published in 1773, in the *Philosophical Transactions* for 1772, q.v.)

"Dissertation traduite de l'Anglois sur certains cercles contenans toutes les couleurs du prisme, formés par des explosions électriques sur la surface des pièces de métal" [Rozier's] *Introduction aux Observations sur la Physique*, &c., 1 (1772), 324–328 [translation of *Philosophical Transactions*, 58 (1768), 68–74].

"Manière d'imprégner l'Eau d'air fixe, & de lui communiquer les propriétés de l'Eau de Pyrmont, & de toutes les Eaux minérales, qui sont connues sous le nom d'Acidules ou Aëriennes" [Rozier's] *Introduction aux Observations sur la Physique*, &c., 2 (August 1772), 323–331. Also: *Manière D'Impregner L'Eau D'Air Fixe*, &c. ([Paris], extrait du *Journal d'observations sur la Physique*, etc. [1772]), 8vo. (This appears to be a separate printing of the above, which, of course, is a translation of *Directions for Impregnating Water*, &c. [London, 1772].)

1773

"Observations on different Kinds of Air." "read March 5, 12, 19, 26, 1772," *Philosophical Transactions*, 62 (1772), 147–252.

———, with an "Appendix, containing an account of some experiments made by Mr. Hey," *Philosophical Transactions*, 62 (1772), 253–256.

———, and a "Letter from Mr. Hey to Dr. Priestley, concerning the Effects of fixed Air applied by way of a Clyster," *Philosophical Transactions*, 62 (1772), 257–264.

———, and a "Correction," *Philosophical Transactions*, 62 (1772), 264. (Considerable sections of this paper were added after the dates given for its reading, as can easily be seen from the context. Furthermore, though the volume is dated 1772, from the preliminary material in it, one can see that it was actually published in 1773.)

"Extrait d'une Lettre de M. Priestley, sur la découverte d'un Air alkalin," [Rozier's] *Introduction aux Observations sur la Physique*, &c., 2 (1773), 389.

"Observations & Expériences sur différentes especes d'air," [Rozier's] *Observations sur la Physique,* &c., 1 (April, May 1773), 292–325, 394–426 [translation of *Philosophical Transactions,* 62 (1772), 147–264].

"Expériences et Observations sur le Charbon, comme conducteur de l'Électricité," [Rozier's], *Observations sur la Physique,* &c. 2 (1773), 89–97 [translation of *Philosophical Transactions,* 60 (1770), 211–227].

1774

Experiments and Observations on different Kinds of Air. London, J. Johnson, 1774, 8vo.

"On the noxious Quality of the Effluvia of putrid Marshes," read 16 December 1773, *Philosophical Transactions,* 64 (1774), 90–95.

————, with "Farther Proofs of the Insalubrity of marshy Situations, in a Letter from the Rev. Dr. Price," read 13 January 1774, *Philosophical Transactions,* 64 (1774), 96–98.

Osservazioni sulle differenti specie d'aria. Trad. dall'inglese da G. Fr. Fromond coll'aggiunta di varie annotazioni consultate coll'autore. Milano, Galeazzi, 1774. 8vo.

Auserlesene kleine Werke dreyer berühmter Englisher Chymisten. Priestley, Henry, und Black, Die Schwängerung des gemeinen Wassers mit fixer Luft, die Magnesia und Kalkerde. Copenhagen und Leipzig, Heineck und Faber, 1774. 8vo.

1775

Hartley's Theory of the Human Mind on the Principle of the Association of Ideas: with Essays relating to the Subject of it. London, J. Johnson, 1775. 8vo.

Philosophical Empiricism: containing Remarks on a Charge of Plagiarism, respecting Dr. H[————]s; interspersed with various Observations relating to different Kinds of Air. London, J. Johnson, 1775. 8vo. ["Dr. H————s" was Bryan Higgins.]

Experiments and Observations on different Kinds of Air, vol. 2. London, J. Johnson, 1775. 8vo.

Experiments and Observations on different Kinds of Air, vol. 1, 2nd ed. corrected. London, J. Johnson, 1775. 8vo.

The History and Present State of Electricity, 3rd ed., corrected and enlarged. London, C. Bathurst, T. Lowndes, J. Rivington, J. Johnson, S. Crowder, G. Robinson, R. Baldwin, T. Becket, T. Cadell, 1775. 2 vols., 8vo.

————, a reprint of the 3rd ed. with the addition of the electrical papers from *Philosophical Transactions*, 60 (1770), 192–210, 211–227; and with an introduction by Robert E. Schofield. New York, Johnson Reprint Corporation, The Sources of Science, No. 18, 1966.

The History and Present State of Electricity, 4th ed., corrected and enlarged. London, C. Bathurst, T. Lowndes, J. Rivington, J. Johnson, S. Crowder, G. Robinson, R. Baldwin, T. Becket, and T. Cadell, 1775. 4to.

"An Account of further Discoveries in Air," read 25 May 1775, *Philosophical Transactions*, 65 (1775), 384–394.

"Luce delle sostanze putride," *Scelti d'Opuscoli Interessanti*, 1 (1775), 210. (Reference from the Indexes of *Opuscoli Scelti sulle Scienze e sulle Arti*.)

"Colori dell' esplosione electrica," *Scelti d'Opuscoli Interessanti*, 1 (1775), 253. (Reference from the Indexes of *Opuscoli Scelti sulle Scienze e sulle Arti*.)

"Color turchino delle ombre," *Scelti d'Opuscoli Interessanti*, 1 (1775), 270. (Reference from the Indexes of *Opuscoli Scelti sulle Scienze e sulle Arti*.)

"Elettricità e flogisto," *Scelti d'Opuscoli Interessanti*, 1 (1775), 365. (Reference from the Indexes of *Opuscoli Scelti sulle Scienze e sulle Arti*.)

1776

Geschichte und gegenwartiger Zustand der Optik, vorsuglich in Absicht auf den Physikalischen Theil dieser Wissenschaft. Leipzig, Johann Friedrich Junius, 1776. 4to.

Experiments and Observations on different Kinds of Air, vol. 2, 2nd ed. London, J. Johnson, 1776. 8vo.

"Observations on Respiration, and the Use of the Blood," read 25 January 1776, *Philosophical Transactions*, 66 (1776), 226–238.

"Aria deflogisticata," *Scelti d'Opuscoli Interessanti*, 2 (1776), 174. (Reference from the Indexes of *Opuscoli Scelti sulle Scienze e sulle Arti*.)

1777

Disquisitions relating to Matter and Spirit, to which is added the History of the Philosophical Doctrine concerning the Origin of the Soul, and the Nature of Matter; with its Influence on Christianity, especially with Respect to the Doctrine of the Pre-existence of Christ. London, J. Johnson, 1777. 8vo.

Experiments and Observations on different Kinds of Air, vol. 3. London, J. Johnson, 1777. 8vo.

A Familiar Introduction to the Study of Electricity, 3rd ed. London, J. Johnson, 1777. 8vo.

Expériences et Observations sur différentes Espèces d'Air, traduit par M. Gibelin. Paris, chez Nyon l'aîné, 1777. 3 vols. 12mo.

"Modo d'impregnar l'acqua d'aria fissa," *Scelti d'Opuscoli Interessanti,* 3 (1777), 16. (Reference from the Indexes of *Opuscoli Scelti sulle Scienze e sulle Arti.*)

"Uso della respirazione," *Scelti d'Opuscoli Interessanti,* 3 (1777), 64. (Reference from the Indexes of *Opuscoli Scelti sulle Scienze e sulle Arti.*)

"Su diverse arie fattizie," *Scelti d'Opuscoli Interessanti,* 3 (1777), 202, 359. (Reference from the Indexes of *Opuscoli Scelti sulle Scienze e sulle Arti.*)

"Effluvia delle acque putride," *Scelti d'Opuscoli Interessanti,* 3 (1777), 314. (Reference from the Indexes of *Opuscoli Scelti sulle Scienze e sulle Arti.*)

1778

A Free Discussion of the Doctrines of Materialism and Philosophical Necessity, in a Correspondence between Dr. Price and Dr. Priestley; to which are added, by Dr. Priestley, an Introduction, explaining the Nature of the Controversy, and Letters to Several Writers who have animadverted on his Disquisitions relating to Matter and Spirit, or his Treatise on Necessity. London, J. Johnson and T. Cadell, 1778. 8vo.

1779

Experiments and Observations relating to various Branches of Natural Philosophy; with a Continuation of the Observations on Air. London, J. Johnson, 1779. 8vo.

1780

A Familiar Introduction to the Theory and Practice of Perspective, 2nd ed., corrected. London, J. Johnson 1780. 8vo.

Expériences et Observations sur différentes Espèces d'Air, traduit par M. Gibelin. Paris, chez Nyon l'aîné, 1780. Vols. 4, 5. 12mo.

1781

Experiments and Observations relating to various Branches of Natural Philosophy; with a Continuation of the Observations on Air, vol. 2. Birmingham, J. Johnson, 1781. 8vo.

Experiments and Observations on different Kinds of Air, vol. 1, 3rd ed., London, J. Johnson, 1781. 8vo.

1782

Disquisitions relating to Matter and Spirit, 2nd ed., improved and enlarged. Birmingham, J. Johnson, 1782. 8vo.

A Free Discussion of the Doctrines of Materialism and Philosophical Necessity, in a Correspondence, 2nd ed. Birmingham, J. Johnson and T. Cadell, 1782. 8vo.

"An Analysis of Two Mineral Substances, viz. the Rowley–ragstone and the Toad-stone," by William Withering, communicated with an introductory letter by Joseph Priestley, read 16 May 1782, *Philosophical Transactions,* 72 (1782), 327–336 (Priestley's letter on page 327).

Expériences et Observations sur différentes Branches de la Physique avec une Continuation des Observations sur l'Air, traduit par M. Gibelin. Paris, 1782. Vols. [1, 2]. 12mo.

1783

"Experiments relating to Phlogiston, and the seeming Conversion of Water into Air," read 26 June 1783, *Philosophical Transactions,* 73 (1783), 398–434.

1784

Experiments and Observations on different Kinds of Air, vol. 2, 3rd ed. London, J. Johnson, 1784. 8vo.

———, extracts from vol. 2, published in *The Discovery of Oxygen,* "Part. I. Experiments by J. Priestley" (Edinburgh, Alembic Club Reprint No. 7, 1894), with subsequent editions.

1785

"Experiments and Observations relating to Air and Water," read 24 February 1785, *Philosophical Transactions,* 75 (1785), 279–309.

"Expériences et Observations relatives à l'Air et à l'Eau . . ." [Rozier's] *Observations sur la Physique*, &c., 27 (September 1785), 167–188 (translation of *Philosophical Transactions*, 75 [1785], 279–309).

"Expériences relatives au Phlogistique et à la Conversion apparente de l'Eau en Air," [Rozier's] Observations sur la Physique, &c., 27 (December 1785), 401–425 (translation of *Philosophical Transactions*, 73 [1783], 398–434).

1786

Experiments and Observations relating to various Branches of Natural Philosophy; with a Continuation of the Observations on Air, vol. 3. Birmingham, J. Johnson, 1786. 8vo.

A Familiar Introduction to the Study of Electricity, 4th ed. London, J. Johnson, 1786. 8vo.

1787

Versuch und Beobachtungen ueber Verschienden Theil der Naturlehr. Wien und Leipzig, 1787.

Expériences et Observations sur différentes Branches de la Physique avec une Continuation des Observations sur l'Air, traduit par M. Gibelin (Paris, 1787), vols. [3, 4]. 12mo.

"Du Charbon des Métaux" [Rozier's] *Observations sur la Physique*, &c., 30 (February 1787), 81–83.

"Sul Carbone de' Metalli," *Opuscoli Scelti sulle Scienze e sulle Arti*, 10 (1787), 288–291.

1788

"Experiments and Observations relating to the Principle of Acidity, the Composition of Water, and Phlogiston," read 7 February 1788, *Philosophical Transactions*, 78 (1788), 147–157.

"Additional Experiments and Observations relating to the Principle of Acidity, the Decomposition of Water, and Phlogiston," with letters to Priestley on the subject by Dr. Withering and James Keir, read 1 May 1788, *Philosophical Transactions*, 78 (1788), 313–330 (Priestley's paper covers pp. 313–319).

1789

"Objections to the Experiments and Observations relating to the Principle of Acidity, the Composition of Water, and Phlogiston, considered; with farther Experiments and Observations on the same Subject," read 27 November 1788, *Philosophical Transactions,* 79 (1789), 7–20.

"Experiments on the Phlogistication of Spirit of Nitre," read 26 March 1789, *Philosophical Transactions,* 79 (1789), 139–150.

"Experiments on the Transmission of the Vapour of Acids through an hot earthen Tube, and further Observations relating to Phlogiston," read 2 July 1789, *Philosophical Transactions,* 79 (1789), 289–299.

"Extrait d'un troisième Mémoire . . . sur la Combustion de l'Air inflammable & de l'Air pur" [Rozier's] *Observations sur la Physique, &c.,* 34 (May 1789), 360–363.

"Sperienze ed Osservazioni . . . Relative ai principj d'acidità, alta composizione dell acqua, e al flogisto . . . ," *Opuscoli Scelti sulle Scienze e sulle Arti,* 12 (1789), 85–93 (translation of *Philosophical Transactions,* 78 (1788), 147–157).

1790

Experiments and Observations on different Kinds of Air, and other Branches of Natural Philosophy, connected with the Subject, in three volumes, "Being the former Six Volumes abridged and methodized, with many additions." Birmingham, J. Johnson, 1790. 8vo.

Hartley's Theory of the Human Mind, 2nd ed. London, J. Johnson, 1790. 8vo.

"Observations on Respiration," read 25 February 1790, *Philosophical Transactions,* 80 (1790), 106–110.

"Expériences sur la Phlogistication de l'Acide du Nitre" [Rozier's] *Observations sur la Physique, &c.,* 36 (April 1790), 241–248 (translation of *Philosophical Transactions,* 79 (1789), 139–150).

"Expériences sur le passage de la Vapeur des Acides dans des Tubes de terre, avec de nouvelles Observations relatives au Phlogistique" [Rozier's] *Observations sur la Physique, &c.,* 37 (July 1790), 35–42 (translation of *Philosophical Transactions,* 79 [1789], 289–299).

1791

"Farther Experiments relating to the Decomposition of dephlogisticated and inflammable Air," read 7 April 1791, *Philosophical Transactions,* 81 (1791), 213–222.

"Observations sur la Respiration" [Rozier's] *Observations sur la*

Physique, &c., 39 (November 1791), 329–331 (translation of *Philosophical Transactions,* 80 (1790), 106–110).

"On the State of the Air in Dining-Rooms," *The Weekly Entertainer,* 18 (1791), 145–146 (extracted from *Experiments and Observations relating to Natural Philosophy* [1779], pp. 278–281).

1792

"Dernières expériences relatives à la décomposition de l'Air déphlogistiqué & de l'Air inflammable" [Rozier's] *Observations sur la Physique,* &c., 40 (February 1792), 91–97 (translation of *Philosophical Transactions,* 81 (1791), 213–222).

"Sperienze Relative alla Decomposizione dell' Aria Deflogisticata e dell' Aria Infiammabile . . . ," *Opuscoli Scelti sulle Scienze e sulle Arti,* 15 (1792), 283–288 (translation of *Philosophical Transactions,* 81 (1791), 213–222).

1793

Experiments on the Generation of Air from Water; to which are prefixed, Experiments relating to the Decomposition of Dephlogisticated and Inflammable Air. London, J. Johnson, 1793. 8vo.

1794

Heads of Lectures on a Course of Experimental Philosophy, particularly including Chemistry; delivered at the New College in Hackney. London, J. Johnson, 1794. 8vo.

The History and Present State of Electricity, 5th ed., corrected. London, J. Johnson, F. & C. Rivington, T. Cadell, R. Baldwin, and H. Lowndes, 1794. 4to.

1796

Experiments and Observations relating to the Analysis of Atmospherical Air; also farther Experiments relating to the Generation of Air from Water. Read before the American Philosophical Society, Feb. 5th & 19th, 1796, and printed in their Transactions. To which are added, Considerations on the Doctrine of Phlogiston, and the Decomposition of Water, addressed to Messrs. Berthollet, &c. London, reprinted for J. Johnson, 1796. 8vo.

Considerations on the Doctrine of Phlogiston and the Decomposition of Water. Philadelphia, by Thomas Dobson, 1796. 8vo.

1797

Considerations on the Doctrine of Phlogiston, and the Decomposition of Water, Part II. Philadelphia, 1797. 8vo.

────── *Considerations on the Doctrine of Phlogiston, and the Decomposition of Water, and Two Lectures on Combustion and an Examination of Dr. Priestley's Considerations on the Doctrine of Phlogiston,* by John Maclean, ed., with a sketch of Dr. Maclean, by W. Foster. Princeton, N.J., Princeton University Press, 1929.

Réflexions sur la doctrine du Phlogistique et la décomposition de l'Eau, traduit . . . & suivi d'une réponse par P. A. Adet. Philadelphia, 1797; Paris, 1798.

1798

"A letter to Dr. Mitchill, in reply to the preceding [An Attempt to accommodate the Disputes among Chemists concerning Phlogiston]," *New York Medical Repository,* 1 (1798; 2nd ed., 1800), 511–512 (same pages as in 2nd ed.).

"A Letter to the Editor," concerning the principles of the new theory of chemistry, 20 December 1797, *Monthly Magazine,* 5 (1798), 159–160.

"A Letter to the Editor," in defence of phlogiston and against the decomposition of Water (essentially a repetition of material in *The New York Medical Repository,* 2 [1799], 163–165, 166–167), 22 August 1798, *Monthly Magazine,* 6 (1798), 237–238.

1799

"Experiments and Observations relating to the Analysis of atmospherical Air," *Transactions of the American Philosophical Society,* 4 (1799), 1–11 (read 5 February 1796).

"Farther Experiments relating to the Generation of Air from Water," *Transactions of the American Philosophical Society,* 4 (1799), 11–21 (read 19 February 1796).

"Appendix to the above Articles," *Transactions of the American Philosophical Society,* 4 (1799), 382–386 (read 23 November 1796 as a letter to B. S. Barton, M.D.).

"A Second Letter from Dr. Priestley to Dr. Mitchill," 14 June 1798, *New York Medical Repository*, 2 (1799, 3rd ed., 1805), 48–49 (45–47 in 3rd ed.).

"On Red Precipitate of Mercury as favourable to the Doctrine of Phlogiston," 20 July 1798, *New York Medical Repository*, 2 (1799), 163–165 (152–155 in 3rd ed.).

"Objections to the antiphlogistic Doctrine of Water," 23 August 1798, *New York Medical Repository*, 2 (1799), 166–167 (155–157 in 3rd ed.).

"Experiments relating to the Calces of Metals, communicated in a fifth Letter to Dr. Mitchill," 11 October 1798, *New York Medical Repository*, 2 (1799), 263–268 (249–254 in 3rd ed.).

"Of some Experiments made with Ivory Black and also with Diamonds," 11 October 1798, *New York Medical Repository*, 2 (1799), 269–272 (254–257 in 3rd ed.).

"On the phlogistic Theory," 17 January 1799, *New York Medical Repository*, 2 (1799), 383–387 (353–358 in 3rd ed.).

"On the same Subject," 1 February 1799, *New York Medical Repository*, 2 (1799), 388–389 (358–360 in 3rd ed.).

"A letter to the Editor," relating to Experiments on the Calces of Metals, 22 December 1798, *Monthly Magazine*, 7 (1799), 261–264 (substantially the same as in the *New York Medical Repository*, 2, 263–268).

"Experiments made on Ivory Black and Diamonds," *Monthly Magazine*, 7 (1799), 353–354 (same as in the *New York Medical Repository*, 2, 269–272).

"A Letter to the Editor" on the phlogistic Theory, 17 January 1799, *Monthly Magazine*, 7 (1799), 354–356 (substantially the same as in the *New York Medical Repository*, 2, 383–387).

1800

The Doctrine of Phlogiston established and that of the Composition of Water refuted. Northumberland, for the Author, 1800. 8vo.

"A Reply to his antiphlogistic Opponents, No. 1," *New York Medical Repository*, 3 (1800, 2nd ed, 1805), 116–121.

"A Reply to his antiphlogistic Opponents, No. 2," *New York Medical Repository*, 3 (1800), 121–124.

"A Reply to his antiphlogistic Opponents, No. 3," *New York Medical Repository*, 3 (1800), 124–127.

"Singular Effects of Gaseous Oxyd of Septon (dephlogisticated nitrous Air)," 30 January 1800, *New York Medical Repository*, 3 (1800), 305.

"Priestley's Sentiments on the Doctrine of Septon," quoted from a letter of 24 July 1799, *New York Medical Repository*, 3 (1800), 307.

"Air produced, without limitation, from Water by freezing," *New York Medical Repository*, 3 (1800), 422–423.

"Singular Effects of Gaseous Oxyd of Septon," *Monthly Magazine*, 9 (1800), 409 (same as in the *New York Medical Repository*, 3 (1800), 305).

1801

"Experiments on the Production of Air by the Freezing of Water," *New York Medical Repository*, 4 (1801; 2nd ed., 1808), 17–21.

"A Letter correcting a Review of his Tract on Phlogiston," 6 July 1800, *New York Medical Repository*, 4 (1801), 103.

"Experiments on heating Manganese in inflammable Air," *New York Medical Repository*, 4 (1801), 135–137.

"Some Observations relating to the Sense of Hearing," 8 May 1800, *New York Medical Repository*, 4 (1801), 247–248.

"Experiments on the Production of Air by the Freezing of Water," *Journal of Natural Philosophy, Science and the Arts*, 4 (1801), 193–196 (same as in the *New York Medical Repository*, 4 (1801), 17–21).

1802

"Experiments on the Transmission of Acids and other Liquors, in the form of Vapours, over several Substances in a hot Earthen tube," *Transactions of the American Philosophical Society*, 5 (1802), 1–13 (read 20 December 1799).

"Experiments relating to the Change of Place in different Kinds of Air, through several interposing Substances," *Transactions of the American Philosophical Society*, 5 (1802), 14–20.

"Experiments relating to the Absorption of Air by Water," *Transactions of the American Philosophical Society*, 5 (1802), 21–27.

"Miscellaneous Experiments relating to the Doctrine of Phlogiston," *Transactions of the American Philosophical Society*, 5 (1802), 28–35.

"Experiments on the Production of Air by the Freezing of Water," *Transactions of the American Philosophical Society*, 5 (1802), 36–41 (read 18 April 1800) (substantially the same as in the *New York Medical Repository*, 4, 17–21.

"Experiments on Air exposed to Heat in Metallic Tubes," *Transactions of the American Philosophical Society*, 5 (1802), 42–50 (read 15 August 1800).

——— The above papers from the *Transactions of the American Philosophical Society* also appeared separately in a prepublication form in the United States as "Six Chemical Essays."

Remarks on the Work entitled "A Brief History of Epidemic and Pestilential Diseases," 4 May 1801, *New York Medical Repository*, 5 (1802), 32–35.

"Some Thoughts concerning Dreams," *New York Medical Repository*, 5 (1802), 125–129.

"Observations and Experiments relating to the Pile of Volta," 16 and 29 September 1801, *New York Medical Repository*, 5 (1802), 152–159.

"Miscellaneous Observations relating to the Doctrine of Air," 30 July 1801, *New York Medical Repository*, 5 (1802), 264–267.

"A Reply to Mr. Cruickshank's Observations in Defence of the New System of Chemistry, in the fifth Volume of Mr. Nicholson's Journal p. 1, &c."; 21 November 1801, *New York Medical Repository*, 5 (1802), 390–392.

"Additional Remarks on the Same," *New York Medical Repository*, 5 (1802), 393.

Reply to Mr. Cruickshank's, *Journal of Natural Philosophy, Science and the Arts*, 1 (new series, 1802), 181–184.

"Experiments on the Pile of Volta," *Journal of Natural Philosophy, Science and the Arts*, 1 (n.s., 1802), 198–204.

"On the Theory of Chemistry," *Journal of Natural Philosophy, Science and the Arts*, 2 (n.s., 1802), 69–70.

"On the Conversion of Iron into Steel," *Journal of Natural Philosophy, Science and the Arts*, 2 (n.s., 1802), 233–234.

"A Letter to the Editor," on Cruickshank, finery cinder, etc., *Monthly Magazine*, 14 (1802), 2–3.

1803

The Doctrine of Phlogiston established and that of the Composition of Water refuted, 2nd ed., with additions. Northumberland, for P. Byrne, Philadelphia, 1803.

The Doctrine of Phlogiston established, with Observations on the

Conversion of Iron into Steel, in a Letter to Mr. Nicholson. London, J. Johnson, 1803.

"Remarks on Mr. Cruickshank's Experiments upon Finery Cinder and Charcoal," 12 April 1802, *New York Medical Repository*, 6 (1803), 24–26.

"Observations on the Conversion of Iron into Steel," *New York Medical Repository*, 6 (1803), 158–159.

"Additional Remarks on Mr. Cruickshank's Experiments on Finery cinder and Charcoal," 15 November 1802, *New York Medical Repository*, 6 (1803), 271–273.

"On Air from Finery cinder and Charcoal with other Remarks on the Experiments and Observations of Mr. Cruickshank," *Journal of Natural Philosophy, Science and the Arts*, 3 (n.s., 1803), 52–54.

"Answer to the Observations of Mr. William Cruickshank upon the Doctrine of Phlogiston," *Journal of Natural Philosophy, Science and the Arts*, 4 (n.s., 1803), 65–69.

1809

"Observations and Experiments relating to equivocal, or spontaneous Generation," read 18 November 1803, *Transactions of the American Philosophical Society*, 6 (1809), 119–129.

"Observations on the Discovery of Nitre, in Common Salt, which had been frequently mixed with Snow," read 2 December 1803, *Transactions of the American Philosophical Society*, 6 (1809), 129–132.

General Bibliography

MANUSCRIPTS OTHER THAN THOSE CITED IN APPENDIX I:

Letter of James Freeman to the Rev. Mr. Lindsey, 16 June 1793; Dr. Williams's Library, London.

Letter of Priestley to Theophilus Lindsey, 4 November 1770; Dr. Williams's Library, London.

Letter of Priestley to Newcome Cappe, 13 April 1777; Burndy Library, Norwalk, Connecticut; and Priestley, *Memoirs*, 105–106.

Letter of Priestley to Benjamin Franklin, 21 Dec. 1780; American Philosophical Society, Philadelphia.

Letter of Priestley to Theophilus Lindsey, 6 March 1800; Dr. Williams's Library, London.

Letter of Matthew Turner to John Seddon, 16 March 1762; Library, Manchester College, Oxford.

Minutes of the Warrington Trustees; manuscript book preserved in the Library, Manchester College, Oxford.

Record Book of the Royal Society, vol. 25 (1763–1766); Archives, Royal Society.

Letter of Priestley to Theophilus Lindsey, 29 May 1797; Dr. Williams's Library, London.

REFERENCE BOOKS

Biographie Universelle [Michaud]. Paris, Madame C. Desplaces, 1843–1865.

Dictionary of National Biography, 22 vols. London, Smith, Elder & Co. A reissue of 1908–1909.

Dizionario Enciclopedico Italiano. Roma, Istituto dell' Enciclopedia Italiana, 1955–1961.

Encyclopaedia Britannica, 11th ed. Cambridge, at the University Press, 1910.

Nouvelle Biographie Générale [Hoefer]. Paris, Fermin Didot Frères, 1853–1866.

J. C. Poggendorff, *Biographisch-Literarisches Handwörterbuch zur Geschichte der Exacten Wissenschaften.* Leipzig, Johann Ambrosius Barth, 1863; reprinted 1945, Edwards Brothers, Ann Arbor, Mich.

Report of the Record Commissioners of the City of Boston, vol. 24. "Boston Births A.D. 1700 to A.D. 1800." Boston, Rockwell & Churchill, 1894.

Vital Records of Salem, Massachusetts to the end of the Year 1849, vol. 6. "Deaths." Salem, Essex Institute, 1925.

BOOKS AND ARTICLES OTHER THAN THOSE BY PRIESTLEY ON SCIENCE LISTED IN APPENDIX III:

Harold J. Abrahams, "Priestley Answers the Proponents of Abiogenesis," *Ambix,* 12 (1964), 44–71.

"Account of Experiments made in Germany with Volta's Galvanic Apparatus, communicated to the French National Institute . . . ," *Philosophical Magazine,* 9 (April, 1801), 221–226.

W. H. G. Armytage, "Joseph Priestley and Edmund Burke: An Unpublished Letter," *Annals of Science,* 12 (1956), 160–161.

Franklin Bache, "Where is Franklin's First Chart of the Gulf Stream?" *Proceedings of the American Philosophical Society,* 76 (1936), 731–741.

[William Bewley], "The History and Present State of Electricity . . . By Joseph Priestley . . . ," *Monthly Review,* 37 (1767), 93–105, 242–254, 449–464.

Henry Carrington Bolton, *Scientific Correspondence of Joseph Priestley.* New York, privately printed, 1892.

Catalogue of the Library of the Late Dr. Priestley . . . for sale by Thomas Dobson. Philadelphia, T. Dobson, 1816.

Henry Cavendish, "Experiments on Air," *Philosophical Transactions,* 74 (1784), 119–153; 75 (1785), 222–227.

I. Bernard Cohen, *Franklin and Newton.* Philadelphia, American Philosophical Society, *Memoirs,* vol. 43, 1956.

James Cook, "The Method taken for Preserving the Health of the Crew of His Majesty's Ship the Resolution during her late Voyage round the World," *Philosophical Transactions,* 66 (1766), 450–475.

A Correspondent [probably Dr. George S. Gibbes], "On the Chemical Effects of the Pile of Volta," [Nicholson's] *Journal of Natural Philosophy, Chemistry and the Arts,* 4 (January–February 1801), 472–473.

A Correspondent, "On the Chemical Effects of the Pile of Volta," [Nicholson's] *Journal of Natural Philosophy, Chemistry and the Arts,* 4 (January–February 1801), 514–515.

Sir Humphry Davy, *Collected Works.* London, Smith, Elder & Co., 1840, vol. 7.

John Davy, ed., *Fragmentary Remains Literary and Scientific, of Sir Humphry Davy.* London, J. Churchill, 1858.

Jean André DeLuc, *Idées sur la Météorologie.* Paris, chez la Veuve Duchesne, 1787.

Sidney Edelstein, "Priestley Settles the Water Controversy," *Chymia,* 1 (1948), 123–127.

"Extract of a Letter from Doctor G. M. to Dr. William Babington . . . On the State of Galvanism and other Scientific Pursuits in Germany," [Nicholson's] *Journal of Natural Philosophy, Chemistry and the Arts,* 4 (January–February 1801), 511–513.

Willem Jacoba Storm v. 'sGravesande, *Mathematical Elements of Natural Philosophy . . . ,* trans. J. T. Desaguliers, 5th ed., 2 vols. London, J. Senex, W. Innys, R. Manly, and T. Longman, 1737.

Henry Guerlac, "Joseph Priestley's First Papers on Gases and their Reception in France," *Journal of the History of Medicine and Allied Sciences,* 12 (1957), 1–12.

Sir Philip Hartog, "Newer Views of Priestley and Lavoisier," *Annals of Science,* 5 (1941), 1–56.

William Henry, *An Estimate of the Philosophical Character of Dr. Priestley.* York, Wilson, 1832.

J. L. E. Dreyer, ed., *Scientific Papers of Sir William Herschel.* London, Royal Society and Royal Astronomical Society, 1912.

R. J. Honeywell, *The Educational Work of Thomas Jefferson.* Vol. 16 of Harvard Studies in Education. Cambridge, Mass., Harvard University Press, 1931.

Theodore Hornberger, *Scientific Thought in the American College, 1638–1800.* Austin, University of Texas Press, 1945.

James Keir, "On the Crystallizations observed on Glass," *Philosophical Transactions*, 66 (1776), 530–542.

Constance A. Lubbock, *The Herschel Chronicle*. Cambridge, at the University Press, 1933.

Douglas McKie, *Antoine Lavoisier*. Philadelphia, J. B. Lippincott [1935].

Douglas McKie, "Joseph Priestley and the Copley Medal," *Ambix*, 9 (1961), 1–22.

Douglas McKie, "Priestley's Laboratory and Library and other of his Effects," *Notes and Records of the Royal Society of London*, 12 (1956), 114–136.

Douglas McKie, "An Unpublished Letter from Priestley to John Parker," *Archives Internationales d'Histoire des Sciences*, No. 35 (1956), 117–124.

Hélène Metzger, *Newton, Stahl, Boerhaave et la Doctrine Chimique*. Paris, F. Alcan, 1930.

[A. Moilliet], *Sketch of the Life of James Keir*. London, privately printed, [1868].

Patrick Muirhead, ed., *Correspondence of the Late James Watt on his Discovery of the Theory of the Composition of Water*. London, John Murray, 1846.

"Benjamin Lynde Oliver, M.D.," *Essex Institute Historical Collections*, 68 (1932), 1–4.

Charles S. Osgood and H. M. Batchelder, *Historical Sketch of Salem, 1626–1879*. Salem, Essex Institute, 1879.

Mary Cathryne Park, "Joseph Priestley and the Problem of Pantisocracy," *Proceedings of the Delaware County Institute of Science*, 10 (1947), 1–60.

J. R. Partington, *A History of Chemistry*, vol. 3. London, Macmillan & Co., Ltd., 1962.

J. R. Partington and Douglas McKie, "Historical Studies on the Phlogiston Theory," Parts I, II, III, and IV, *Annals of Science*, 2 (1937), 361–404; 3 (1938), 1–58; 4 (1938), 337–371; 5 (1939), 113–149.

Joseph Priestley, *Additional Letters to a Philosophical Unbeliever*. . . . Birmingham, for J. Johnson, 1782.

Joseph Priestley, *An Appeal to the Public, on the Subject of the Riots in Birmingham*. Birmingham, J. Thompson for J. Johnson, 1791.

Joseph Priestley, *Description of a Chart of Biography*. Warrington, for the Author and sold by himself and J. Bowles, London, 1765.

Joseph Priestley, *An Examination of Dr. Reid's Inquiry into the Human Mind on the Principles of Common Sense, Dr. Beattie's Essay on the Nature and Immutability of Truth, and Dr. Oswald's Appeal to Common Sense in Behalf of Religion.* London, J. Johnson, 1774.

Joseph Priestley, *Familiar Letters Addressed to the Inhabitants of Birmingham.* Birmingham, J. Thompson for J. Johnson, 1790.

Joseph Priestley, *Hartley's Theory of the Human Mind on the Principle of the Association of Ideas; with Essays relating to the Subject of It.* London, J. Johnson, 1775.

"Letter of Joseph Priestley to Marsilio Landriani," [Carlo Amorette], ed. *Opuscoli Scelti sulle Scienze e sulle Arti,* 1 (1778), 271–272.

"Letters of Joseph Priestley," *Proceedings of the Massachusetts Historical Society,* 3 (2nd series, 1886–1887), 11–40.

Joseph Priestley, *Letters to the Inhabitants of Northumberland.* Northumberland, A. Kennedy, 1801.

Joseph Priestley, *The Memoirs of Dr. Joseph Priestley, to the Year 1795. . . .* London, J. Johnson, 1806.

Timothy Priestley, *A Funeral Sermon Occasioned by the Death of the late Rev. Joseph Priestley.* London, Alex. Hogg and Co., 1805.

Sir John Pringle, *A Discourse on the Different Kinds of Air, Delivered at the Anniversary Meeting of the Royal Society, November 30, 1773.* London, for the Royal Society, 1774.

A Report of the State of Warrington Academy, by the Trustees at their Annual Meeting, June 5, MDCCLXI (n.p.).

A Report of the State of Warrington Academy, by the Trustees at their Annual Meeting, June 30th, MDCCLXII.

A Report of the State of Warrington Academy, by the Trustees at their Annual Meeting, June 26th, MDCCLXVI.

Myron Robinson, "A History of the Electric Wind," *American Journal of Physics,* 30 (1962), 366–372.

John Towill Rutt, *Life and Correspondence of Joseph Priestley.* 2 vols. London, R. Hunter, 1831–1832.

Charles William Scheele, *Chemical Observations and Experiments on Air and Fire,* translated by J. R. Forster. London, J. Johnson, 1780.

Robert E. Schofield, "Electrical Researches of Joseph Priestley," *Archives Internationales d'Histoire des Sciences,* No. 64 (1963), 277–286.

Robert E. Schofield, "Introduction," in Joseph Priestley, *History of Electricity*, reprint of the 3rd ed. of 1775. New York, Johnson Reprint Corporation, 1966.

Robert E. Schofield, "Joseph Priestley, the Theory of Oxidation and the Nature of Matter," *Journal of the History of Ideas*, 25 (1964), 285–294.

Robert E. Schofield, "Joseph Priestley's American Education," in *Early Dickinsoniana, The Boyd Lee Spahr Lectures in Americana, 1957–1961* (Carlisle, Pa., Dickinson College, 1961), pp. 117–138.

Robert E. Schofield, "Josiah Wedgwood, Industrial Chemist," *Chymia*, 5 (1959), 180–192.

Robert E. Schofield, "The Scientific Background of Joseph Priestley," *Annals of Science*, 13 (1957), 148–163.

Robert E. Schofield, "Still More on the Water Controversy," *Chymia*, 9 (1964), 71–76.

"Second Problème de Chymie à Résoudre: Déterminer s'il y a plusieurs espèces de Gas Inflammable, ou s'il n'y a que d'une seule espèce," [Rozier's] *Observations sur la Physique*, 9 (1777), 321–322.

"Letters and Papers of the Rev. John Seddon," *The Christian Reformer; or Unitarian Magazine and Review*, 10 (n.s., 1854), 625–629.

J. W. Ashley Smith, *The Birth of Modern Education* (London, Independent Press Ltd., 1954).

". . . Sur l'Air des Marais & les différentes espèces de Gaz Inflammable," [Rozier's] *Observations sur la Physique*, 19 (1782), 459–462.

Jared Sparks, ed., *Works of Benjamin Franklin*. Boston, Hilliard Gray and Company, 1838.

William Turner, *The Warrington Academy*, edited, with an introduction by G. A. Carter. Warrington, Library and Museum Committee, 1957.

Epistolario di Alessandro Volta, Francesco Massardi *et al.*, eds., vol. 1 Bologna, edizione nazionale, Nicola Zanichelli, 1949.

William Wales and William Bayly, *The Original Observations made in the Course of a Voyage towards the South Pole and Round the World, in His Majesty's Ships the Resolution and Adventure. . . .* London, W. and A. Stratian, 1777.

C. R. Weld, *History of the Royal Society*. London, John W. Parker, 1848.

George Walker, *Essays on Various Subjects, to which is prefixed a Life of the Author*. London, J. Johnson, 1809.

Lancelot Law Whyte, ed., *Roger Joseph Boscovich S.J., F.R.S., 1711–1787*. London, George Allen & Unwin, 1961.

John Williams, *Memoirs of the Late Reverend Thomas Belsham*. London, for the Author, 1833.

L. Pearce Williams, *Michael Faraday*. London, Chapman & Hall, 1965.

George Wilson, *Life of the Honorable Henry Cavendish*. London, Cavendish Society, 1851.

Abraham Wolf, *A History of Science, Technology and Philosophy in the 18th Century*, 2nd ed., revised by Douglas McKie. London, Allen & Unwin [1952].

Thomas Young, *A Course of Lectures in Natural Philosophy*. 2nd ed. London, Taylor & Walton, 1845.

Index

Acid
  produced by inflammable air with
    dephlogisticated airs, 249, 250,
    271
  airs, 147, 150
Acid of nitre. *See* Nitrous acid
Acidity, Priestley concedes caused by
    oxygen, 294, 325
Adet, Pierre August, 293
Adlum, John, 290
Admiralty, Lords of the, 52, 131
Aeolipyle, 36
Aepinus, Franz Ulrich Theodor
  First Account of the Tourmalin, 16,
    17, 18, 28
  *Testamen theoria electricitatis et
    magnetismi,* 30
Agriculture, 210, 218, 219
  Priestley's theories applied to, 223–
    224
  test airs for, 246–247
  tests water for Arthur Young, 225
Aikin, John, 8, 59, 70, 80
Air
  atmospheric, 185
    constitution of, 295–296
    source of, 216, 217, 218
  See also Common air
Air balloons, to explore upper atmo-
    sphere, 229

Airs
  absorption by
    iron filings and brimstone, 182
    plants, 165, 171–172, 174, 176, 177
  adsorption by charcoal, 165
  color of
    electric spark in, 65
    flame in, 107
  concept of "fixing," 328
  consumption by fires and volcanoes,
    268
  diffusion of, 65, 154, 156
  diffusion, encouraging by physical
    manipulation, 64
  doctrine of, 51
  experiments on, 64–65, 69
  extraction from
    metals, 112
    rocks and minerals, 203, 204–205,
      267
  first paper on, 72; additions to, 113
  generate different kinds of, 146
  generation from water, 286, 287–288,
    313; by freezing, 301–302, 303,
    305, 325; by heating, 325; by vac-
    uum, 305, 325
  made noxious by respiration and
    burning, 107
  marsh gas, 159
  nitrous air, test by, 104–105, 147, 174,
    181

[401]